P9-EES-377

ALSO BY *Barry Bluestein*
AND *Kevin Morrissey:*

Dip It!

Light Sauces

Quick Breads

The 99% FAT-FREE Cookbook

Doubleday

NEW YORK   LONDON
TORONTO
SYDNEY   AUCKLAND

ALPHA PUBLISHING™
A DIVISION OF ALPHA CORPORATION

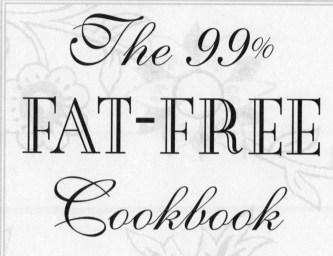

The 99% FAT-FREE Cookbook

MORE THAN 125

UP-TO-THE-MINUTE

RECIPES WITH NO MORE

THAN 1 GRAM OF FAT

Barry Bluestein

AND *Kevin Morrissey*

PUBLISHED BY DOUBLEDAY

a division of Bantam Doubleday Dell Publishing Group, Inc.
1540 Broadway, New York, New York 10036

DOUBLEDAY and the portrayal of an anchor with a dolphin are
trademarks of Doubleday, a division of Bantam Doubleday Dell
Publishing Group, Inc.

Book design by Marysarah Quinn

Library of Congress Cataloging-in-Publication Data
Bluestein, Barry.
    The 99% fat-free cookbook : more than 125 up-to-the-minute recipes
with no more than 1 gram of fat / Barry Bluestein and Kevin
Morrissey. — 1st ed.
        p.   cm.
    1. Low-fat — Recipes.   I. Morrissey, Kevin.   II. Title.
III. Title: Ninety-nine percent fat free cookbook.
RM237.7.B58   1994
641.5'638 — dc20   93-25293
                                                    CIP

Doubleday Canada ISBN 0-385-25641-8

Copyright © 1994 by Barry Bluestein and Kevin Morrissey

All Rights Reserved

Printed in the United States of America

For information on this special edition contact
Alpha Publishing™
151 Bloor Street West, Suite 890
Toronto, Ontario, Canada M5S 1S4

Alpha ISBN 1-896391-07-9

ALPHA PUBLISHING™
A DIVISION OF ALPHA CORPORATION

DEDICATED TO

Jeff Wilson

WHO WAS ALWAYS THERE

Acknowledgments

We gratefully acknowledge the assistance of Lisa Schumacher Newkirk, Claudia Clark Potter, Colin Reeves, William Rice, and Jill Van Cleave for their ideas and advice as this book took shape. For their help in recipe development and testing, we would like to thank Ann Bloomstrand and Elaine Brooks, our bread maven in the Berkshires.

Elaine Barlas earned a special place in paradise for her dual role of culinary cheerleader and sous chef for our tastings. Appreciation for their constructive feedback goes to our panel of tasters, who included: Ricardo Alcaraz, Bob and Jo Ann Bassi, Harry and Eleanor Bluestein, Cheryl Blumenthal, Linda Gray, Jerry and Pat Grose, Rob Humrickhouse, John Koulias, Marlis Levin, Emmie and Bill Ruffin, Art Smith, Greg Snider, and John Vranicar.

We extend heartfelt thanks to Judith Kern, our editor, without whose vision and knowledge our idea would not be a book. Lastly, we acknowledge the contributions of Carol Siegel, for her thoughtful copy editing, and of Susan Ramer, our always supportive literary agent.

Contents

Introduction

The American way of eating has changed irrevocably during the past decade. The pursuit of a lighter and more healthful diet has become the driving force behind a quiet but steady revolution taking place in homes across the nation.

The new passion for setting a healthful dining table has entered the mainstream with a vengeance. As a people, we are finally taking heed of a generation of scientific data demonstrating the links between the traditional, high-fat American diet and numerous preventable, dietary-related health problems.

Long conscious of the need to limit our intake of so-called fattening foods, we are now learning the very important distinction between simple calories and the fat content of the foods we eat. We are quickly coming to appreciate that counting calories without looking at fat content is to focus on the battle while disregarding the war.

Yet there is a troubling lag between acquiring knowledge and learning to use it. Even as "fat free" has become the rallying slogan for the marketing of commercially prepared synthetic products, home cooks struggling to eliminate fat in the preparation of fresh, natural foods labor methodically to revise individual recipes. The majority of cookbooks now on the market provide little in the way of an overall guiding technique; and the majority of recipes, even in those books with a "light" or "healthy-eating" focus, still contain at least 5 or 10 grams of fat per serving.

We believe the problem is a basic conceptual one: Simply stated, we must learn to cook fat free in order to eat fat free. Most recipes rely on traditional cooking methods, which require the use of fatty ingredients. Revisions that purport to be light in most cases simply reduce the amount of fat used in the recipe or downscale the size of the portion—the culinary equivalent of the old binge-and-starve approach to dieting.

Just as we have learned to pursue a more healthful diet by changing our everyday eating habits, we must learn to prepare more healthful food by changing our cooking techniques. The next logical step in the dietary revolution is to shift responsibility for fat-free eating from the dining table to the kitchen.

The 99% Fat-Free Kitchen

In the *The 99% Fat-Free Cookbook*, we offer a guiding philosophy and simple techniques for eliminating as much fat as possible at the source, your kitchen. We include only recipes with 1 gram of fat or less per serving.

Our premise that fat-free eating derives from fat-free cooking requires reeducating the cook, not depriving the diner. In testing recipes for this book, we found that most of our guests did not realize the dishes we served them were fat free until we told them so.

Fat-free cooking entails discriminating selection and innovative preparation of ingredients, not deletion of favorite dishes from our menus. Essentially, we have broken traditional recipes and method-ologies down to their basic components and rebuilt them in ways that eliminate superfluous fats—fats that contribute little to—and may even mask—intrinsic flavor.

It's not necessary to banish chocolate recipes from the fat-free kitchen, just to avoid the use of cocoa butter in their preparation. Cakes and cookies can be made without butter, cream, and egg yolks. You don't have to sacrifice roux-based dishes, as long the roux is made without fat. While the fat content of red meat is too high for inclusion in fat-free recipes, poultry and seafood can be used judiciously to enhance flavor and texture.

Think of the common use of fats in everyday cooking as a troublesome habit to be broken. Why, for example, must we automatically reach for that fat-laden bottle of oil every time we perform as basic a first step as sautéing? The oil isn't necessary and may well make the difference between keeping the subsequent recipe in a healthy-cooking repertoire or discarding it. Substituting canola oil for vegetable oil is no answer; it merely begs the more fundamental question.

While no one can—or should—eliminate *all* fat, few now disagree that a major overhaul of the fatty American diet is essential. *The 99% Fat-Free Cookbook* offers a painless approach for trimming gratuitous fat from meals. Use it as a guide and as a point of departure. If you systematically work 99% fat-free recipes into your cooking repertoire, you will reduce substantially the fat content of the table you set in no time—allowing for a rich and varied menu and enabling the occasional splurge without undue guilt.

99% Fat-Free Cooking Techniques

Replacing traditional cooking methods with fat-free techniques is fundamental. Detailed recipe directions build on a few basic concepts, which include:

- **BAKING:** Oil, shortening, and egg yolks are not needed. We substitute egg whites, fruit purees, buttermilk, and light corn syrup.

- **BINDING:** We use potato or vegetable purees or egg whites rather than whole eggs to bind savory cakes and fillings.

- **BROWNING:** We use juice, stock, or bread crumbs in place of melted butter and oil.

- **FLAVORING:** To achieve the smoky taste usually derived from the inclusion of ham or pork, we cook with a little smoked turkey or steam ingredients with a few bacon cubes added to the water in the bottom of the steamer. In desserts, sauces, and dressings, we use buttermilk for the rich, creamy taste of butter.

- **FRYING:** Slow baking, which imparts the same crispness as frying to many foods, is our preferred method. It is done dry or with a touch of light cooking spray, eliminating the heavy oils needed for frying.

- **GLISTENING:** The gloss on a bowl of pasta usually comes from tossing the noodles in oil, and the sheen of a sauce usually comes from one of a variety of fats. We toss pastas in stock, instead, and finish sauces with a little stock and corn-starch.

✄ SAUTÉING: Instead of using oil, butter, or shortening over medium to high heat, we "sweat" vegetables over low heat, which releases their own moisture, or add just a little water. For seafood and poultry, we use water, stock, or other fat-free liquid, also over low heat.

✄ THICKENING: To thicken soups, sauces, and stews, we replace butter and flour with either vegetable purees or buttermilk. For salad dressings that cling, we use corn syrup or honey instead of oil.

1

The 99%
FAT-FREE
Pantry

A Word on Counts, Portions, and Equivalents

Total fat per serving has been calculated for each recipe to the nearest $\frac{1}{100}$th of a gram. For commercial products, we use the lowest-fat brands readily available. Counts are based to the greatest extent possible on actual data rather than on the liberally rounded off figures manufacturers have sometimes used on product labels. Recently standardized federal labeling guidelines should help consumers in their selection of commercial products. Read and compare product labels carefully.

Although serving sizes vary some among the recipes, we have tried to maintain consistent portions, averaging 6 to 8 ounces for main courses.

To give you a better idea how much to buy at the market, equivalents are provided for ingredient measures, unless the measured item is too small, that is, less than a whole. For example:

1 cup chopped white onion (1 medium onion);
½ tablespoon chopped garlic (about 2 cloves);
2 large red bell peppers (14 to 16 ounces total);
4 cups cubed red potatoes (about 1½ pounds potatoes).

The Pantry

BACON SMOKING: In several recipes, we impart the smoky flavor of pork products, without the fat, by cooking ingredients in a steamer and adding cubed bacon to the water in the bottom of the steamer. The trick is to make sure the water level is low enough so as not to bubble up through the holes in the bottom of the steamer basket, since you don't want the fat from the bacon to come into contact with the ingredients above. Use real smoked, not cured, bacon for its strong flavor.

Smoked turkey skin works as well as smoked bacon for this purpose and can be frozen for convenient storage.

BASIL VINEGAR: To make basil vinegar, add 4 to 6 sprigs fresh basil for every 3 cups white wine vinegar and set aside in a clean jar for about 1 week.

BEANS: A few of our recipes call for canned beans because there are commercial products available that have less fat than beans cooked at home. This is the case with butter beans, garbanzo beans, and kidney beans. Compare product labels.

BREAD CRUMBS: As all of the prepared bread crumbs we've found have a higher fat content than we budgeted for this ingredient, we make our own. One slice of white, Italian, or oatmeal sandwich bread yields 4 to 5 tablespoons bread crumbs. Break up the bread into the bowl of a food processor and pulse a few times to make uniform-sized crumbs. Compare the fat content of "light" breads now available from commercial manufacturers.

CHICKEN STOCK: We strongly recommend that you use 99% Fat Free Chicken Stock (page 10), because making your own provides greater control over taste and fat content. If you do use commercial chicken stock, refrigerate it and then skim and strain before heating, according to our recipe directions.

COCOA POWDER: Our recipes are based upon the use of Dutch-processed cocoa powder, which produces a different chemical reaction from other cocoas, which are not treated with an alkali. Compare product labels among Dutch or European-style cocoa powders, which vary in fat content.

CORN: As canned or frozen corn contains less fat than fresh, we call for these varieties in recipes where their use makes a significant difference in fat content without appreciably affecting taste. Compare product labels.

EGG SUBSTITUTE AND EGG WHITE: We use liquid egg substitute a lot for convenience and shelf life (it can be stored in the freezer and kept far longer than shell eggs). Brands that are "nonfat" are clearly marked as such; these are pasteurized egg products from which the fatty yolks have been removed. For those recipes in which we specifically call for egg white, egg substitute should not be used. An equal volume of egg white may be used if you prefer in all recipes calling for liquid egg substitute, with the exception of the Pasta Frittata (page 90), which needs the color provided by the egg substitute.

GROUND TURKEY: Don't use packaged preground turkey, which contains a considerable amount of fat. Have your butcher grind trimmed turkey breast, or prepare it yourself using a meat grinder or the grinder attachment to a stationary electric mixer or food processor.

PASTA: We make our own pasta (page 7), which is very low in fat; if you buy commercially prepared pasta, buy a "light" variety and compare product labels.

PEAS: Some recipes call for canned or frozen peas because these have less fat than fresh peas.

SALT: We often call for coarse kosher salt, which can be used in all but baking recipes. Readily available in most supermarkets, kosher salt has less sodium per measure than finer-grain table salt.

SUN-DRIED TOMATOES: Sun-dried tomatoes can be purchased already prepared, or you can make them at home. To dry your own tomatoes, preheat the oven to 140 degrees. Cut plum tomatoes in half lengthwise and place them on a cookie sheet, cut side up. Bake for about 18 hours, until the tomatoes are dry, deep reddish brown in color, and still somewhat elastic. Do not allow them to blacken or become brittle.

TOMATOES: Since fresh tomatoes do contain more fat, we call for canned tomatoes (preferably the Italian pear or plum variety) when necessary to keep the fat content of a particular recipe at an acceptable level. Canned tomatoes are actually preferable to hothouse tomatoes, since they are allowed to ripen longer on the vine.

TORTILLAS: The fat content of corn tortillas varies widely. Read nutritional labels carefully.

WHITE RICE: Several brands of long-grain white rice are well within our guidelines for fat content if cooked without butter.

YOGURT CHEESE: To make yogurt cheese, suspend a yogurt funnel (available from kitchenware stores) or a strainer that has been lined with a coffee filter atop a nonreactive bowl. Empty plain nonfat yogurt into the funnel or strainer and place the bowl in the refrigerator for at least 8 hours, preferably overnight, until all the liquid whey has dripped through into the bowl. The substance remaining in the funnel or strainer is pure yogurt cheese.

Homemade Pasta

2 cups all-purpose flour, plus a little extra for flouring during preparation   *¼ cup nonfat liquid egg substitute*

Put the flour into the bowl of a food processor. Pulse while adding the egg substitute. This will produce a soft ball of dough.

Turn out onto a floured board and knead the dough into a single ball that is glossy and elastic. Enclose in plastic wrap and set aside for 30 minutes.

Flour the rollers of a pasta machine. Cut the dough in quarters, flour all over, and flatten. Put the first piece of dough through the largest opening on the pasta machine 3 times, folding the dough in half after each time through. Then put it through each successively smaller opening, until it has gone through the smallest. Repeat this process for the remaining 3 pieces of dough.

Put each of the thin pieces of dough through the wide cutters on the pasta machine. Hang and dry the strands of pasta for about 10 minutes.

Yield — 1 pound

99% Fat-Free Smoked Turkey Stock

3 pounds smoked turkey bones, with a few
    scraps of meat left on
1 large yellow onion, peels reserved
1 tomato, quartered; or 3 plum tomatoes,
    halved

2 unpeeled carrots, trimmed and halved
    lengthwise
2 stalks celery, trimmed and halved
4 bay leaves
About 5 quarts water

Preheat the oven to 450 degrees.

Place the turkey bones in an aluminum foil–lined baking pan just large enough to hold them all in a single layer. Bake for about 30 minutes, until the bones are very brown, turning once after 15 minutes. Remove from the baking pan and place on paper towels to drain off any remaining fat.

Meanwhile, put the vegetables into a second baking pan and bake for 20 minutes, turning once after 10 minutes.

Put the baked turkey bones, vegetables, reserved onion peels, and the bay leaves into a large stockpot. Cover with the water. Bring to a rapid boil over high heat and skim the foamy residue off the top. Turn the heat down to low and simmer, uncovered, for about 4 hours, periodically skimming the residue off the top.

Remove from the heat and discard all the solid ingredients. Be sure to remove the bay leaves. Strain the liquid into a large bowl and refrigerate, uncovered, for at least 2 to 3 hours. If refrigerating overnight, cover after 2 to 3 hours.

Remove the stock from the refrigerator and, using a large spoon, lift off the layer of fat that has settled on top. Then, scrape along the top of the stock with a dinner knife to catch any small pieces of fat still remaining. Return the stock to a large pot and cook over medium heat for 2 to 3 minutes, until the stock has liquefied. Pour the liquefied stock through a strainer lined with a double layer of cheesecloth into a clean bowl.

The turkey stock will keep for 3 days in the refrigerator or 6 months in the freezer. We freeze it in 2– and 4–cup portions in re-sealable plastic bags.

Yield—about 1⅔ quarts

99% Fat-Free Chicken Stock

4 pounds chicken bones, with a few scraps of meat left on
3 unpeeled carrots, trimmed and cut into chunks
2 unpeeled parsnips, trimmed and quartered lengthwise

1 large yellow onion, cut into 1-inch chunks
5 stalks celery, trimmed and quartered
15 sprigs fresh parsley, ends trimmed
About 5 quarts water
12 whole black peppercorns

Put the chicken bones, vegetables, and parsley in a large stockpot. Cover with the water. Bring to a rapid boil over high heat, then skim the foamy residue off the top. Reduce the heat to low and simmer for about 4 hours, uncovered, until the bones begin to disintegrate. Periodically skim the residue off the top.

Remove the pot from the heat. Discard all the solid ingredients and strain the liquid into a large bowl. Add the peppercorns and refrigerate, uncovered, for at least 2 to 3 hours. If refrigerating overnight, cover after 2 to 3 hours.

When you take the stock out of the refrigerator, use a large spoon to lift off the layer of fat that has settled on top. Then, using a dinner knife, scrape along the top of the stock to catch any small pieces of fat still remaining. Place the stock in a large pot and cook over medium heat for 2 to 3 minutes, until the stock has liquefied. Pour the liquefied stock through a strainer lined with a double layer of cheesecloth (to strain the sediment) into a clean bowl.

The chicken stock will keep for 3 days in the refrigerator or 6 months in the freezer. We freeze it in 2– and 4–cup portions in resealable plastic bags.

Yield—about 1⅔ quarts

2

First

COURSES

Corn Crabcakes with Cayenne Cream

CRABCAKES:
8 ounces uncooked crabmeat
1 large egg, white only
About 5 tablespoons homemade bread
    crumbs (see Pantry)
⅓ cup corn kernels
3 drops hot sauce
½ tablespoon freshly squeezed lemon juice
1 teaspoon Dijon mustard
⅛ teaspoon freshly ground black pepper
1 tablespoon nonfat sour cream
1 teaspoon Worcestershire sauce

CAYENNE CREAM:
¼ cup plain nonfat yogurt
¼ cup nonfat sour cream
1½ tablespoons minced cornichons
1 tablespoon minced fresh parsley
⅛ teaspoon cayenne pepper
⅛ teaspoon freshly ground black pepper
2 teaspoons freshly squeezed lemon juice

Rinse the crabmeat in a colander under cold running water, picking out any filament or shell. Squeeze out any excess water.

Combine all the crabcake ingredients in a large bowl and mix well. Scoop out a generous 2 tablespoons, roll as you would a meatball, and flatten into a cake. Repeat until you have formed 8 cakes. Place the crabcakes on a nonstick baking sheet, cover, and refrigerate for 30 minutes.

Preheat the oven to 450 degrees.

Bake the crabcakes for about 20 minutes, until golden, flip, and bake for about 10 minutes on the other side.

Meanwhile, combine all the ingredients for the cayenne cream and mix until thoroughly blended.

For each portion, serve 2 crabcakes with a little cayenne cream on the side.

Yield—4 servings
Fat per serving—0.95 g.

Most crabcake recipes derive their fat content from adding superfluous ingredients and then frying the cakes, both of which methods actually obscure the essence of the crab. After trying these crabcakes, with their simple, intense crab flavor, you'll never return to the more common version. Use canned crab if you must, but we think you will appreciate the difference fresh crab makes in this recipe.

Tricolor Peppers on Garlic-Polenta Crostini

This dish is unique in both appearance and texture—a bright multicolored splash of chilled pepper served atop a pinwheel of warm, pale crostini made from polenta rather than bread.

PEPPERS:
2 large red bell peppers (about 14 ounces total), halved lengthwise and seeded
2 large green bell peppers, halved lengthwise and seeded
2 large yellow bell peppers, halved lengthwise and seeded
4 cloves garlic
¼ cup balsamic vinegar
½ cup chopped fresh basil
1 teaspoon sugar
1 teaspoon salt
1 teaspoon freshly ground black pepper

CROSTINI:
3 cloves garlic, quartered
¼ cup water
2 cups skim milk
⅔ cup buttermilk
¼ teaspoon salt
1 teaspoon sugar
1 cup instant polenta

Preheat the broiler and cover the rack with aluminum foil.

Place the bell peppers on the rack, cut side down, 2 to 3 inches from the heat source. Broil for about 5 minutes, until charred. Remove carefully and seal in an airtight plastic bag. Let cool for about 10 minutes.

Remove the peppers from the plastic bag, rub off the skin, slice into narrow strips, and set aside in a nonreactive bowl.

With a press, crush the garlic cloves into a small bowl. Add the remaining ingredients. Mix until the sugar is completely dissolved. Pour this mixture over the sliced peppers and mix well, making sure the peppers are thoroughly coated. Cover and chill in the refrigerator for 2 hours, to allow the flavors to meld.

To make the crostini, put the quartered garlic and water in a small saucepan and bring to a boil over medium heat. Cover, lower the heat, and simmer for about 10 minutes, until the garlic is tender.

Transfer the contents of the saucepan to a small bowl and mash the garlic with a fork. The mixture will not be completely smooth but should be free of any large pieces of garlic.

Combine the skim milk, buttermilk, salt, and sugar in a saucepan and bring to a simmer over medium heat. Whisk in the mashed garlic. Slowly add the instant polenta while whisking, then lower the heat. Continue to cook for about 5 minutes, stirring with a wooden spoon, until the mixture is thick, smooth, and separates easily from the sides of the pan.

Pour into a nonstick 8-inch loaf pan, cover, and refrigerate for 2 hours.

Preheat the grill or broiler.

Remove the polenta from the pan and cut it into ½-inch slices. Cut each slice in half on the diagonal. Grill or broil 1 to 2 minutes per side, until brown. If using the grill, you may want to brown the short sides as well, 30 seconds to 1 minute each.

For each portion, serve 4 pieces of grilled polenta placed on the plate in a pinwheel arrangement and topped with chilled marinated pepper slices.

Yield — 8 servings
Fat per serving — 0.92 g.

Shrimp with Chayote and Snow Peas

Serves 4 unless Barry's invited.

1 cup peeled, chopped chayote
4 ounces snow peas, trimmed and cut into
   thirds on the diagonal
3 ½ ounces cooked shrimp, peeled, deveined,
   and halved
½ red onion, sliced into half rounds
   (about ¾ cup)

1 tablespoon stone-ground mustard
1 tablespoon champagne vinegar
2 tablespoons plain nonfat yogurt
½ tablespoon sugar

Bring a saucepan half filled with water to a boil. Add the chayote and boil for 10 minutes. Add the pea pods and cook for another 20 seconds. Drain and rinse the vegetables immediately under cold running water. Transfer to a bowl and add the shrimp and onion.

In a small bowl, combine the mustard and vinegar. Whisk in the yogurt, then the sugar.

Pour the dressing over the shrimp mixture and toss to coat all ingredients well. Chill for at least 1 hour before serving.

Yield—4 servings
Fat per serving—0.70 g.

Mushroom Strudel

8 ounces white button mushrooms
8 ounces portobello mushrooms
¼ teaspoon chopped fresh tarragon
⅛ teaspoon freshly grated nutmeg
⅛ teaspoon freshly ground black pepper

½ teaspoon salt
1 cup evaporated skim milk
4 sheets phyllo dough (about 3 ounces)
¼ cup 99% Fat-Free Chicken Stock
  (page 10)

Clean and slice the mushrooms. Put them in a nonstick frying pan and cook for 4 minutes over medium heat, stirring constantly. Stir in the tarragon, nutmeg, pepper, and salt. Add the evaporated milk. Lower the heat and simmer for about 15 minutes, uncovered, until the liquid thickens.

Transfer to a food processor or blender and puree. Cover and refrigerate for 30 minutes to thicken and chill.

Preheat the oven to 375 degrees.

Lay out the sheets of phyllo dough and cover with a slightly dampened towel during assembly.

Cut a piece of baker's parchment to fit a baking sheet, then lay it on the countertop. Lay a rectangular sheet of phyllo dough lengthwise on the paper and paint it with chicken stock.

Lay a second sheet, and then a third, directly on top, painting each with stock after positioning. Lay the remaining sheet on top, but do not paint it.

Spoon the mushroom filling onto a short end of the phyllo rectangle, covering about a quarter of the dough and leaving a ¼-inch outer border. Lift the outer edge alongside the filling and roll the dough over onto itself to form a log. Carefully reposition the log so that it rests lengthwise on the baker's parchment, seam side down. Transfer the paper and log to the baking sheet. Paint the exposed dough surface with the remaining chicken stock.

Bake for about 30 minutes, until golden.

Slice into 6 portions.

Yield—6 servings
Fat per serving—0.56 g.

This versatile savory pastry also works well as a side dish to accompany poultry. Don't be intimidated by the idea of working with phyllo dough; it's really quite easy. The amount of white mushrooms called for can be doubled if portobello aren't available.

Fish Sausage with Fennel Sauce

The use of plastic wrap in this recipe to form the sausages and hold them together during cooking replaces the laborious preparation steps in traditional recipes. We're partial to fennel sauce atop this sausage, but try Roasted Red Pepper Cream (page 30) instead if you don't have a juice extractor, necessary for preparing the fennel sauce.

FISH SAUSAGE:
One 8-ounce uncooked cod fillet, quartered
2 tablespoons homemade bread crumbs
  (see Pantry)
Pinch of cayenne pepper
2 tablespoons chopped fresh parsley
1 tablespoon brandy
¼ cup nonfat liquid egg substitute,
  lightly beaten
½ cup evaporated skim milk
4 ounces uncooked scallops

¼ cup trimmed, finely chopped scallions
  (2–3 scallions)
4 sheets heavy plastic wrap, for poaching
  sausage

FENNEL SAUCE:
2 large fennel bulbs (about
  1¾ pounds total)
2 teaspoons cornstarch
½ teaspoon freshly squeezed lemon juice

To make the sausage, put the cod, bread crumbs, cayenne pepper, parsley, and brandy into the bowl of a food processor. Turn on the machine and immediately add the egg substitute, then the evaporated milk, through the feed tube. Turn off the machine and add the scallops. Process for 15 seconds.

Transfer the mixture to a bowl and fold in the scallions. Cover and chill in the refrigerator for 1 hour.

Spread a sheet of heavy plastic wrap on the countertop. Put a quarter of the chilled fish mixture at one end of the sheet and roll it into a sausage-shaped log about 3 inches long and 1 inch thick. Twist the ends of the plastic wrap closed. Repeat with the remaining plastic and fish.

Fill a deep-sided sauté pan at least halfway with water and bring to a boil over medium heat. Lower the heat, put the plastic-encased sausages into the water, and bring back to a bare simmer. Cover and poach for 10 minutes.

Remove the sausages with a slotted spoon and allow them to cool for 10 minutes. Unwrap and slice each sausage into 4 rounds about ¾ inch long.

For the sauce, trim the fennel bulbs, reserving the leaves. Cut each bulb into 5 slices lengthwise, then cut each slice in half. Put the pieces through a juice extractor. (This should produce about 2 cups fennel juice.)

Snip enough of the fennel leaves to yield 2 tablespoons and set aside.

Put the cornstarch into a bowl and mix in 4 teaspoons of the fennel juice.

Combine the lemon juice and the remaining fennel juice in a saucepan and cook for about 3 minutes over medium heat, until just beginning to boil. Remove from the heat, whisk, then add the dissolved cornstarch while still whisking. Return to low heat and cook for about 2 minutes, whisking constantly, until the mixture begins to thicken. Stir in the 2 tablespoons of fennel leaves. Continue to cook for about 3 minutes, stirring with a spoon, until fully thickened to sauce consistency.

Serve 4 rounds of fish sausage on each plate, with some of the fennel sauce drizzled on top.

Yield — 4 servings
Fat per serving — 0.95 g.

Squid with Pasta

Most fish markets sell cleaned squid, which makes preparation almost effortless. Be sure not to overcook the squid, as this will toughen the naturally tender meat.

12 ounces cleaned, trimmed squid (bodies and tentacles)
1 cup chopped white onion (about 1 medium onion)
One 28-ounce can peeled Italian-style plum tomatoes, seeded and chopped, juice reserved
½ tablespoon minced garlic (about 2 cloves)

1 cup seeded, chopped yellow bell pepper (about 1 medium bell pepper)
½ cup dry red wine
2 teaspoons chopped fresh oregano
1 tablespoon tomato paste
5 ounces uncooked thin-strand pasta (see Pantry)

Slice the squid bodies into ¼-inch rings.

In a saucepan, combine the onion and 4 tablespoons of the juice from the tomatoes and sauté for about 6 minutes over medium-low heat, until the onion is wilted. Add the garlic and bell pepper and cook for another 2 minutes.

Add the wine, squid, chopped tomatoes, the remaining juice from the tomatoes, the oregano, and the tomato paste. Raise the heat to high and bring to a boil. Cover and boil for 5 minutes, then reduce the heat to low and simmer for 45 minutes.

Remove the cover and continue to simmer for about 15 minutes longer, until the sauce thickens.

While the squid simmers, bring a large pot of water to a boil, add the pasta, and cook to desired tenderness (3 to 4 minutes for homemade or other fresh pasta, 8 to 10 minutes for dry). Drain the pasta, distribute it among 6 pasta bowls, and top each portion with equal amounts (about 7 ounces each) of the squid mixture.

Yield — 6 servings
Fat per serving — 0.99 g.

Hummus with Sweet Potato Chips

HUMMUS:

8 ounces canned garbanzo beans, drained
    and rinsed
½ cup plain nonfat yogurt
3 tablespoons freshly squeezed lemon juice
3 tablespoons chopped flat-leaf parsley
⅛ teaspoon ground cumin
2 cloves garlic

SWEET POTATO CHIPS:

1 pound sweet potato, peeled
Light vegetable oil cooking spray
1 tablespoon seasoned salt

Preheat the oven to 300 degrees.

For the hummus, combine the beans, yogurt, lemon juice, parsley, and cumin in the bowl of a blender. Press in the garlic and puree until smooth. (This should yield about 1 cup of hummus.)

Thinly slice the sweet potato, using a mandoline slicer.

Lightly spray a nonstick baking sheet twice with the vegetable oil spray and rub the oil evenly over the surface. Arrange the potato slices on the baking sheet in a single layer and place in the oven.

After 5 minutes, sprinkle about half the seasoned salt over the potatoes. After another 5 minutes, turn the slices and salt the other side. When the potatoes have cooked a total of 15 minutes, remove any browned chips. Flip the uncooked slices and move them to the outer edges of the pan. It may take another 5 minutes to cook all the chips. (This should yield about 90 chips.)

Serve the hummus in a bowl centered on a large plate, surrounded by sweet potato chips.

Yield—6 servings
Fat per serving—0.85 g.

This is an extremely light and refreshing hummus, made without fat-laden tahini and oil. We call for the use of a blender to puree the hummus because it yields a smoother consistency; if chunkier hummus is desired, use a food processor. Sweet potato chips can burn quickly and require more diligent watching than is needed for oven roasting white potatoes, but they are well worth the extra effort.

Lobster Tostadas

The sublime decadence of lobster paired with the earthy tortilla makes a wonderful Sunday brunch item. Serve these with jalapeño-spiked Bloody Marys.

SALSA:
1 small jalapeño pepper, halved and seeded
1 small white onion (about 3 ounces), halved
1 large clove garlic
½ cup fresh cilantro leaves
3 red plum tomatoes (about 6 ounces total), cored and quartered
1 yellow tomato (about 6 ounces), cored and quartered
2 teaspoons freshly squeezed lime juice

Four 6-inch corn tortillas
6 tablespoons dry white wine
12 ounces cooked lobster meat, sliced
6 large leaves red-leaf lettuce, shredded

Preheat the oven to 375 degrees.

For the salsa, put the jalapeño pepper, onion, garlic, and ¼ cup of the cilantro into the bowl of a food processor and process to a fine mince. Add the red and yellow tomatoes and pulse to a coarse chop. Transfer to a bowl, stir in the lime juice, and set aside.

Put the tortillas into the oven directly on the middle rack. Bake for about 5 minutes, until toasted.

Meanwhile, combine the remaining ¼ cup cilantro and the wine in a nonstick frying pan. Cook for 1 minute over low heat, just until the liquid begins to smoke. Stir in the lobster meat, cover, and cook for 3 minutes. Remove from the heat.

Put the toasted tortillas on individual serving plates, topped with a handful of lettuce. Divide the salsa and lobster meat among the 4 tostadas, and spoon a little of the cilantro and wine mixture over each serving.

Yield—4 servings
Fat per serving—0.91 g.

Zucchini Ravioli with Caramelized Onion and Roasted Tomato Sauce

DOUGH:
2 cups all-purpose flour, plus a little extra
   for flouring during preparation
1 cup nonfat liquid egg substitute

FILLING:
¼ cup finely chopped yellow onion
¼ cup water
1 teaspoon minced garlic (about 1
   large clove)
2 cups peeled, diced zucchini (about 1
   large zucchini)
¼ teaspoon dried oregano
Pinch of freshly ground black pepper
¼ teaspoon salt
½ cup homemade bread crumbs
   (see Pantry)
1 tablespoon nonfat liquid egg substitute

SAUCE:
2 large tomatoes (about 1 pound total)
2 cups thinly sliced white onion
   (about 1 large or 2 small)
½ cup plus 3 tablespoons freshly squeezed
   orange juice
1½ cups water
⅛ teaspoon dried thyme

ASSEMBLY:
2 tablespoons nonfat liquid egg substitute
1 teaspoon water

We assemble and freeze the ravioli to cook on cold winter nights that beg for hearty, satisfying, one-course meals. As a dinner for two, the portions contain more than 1 gram fat, but are nonetheless light and healthful. Put the fresh ravioli into the freezer in a single layer on a cookie sheet and transfer to a large airtight bag once they are frozen.

To make the dough, put the flour into the bowl of a food processor. Turn the machine on and slowly pour the egg substitute through the feed tube. Process until all the liquid has been absorbed, forming a ball of dough.

Remove the dough and knead for 1 minute. Enclose in plastic wrap and set aside.

For the filling, combine the chopped onion and the water in a nonstick frying pan. Cook for 8 minutes over the lowest possible heat. Add the garlic and cook for about 2 minutes, stirring constantly, until almost all the water is absorbed. Add the zucchini and cook, stirring, for 1 minute more. Stir in the oregano, pepper, and salt. Cover and cook for about 20 minutes, until the zucchini is very soft.

Remove from the heat, scrape the mixture into the bowl of a food processor or blender, and puree to a very soft consistency.

Transfer to a mixing bowl. Mix in the bread crumbs and egg substitute, blending well. Cover and refrigerate until ready to use.

Preheat the oven to 400 degrees.

To make the sauce, place the tomatoes in a shallow baking dish lined with aluminum foil. Put them in the oven and roast for 50 minutes.

Meanwhile, preheat a nonstick frying pan over medium heat. Add the sliced onion and cook for about 8 minutes, stirring constantly, until the onion becomes dry and begins to stick to the pan. Stir in 1 tablespoon of the orange juice and cook for 5 minutes. Add another tablespoon of orange juice, stir, and cook for an additional 5 minutes. Stir in a third tablespoon of orange juice and cook for about 2 minutes more, stirring constantly, until the liquid is totally absorbed and the onion is golden. Remove from the heat and transfer to a food processor or blender.

When the tomatoes are done and cool enough to handle, cut out the cores and add the tomatoes to the onion in the food processor or blender. Puree until smooth.

Return the puree to the frying pan. Cook for 10 to 12 minutes over medium heat, stirring occasionally, until the mixture is thick and dry. Remove from the heat and stir in the water, the remaining ½ cup orange juice, and the thyme.

Return to the heat and bring to a boil. Lower the heat and simmer for 20 minutes, until the mixture is reduced by about a third to a saucelike consistency. Remove from the heat.

To make the ravioli, flour the rollers of a pasta machine. Unwrap the dough, cut it in thirds, and then cut each third in half. Flour and flatten each piece of dough.

Put one piece of dough through the largest opening on the pasta machine 3 times, folding it in half after each time through.

Then put it through each successively smaller opening, until it has gone through the smallest. Repeat for each of the remaining pieces of dough.

Place 3 of the flat, rectangular sheets of dough on a countertop. Onto each sheet, scoop 12 small mounds of filling (½ teaspoonful for each mound) spaced 1½ inches apart. Whisk the egg substitute with the water and paint all of the exposed dough surface with this mixture.

Top each with a second sheet of dough. Pressing down firmly with the side of your hand, make indentations in the dough, equally spaced between the mounds, to form the borders of the 12 ravioli on each sheet. Cut along the indentations to separate the ravioli. (The prepared ravioli can be frozen at this point. See head note.)

Bring a large pot of water to a boil. Drop in the ravioli and cook over medium heat for about 5 minutes. When the ravioli rise to the surface of the boiling water, they are done.

While the ravioli are cooking, reheat the sauce over low heat.

Serve 6 ravioli per person and spoon some of the sauce over each serving.

Yield—6 servings
Fat per serving—0.80 g.

Stuffed Squid Rings

This recipe works well as a plated appetizer, or it can be doubled and passed as an hors d'oeuvre.

3 sun-dried tomatoes (see Pantry)
1 clove garlic
3 cups boiling water
3 large spinach leaves, washed and stemmed
3 large cleaned squid with tentacles (about 3 ounces)

½ cup cooked white rice
1 teaspoon chopped scallion
½ cup white wine
¼ cup soy sauce

Combine the tomatoes, garlic, and ⅓ cup of the boiling water and set aside to steep.

Put the spinach leaves in a colander, pour the rest of the boiling water over them, and let drain.

Remove the reconstituted tomatoes from the soaking liquid and sliver them.

To make the stuffing, cut up the squid tentacles and mix them with the rice, scallion, and slivered tomatoes. Divide this mixture among the 3 spinach leaves. Roll each spinach leaf and stuff it into a squid. Secure closed with toothpicks.

Bring the wine and soy sauce to a boil in a saucepan. Add the stuffed squid to the saucepan, lower the heat, cover, and simmer for about 25 minutes, until they are fork tender.

Refrigerate the stuffed squid for 15 minutes, then cut each one into 4 rings. Serve 3 rings per person.

Yield—4 servings
Fat per serving—0.42 g.

Tequila Scallops

8 ounces uncooked bay scallops
¼ cup tequila
2 tablespoons freshly squeezed lime juice
1 medium ruby red grapefruit, peeled and
    cut into segments, juice reserved
    (collected juice from seeding and
    sectioning grapefruit should yield
    about ¼ cup)

4 teaspoons chopped fresh cilantro,
    for garnish

Combine the scallops, tequila, and lime juice in a nonstick frying pan. Sauté for about 5 minutes over medium heat, until the scallops are firm and opaque. Transfer to a plate with a slotted spoon.

Add the grapefruit juice to the pan, lower the heat, and simmer for 2 to 3 minutes, until the liquid is reduced by about half and thickened.

Add the grapefruit segments and scallops. Toss to mix, remove from the heat, and serve garnished with cilantro.

Yield—4 servings
Fat per serving—0.46 g.

Now you can have your ceviche and heat it too, a good thing given the emerging health concerns about eating raw seafood.

Cold Vegetable Terrine in Basil Aspic

We like to slice and plate the terrine so that the exposed layers of vibrantly colored vegetables lend a warm welcoming feel to the dinner table. The terrine can also be served whole for a dramatic buffet presentation. The addition of basil to the aspic water provides a tasty enhancement.

1¼ cups boiling water
½ cup chopped fresh basil
2 large carrots (about 10 ounces total), peeled and thinly sliced lengthwise
1 large zucchini (about 12 ounces), sliced into paper-thin rounds
Salt and freshly ground black pepper, to taste
6 large portobello mushrooms (about 6 ounces), thoroughly cleaned, stems snapped off

2 plum tomatoes (about 6 ounces total), sliced into rounds
6 ounces thin asparagus, cut into 3-inch spears
1 large red bell pepper (about 10 ounces), seeded and sliced
1 small eggplant (about 10 ounces), thinly sliced
4 teaspoons unflavored gelatin (2 packets)

Mix the boiling water with the basil and set aside.

Line a 9¼-inch loaf pan with plastic wrap, leaving enough overlap to seal the terrine after the pan has been filled.

Bring a pot of water to a boil. Blanch the carrots for 2 minutes in boiling water, transfer them to a colander, rinse with cold water, and drain on paper toweling. While the carrots are draining, blanch the zucchini for 15 seconds, rinse, and drain.

Place the carrots lengthwise on the bottom of the plastic-lined loaf pan, then stand any remaining slices upright along all the sides, allowing the strips to drape over the sides of the pan. Reserve any leftover slices. Layer the zucchini over the carrot, overlapping rounds in a fish scale pattern. Dust with salt and pepper.

Blanch the mushrooms for 10 seconds, and drain. Dump the water from the pot, refill, and bring to a boil. Salt and pepper both sides of the mushrooms lightly, then layer them in the pan over the zucchini, cutting the mushrooms as needed to fit.

Next, add a layer of sliced tomatoes; dust with salt and pepper. When the fresh water has come to a boil, add the asparagus spears and blanch for 15 seconds. Rinse and drain. Layer the spears lengthwise to cover the tomatoes and dust them with salt and pepper.

Blanch the red pepper strips for 30 seconds, rinse, drain, and layer over the asparagus.

Blanch the eggplant for 30 seconds, rinse, drain, and layer on top.

Put the basil water in a small saucepan and place over medium heat just until the liquid begins to give off steam. Add the gelatin, reduce the heat to low, and stir with a wooden spoon until the gelatin is completely dissolved and the mixture begins to thicken. Pour over the vegetables in the loaf pan.

Fold the overhanging carrot strips over the top and add any that were reserved from the first step of assembly. Don't worry about any gaps or irregularities on the surface, as this will be the bottom of the finished terrine. Close the plastic wrap over the pan and top with an additional layer of doubled plastic wrap to seal.

Put the loaf pan onto a large plate and weigh the pan down with another loaf pan of the same size filled with water, bags of dried beans, or anything else sufficiently heavy, or with a brick. Refrigerate for at least 3 hours to allow the basil aspic to form and the terrine to set.

To unmold, open the plastic wrap, put a serving plate upside down on top of the loaf pan, flip, and remove the plastic. Cut into 8 slices.

Yield — 8 servings
Fat per serving — 0.35 g.

Simply elegant potato cakes surrounded by a robust sauce.

Potato Cakes with Roasted Red Pepper Cream

POTATO CAKES:
4 cups peeled, cubed new red potatoes
 (about 1½ pounds)
1 tablespoon trimmed and chopped
 scallion (about 1 scallion)
¼ cup nonfat liquid egg substitute
1 teaspoon finely grated lemon rind
¼ cup nonfat sour cream
⅛ teaspoon coarse kosher salt
⅛ teaspoon white pepper

ROASTED RED PEPPER
CREAM:
One 8-ounce red bell pepper, halved
 and seeded
½ cup buttermilk
¼ teaspoon salt
⅛ teaspoon white pepper

To make the cakes, put the potatoes in a 3-quart saucepan with water to cover. Bring to a boil over high heat and continue to boil for about 20 minutes, until the potatoes are fork tender.

Drain well, transfer to a large mixing bowl, and mash. Set aside and allow to cool completely to room temperature.

When the potatoes have cooled, add the remaining ingredients for the cakes. Mix well. Form into 12 cakes, using about a tablespoon of the mixture for each cake. Place the cakes on a nonstick baking sheet, cover with plastic wrap, and refrigerate for at least 1 hour.

For the cream, about 30 minutes before you want to serve, preheat the broiler and line the rack with aluminum foil.

Place the bell pepper on the rack, cut side down, 2 to 3 inches from the heat source. Broil for about 5 minutes, until charred. Remove the pepper and turn the oven down to 500 degrees.

Carefully transfer the pepper to an airtight plastic bag, seal, and let cool for about 10 minutes.

Remove the pepper from the plastic bag and rub off the skin. Put the pepper into a food processor or blender and puree to a smooth consistency while pouring in ¼ cup of the buttermilk. Set aside.

Remove the baking sheet from the refrigerator, uncover, and put in the oven. Bake for about 15 minutes, until the potato cakes are browned.

When the cakes are almost done, transfer the pepper puree to a small saucepan over low heat. Whisk in the remaining ¼ cup of buttermilk, the salt and white pepper. Cook for 1 minute more to heat thoroughly.

Serve 2 cakes per person, browned side up, and surround with red pepper cream.

Yield — 6 servings
Fat per serving — 0.33 g.

Pumpkin Ravioli

This subtle yet sophisticated first course proves just how far fat-free cooking has come since the days of cottage cheese and crackers. Our crescent-shaped pies are actually lunettes, rather than the more traditional square ravioli. The sweet apple and carrot sauce requires a juice extractor. If you don't have one, try the Caramelized Onion and Roasted Tomato Sauce (page 23) from our Zucchini Ravioli.

DOUGH:
2 cups all-purpose flour, plus a little extra for flouring during preparation
⅔ cup nonfat liquid egg substitute

FILLING:
½ cup pumpkin puree
1 tablespoon nonfat liquid egg substitute
1 teaspoon ground cumin

ASSEMBLY:
1 tablespoon nonfat liquid egg substitute

SAUCE:
2 MacIntosh apples (about 10 ounces total), quartered
2 large carrots (about 10 ounces total)
2 teaspoons cornstarch
4 teaspoons water
Chopped fresh parsley, for garnish

To make the dough, put the flour into the bowl of a food processor and pulse while adding the egg substitute. This will produce bits of dough about the size of large peas.

Turn out onto a floured board and knead the dough into a single ball that is glossy and elastic. Enclose in plastic wrap and set aside for 30 minutes.

While the dough is resting, mix all the filling ingredients together well. Set aside.

Flour the rollers of a pasta machine. Cut the dough in half, flour all over, and flatten. Put the first piece of dough through the largest opening on the pasta machine 3 times, folding it in half after each time through. Then put it through each successively smaller opening, until it has gone through the smallest. Repeat with the second piece of dough.

From each thin piece of dough, cut twelve 3-inch circles. Put 1 teaspoon of filling in the center of each circle. Paint the exposed dough with egg substitute (1 tablespoon should suffice to paint all 24 circles). Fold each circle in half to form a crescent-shaped ravioli and crimp the edges together to seal.

For the sauce, run the apples and carrots through a juice extractor. You should have about 1 cup of juice.

In a small bowl, combine the cornstarch and water.

Put the juice in a small saucepan and cook over medium heat just until the liquid begins to give off steam, about 2 minutes. Remove from the heat, whisk in the cornstarch mixture, return to heat, and cook for 2 minutes more. Reduce the heat to very low to keep warm while the ravioli cook.

Bring a large saucepan of water to a boil. Drop in the ravioli and cook over medium heat for about 5 minutes. When the ravioli rise to the surface of the boiling water, they are done.

Serve 3 ravioli per portion, topped with some of the apple-carrot sauce and a sprinkling of parsley.

Yield—8 servings
Fat per serving—0.47 g

Peppered Potatoes

1 pound small unpeeled new red potatoes (about 10 potatoes), quartered

½ cup peppered vodka

Fill the bottom of a steamer with water and bring to a boil. Put the potatoes into the steamer basket, cover, and steam for 8 to 10 minutes, until fork tender. Remove from the heat and drain the potatoes.

Transfer to a bowl. Pour the vodka over the potatoes and toss a minute or two to allow the vodka to be absorbed.

Yield — 10 servings
Fat per serving — 0.03 g.

3

SOUPS

Roasted Acorn Squash Soup with Maple Cream

1 acorn squash (about 1½ pounds)
1 cup chopped celery (about 2 stalks)
⅔ cup peeled, chopped carrot
    (about 1 carrot)
1¼ cups coarsely chopped yellow onion
    (about 1 onion)
2 cups 99% Fat-Free Chicken Stock
    (page 10)

¼ teaspoon ground nutmeg
Up to ⅛ teaspoon cayenne pepper, to taste
½ cup Yogurt Cheese (see Pantry)
¼ cup pure maple syrup
1 tablespoon trimmed and finely chopped
    scallion (about 1 scallion), for garnish

Preheat the oven to 350 degrees.

Cut the squash in half, scoop out and discard the seeds. Place, cut side down, on a foil-lined baking sheet. Bake for about 45 minutes, until the squash is fork tender. Let cool a bit, then peel.

Combine the celery, carrot, and onion in a heavy saucepan. Cover and cook for about 10 minutes over low heat, until the onion has wilted. Add the chicken stock and bring to a boil over medium heat. Lower the heat, cover, and simmer for 20 minutes.

Puree the soup mixture with the squash in a food processor or blender until smooth. Return to the pan, add the spices, and cook for 3 minutes more, until thoroughly heated.

Meanwhile, combine the yogurt cheese and maple syrup.

Top each bowl of soup with about 1½ tablespoons maple cream and a sprinkling of scallion.

Yield—4 servings
Fat per serving—0.55 g.

Oven-roasting the acorn squash intensifies its sweet, nutty taste. Using yogurt cheese as a base lends the maple cream enough body to garnish this rich soup.

Creamy Leek Soup

Pureed potato gives this soup the thick, creamy texture normally provided by dairy products.

5 cups trimmed, sliced leek, white and light green parts only (about 1 pound)

2½ cups peeled, cubed red potatoes (about 1 pound)

4 cups 99% Fat-Free Chicken Stock (page 10)

Chopped fresh chives, for garnish

Combine all the ingredients except the chives in a large saucepan and bring to a boil. Lower the heat, cover, and simmer for 1 hour.

Transfer to a food processor or blender and puree. Return the soup to the pan and reheat for 3 minutes.

Garnish with the chopped fresh chives and serve immediately.

Yield — 6 servings
Fat per serving — 0.16 g.

Winter Vegetable Soup

1 cup trimmed and sliced leek, white and
    light green parts only (3–4 ounces)
1½ cups thinly sliced yellow onion
    (about 1 onion)
2 teaspoons chopped garlic
    (about 3 cloves)
1 cup chopped celery (2–3 stalks)
1½ cups peeled, chopped carrots
    (about 3 carrots)
1½ cups peeled, chopped parsnips
    (about 2 parsnips)
1 cup peeled, finely chopped red potato
    (about 1 medium potato)

1 bay leaf
2 tablespoons chopped flat-leaf parsley
2 teaspoons dried basil
½ teaspoon ground sage
⅛ teaspoon cayenne pepper
7 cups water
2 cups shredded savoy cabbage
    (about 8 ounces)
15½ ounces canned butter beans, drained
    and rinsed
1 cup peeled, seeded, and chopped fresh
    tomatoes (about 2 tomatoes)

Our version of the classic minestrone. Instead of floating butter beans in the soup, we puree them for use as a thickening agent in lieu of butter and flour.

Combine the leek, onion, garlic, celery, and carrots in a nonstick stockpot. Cook for about 20 minutes over low heat, stirring occasionally, until the vegetables look dry.

Add the parsnips and potato. Mix in the bay leaf, parsley, basil, sage, and cayenne pepper. Add the water. Bring to a boil, lower the heat, cover partially, and simmer for 40 minutes.

Stir in the cabbage and cook for another 5 minutes. Remove the bay leaf. Transfer 1 cup of liquid from the stockpot to a food processor or blender, add the beans, and puree. Stir back into the stock. Raise the heat to medium, bring to a boil, and cook for 10 minutes. Add the tomatoes and cook for an additional 2 to 3 minutes.

Yield—8 servings (6 as a main course)
Fat per serving—0.42 g. (0.56 g. for main course)

Tortilla Soup

We broil the tortilla chips to obtain the crispness usually achieved by frying.

Six 6-inch corn tortillas
3 cups 99% Fat-Free Chicken Stock
   (page 10)
1 tablespoon freshly squeezed lime juice
⅛ teaspoon ground cumin
¼ teaspoon ground turmeric
Dash each of salt and cayenne pepper,
   to taste

½ cup corn kernels (about 1 ear)
3 tablespoons chopped fresh cilantro
3 tablespoons seeded, very finely chopped
   fresh jalapeño pepper (about 1 large
   pepper), for garnish (optional)

Preheat the broiler.

Cut the tortillas into long, ½-inch-wide strips. Place them under the broiler until crisp, about 1 minute per side, taking care not to burn them. Remove from the oven and set aside.

Combine the chicken stock, lime juice, and spices in a saucepan and cook for 10 minutes over medium heat.

Divide the toasted tortilla strips, corn kernels, and cilantro among 6 small bowls, and pour the hot soup on top. Garnish, if desired, with the chopped jalapeño pepper. Serve immediately.

Yield — 6 servings
Fat per serving — 0.21 g.

Cucumber Soup

4 cups peeled, coarsely chopped cucumber
    (about two 1-pound cucumbers)
½ teaspoon salt
¼ cup champagne vinegar
1½ cups 99% Fat-Free Chicken Stock
    (page 10)

¼ cup dry vermouth
¼ teaspoon white pepper
½ cup chopped fresh dill weed, plus
    additional for garnish
About 6 tablespoons plain nonfat yogurt,
    for garnish

Combine the cucumber and salt in a nonreactive bowl and toss to coat the cucumber well. Set aside for about 30 minutes.

Rinse the cucumber under cold running water for about 1 minute, shake off the excess water, and pat dry. Transfer to a food processor or blender, add the vinegar, and puree to a smooth consistency.

Combine the chicken stock, vermouth, and pepper in a medium saucepan. Bring to a boil over medium heat. Whisk in the cucumber puree and the chopped dill and cook for another 2 minutes, stirring occasionally.

Ladle into 6 soup bowls and garnish each serving with a dollop of yogurt and a sprinkling of fresh dill.

Yield — 6 servings
Fat per serving — 0.20 g.

Whereas most cucumber soups are cold summertime fare, this version is served warm year-round.

Cream of Pumpkin Soup

1 cup chopped white onion (about
   1 medium onion)
3 tablespoons water
½ teaspoon freshly grated ginger
¼ teaspoon coarse kosher salt
¼ teaspoon curry powder
⅛ teaspoon freshly ground black pepper

1 cup pumpkin puree
1 cup 99% Fat-Free Chicken Stock
   (page 10)
½ cup skim milk
½ cup evaporated skim milk
Snipped fresh chives, for garnish

Put the onion and water in a saucepan over low heat. Cook for about 12 minutes, until all the water has evaporated and the onion is tender.

Remove from the heat and stir in the seasonings, mixing until the onion is coated. Add the pumpkin and mix until well incorporated. Stir in the stock and skim milk until blended.

Return to medium heat and bring to a boil, stirring constantly. Lower the heat and simmer, uncovered, for 10 minutes. Stir in the evaporated milk and cook for another 4 minutes.

Ladle into 4 small soup bowls, garnish with chives, and serve.

Yield — 4 servings
Fat per serving — 0.18 g.

Cream of Garlic Soup

2 cups 99% Fat-Free Chicken Stock
  (page 10)
10 cloves garlic (about 2 ounces)
⅔ cup peeled, diced red potato (about 1
  small potato)
½ cup trimmed, sliced leek, white and light
  green parts only (about 1½ ounces)

¼ cup plain nonfat yogurt
⅛ teaspoon white pepper
¼ teaspoon salt
Snipped fresh chives, for garnish

Combine the stock, garlic, potato, and leek in a saucepan and bring to a boil. Lower the heat and simmer for about 25 minutes, uncovered, until the vegetables are tender.

Strain the mixture through a sieve, reserving the liquid. Put the solids in the bowl of a food processor or blender, add ½ cup of the liquid, and puree.

Return the puree and the remainder of the reserved liquid to the saucepan and set over low heat. Whisk in the yogurt, salt, and pepper. Cook for another 2 minutes while whisking, until the soup begins to steam.

Put about a teaspoon of chives into each of 4 small bowls and pour the soup over.

Yield—4 servings
Fat per serving—0.34 g.

Pungent, intense, and aromatic—for garlic lovers only!

Yellow Split-Pea Soup

This soup provides a truly hearty antidote to winter chills. Using smoked turkey stock supplies the nuance of ham without the fat.

2 medium white onions (about 14 ounces total), cut into 1-inch cubes
1 tablespoon chopped garlic (3–4 cloves)
2 cups yellow split peas (about 1 pound)
1 teaspoon dried oregano
½ teaspoon dried thyme
1 teaspoon salt

1 teaspoon freshly ground black pepper
⅛ teaspoon hot sauce
2 cups 99% Fat-Free Smoked Turkey Stock (page 8)
4 cups 99% Fat-Free Chicken Stock (page 10)

Put the onion in a large nonstick saucepan over medium-low heat. Cook for about 5 minutes, stirring constantly, until the onion is wilted and translucent. Add the garlic, stir, and continue to cook for 1 minute.

Stir in the split peas, then the seasonings, hot sauce, and stocks. Raise the heat to medium and bring to a boil. Reduce the heat to low, cover, and simmer for about 1 hour, until the soup is fairly thick. Remove the cover and stir well before serving.

Yield — 6 servings
Fat per serving — 0.84 g.

Asparagus Soup

⅔ cup chopped yellow onion (about 1 small onion)
⅓ cup chopped shallot (about 2 shallots)
2 tablespoons water
3½ cups chopped asparagus tips (about 1 pound)
4 cups 99% Fat-Free Chicken Stock (page 10)

1 cup shredded spinach leaves, packed (about 2 ounces)
2 teaspoons chopped fresh tarragon
⅛ teaspoon freshly grated nutmeg, plus a dash for garnish
½ teaspoon salt
¼ teaspoon freshly ground black pepper

Combine the onion, shallot, and water in a nonstick frying pan. Cook for about 6 minutes over medium heat, stirring constantly, until onions are wilted. Stir in the asparagus and cook, stirring, for 1 minute more.

Add the stock and bring to a boil. Cover, lower heat, and simmer until the onion and asparagus are tender, about 30 minutes.

Transfer the contents of the pan to a food processor or blender. Add the spinach and tarragon, and puree until smooth. Add the nutmeg and process to blend. Return the mixture to the pan, add the salt and pepper, and reheat for about 3 minutes.

Garnish each serving with a small scraping of nutmeg.

Yield—6 servings
Fat per serving—0.34 g.

Cream of Broccoli Soup

1 pound broccoli flowerets and tender
    stems (about 1 head)
2½ cups peeled, cubed small red potatoes
    (about 1 pound)
1 cup trimmed and chopped celery
    (about 2 stalks)
1 cup chopped yellow onion
    (about 1 onion)

2 cloves garlic, quartered
4 cups 99% Fat-Free Chicken Stock
    (page 10)
½ tablespoon chopped fresh tarragon
Chopped fresh chives, for garnish
Grated lemon rind, for garnish

Combine the broccoli, potatoes, celery, onion, garlic, and chicken stock in a 4-quart saucepan or pot over medium heat. Add the tarragon and bring to a boil. Lower the heat, cover, and simmer for 45 minutes.

Transfer the contents of the pot to a food processor or blender and puree. Return the soup to the pot and reheat for 3 minutes.

Garnish each serving lightly with chives and lemon rind.

Yield—6 servings
Fat per serving—0.27 g.

Curried Chicken and Rice Soup

2 cups 99% Fat-Free Chicken Stock
  (page 10) or bouillon
1½ cups water
5 ounces skinless, boneless chicken breast,
  trimmed of all fat
½ cup finely chopped white onion
  (about 1 small onion)
2 large carrots (about 10 ounces total),
  peeled, trimmed, and cut into ½-inch
  chunks

2 stalks celery (about 4 ounces total),
  trimmed and cut into ½-inch chunks
¾ teaspoon curry powder
⅛ teaspoon freshly ground black pepper
¼ teaspoon coarse kosher salt
⅛ teaspoon ground cardamom
⅓ cup uncooked long-grain white rice
1 large fresh tomato (about 8 ounces),
  peeled, seeded, and chunked

Combine the chicken stock and water in a saucepan over medium heat and bring to a boil. Add the chicken breast and allow to come back to a boil. Lower the heat, cover, and simmer for about 15 minutes, until the chicken is fork tender. Remove and reserve the chicken. Stir in the onion, carrots, celery, and seasonings.

Rinse the rice under cold running water and drain.

Cut the chicken into small chunks. (You should have about ½ cup chunked chicken.)

Add the rice, chicken, and tomato to the saucepan, raise the heat to medium, and bring to a boil. Lower the heat, cover, and simmer for another 15 minutes.

Yield—6 servings
Fat per serving—0.75 g.

Bouillon can be substituted in this recipe for the richer chicken stock, since we add flavor by precooking the chicken in the base. Make sure to trim all fat from the chicken breast.

Cranberry Soup

The blend of celery root and orange adds character to this surprisingly mellow cold soup, which has none of the tartness usually associated with cranberries.

1 cup cranberries (about 4 ounces)
½ cup peeled, trimmed, and grated celery root (about 2 ounces)
1 cup water

1½ cups freshly squeezed orange juice
2 tablespoons sugar
⅛ teaspoon ground sage
1 tablespoon port wine

Put the cranberries, celery root, and ½ cup of the water in a saucepan. Cook for about 10 minutes over medium-low heat, until all the cranberries have burst and are soft enough to mash.

Puree the mixture in a food processor or blender and return the puree to the pan.

Add the remaining ½ cup of water, the orange juice, sugar, and sage. Whisk well and cook over low heat for 10 minutes, uncovered. Add the port, and cook for 2 minutes longer.

Cover and refrigerate the soup for at least 2 hours, until thoroughly chilled.

Yield — 4 servings
Fat per serving — 0.30 g.

Minted Melon Soup

6 cups peeled, seeded, and cubed honeydew
  melon (about one 4-pound melon)
¼ cup freshly squeezed lemon juice
  (about 1 lemon)
2 cups plain nonfat yogurt, plus
  additional for garnish

¼ cup chopped fresh mint, tightly packed,
  plus 6 whole sprigs for garnish
1 cup peeled, chopped cucumber
  (about 1 large cucumber)

Combine the melon, lemon juice, yogurt, and chopped mint in a food processor or blender and puree. Cover and refrigerate for at least 2 hours, until thoroughly chilled.

Stir the cucumber into the puree and serve in small chilled bowls, garnished with a sprig of mint and a little yogurt.

Yield — 6 servings
Fat per serving — 0.29 g.

A deceptively simple recipe with a delightfully complex result.

Pear Port Soup

A refreshing and sweet summertime repast. The long simmering takes the edge off the wine, leaving only its distinctive flavor. The better the wine used in this recipe, the better the soup.

8 cups peeled, cored, and chopped ripe
   Anjou pears (about 3 pounds)
1 cup sugar

5 cups tawny port wine
1½ cups water

Combine all the ingredients in a saucepan and simmer for 45 minutes, uncovered, until the pears are tender enough to be easily mashed with a wooden spoon.

Puree in a food processor or blender and chill for at least 2 hours before serving.

Yield—6 servings
Fat per serving—0.85 g.

Carrot Soup

6 cups peeled, trimmed, and shredded
   carrots (about 2 pounds)
⅔ cup peeled, finely diced red potato
   (about 1 small potato)
½ cup grated white onion
   (about 1 small onion)
½ teaspoon coarse kosher salt
1 teaspoon chopped fresh thyme

1 tablespoon chopped fresh dillweed, plus
   additional for garnish
4 cups water
1 clove garlic
½ cup plain nonfat yogurt, plus additional
   for garnish
½ cup buttermilk

Combine the carrots, potato, onion, salt, thyme, dillweed, and water in a saucepan. Press in the garlic and bring to a boil over medium heat. Lower the heat and simmer for 20 minutes, uncovered.

Puree the mixture in a food processor or blender. Transfer to a bowl and whisk in the yogurt and buttermilk. Cover and refrigerate for at least 2 hours, until well chilled.

Garnish each serving with a little yogurt and dill.

Yield — 6 servings
Fat per serving — 0.41 g.

Watercress Vichyssoise

The marriage of two distinguished cold soups. Our version uses yogurt in place of the traditional heavy cream and butter.

2 cups stemmed, chopped watercress, plus
   6 whole sprigs for garnish
   (about 12 ounces total)
4 cups peeled, finely cubed red potatoes
   (about 1½ pounds)
2½ cups skim milk
1 teaspoon coarse kosher salt

¼ teaspoon white pepper
½ cup chopped white onion
2 cups peeled, chopped cucumber (about
   one 1-pound cucumber)
¾ cup plain nonfat yogurt, plus additional
   for garnish

Combine the chopped watercress, potatoes, milk, salt, white pepper, and onion in a saucepan. Bring to a boil over medium heat, lower the heat, and simmer for 20 minutes, uncovered.

Transfer to a food processor or blender and puree while adding the cucumber. Transfer the puree to a bowl, whisk in the yogurt, and cover. Refrigerate for at least 2 hours, until very well chilled.

Garnish each serving with a sprig of watercress and, if desired, a dollop yogurt.

Yield — 6 servings
Fat per serving — 0.45 g.

Cantaloupe Soup

3⅓ cups peeled, seeded, and cubed
   cantaloupe (about one 2½-pound
   melon)
¾ cup apricot nectar

2 teaspoons grated lemon rind
4 teaspoons freshly squeezed lemon juice
½ teaspoon ground clove
4 sprigs fresh mint, for garnish

Combine the melon, nectar, and lemon rind in a food processor or blender and puree. Transfer to a mixing bowl and whisk in the lemon juice and clove. Cover and chill in the refrigerator for at least 2 hours before serving.

    Garnish each serving with a sprig of fresh mint.

Yield—4 servings
Fat per serving—0.39 g.

Roasted Beet and Red Pepper Borscht

1 pound whole baby beets, trimmed
One 4-ounce red bell pepper
4 teaspoons freshly grated ginger
2 cups water
4 teaspoons freshly squeezed lemon juice

2 teaspoons sugar
1⅓ cups plain nonfat yogurt, plus
  additional for garnish
Chopped fresh chives, for garnish

Preheat the oven to 375 degrees.

Wrap the beets in aluminum foil and roast them for about 45 minutes, until just tender when pierced with a wooden skewer. Remove from the oven, unwrap, and set aside.

Turn the oven up to preheat the broiler and line the rack with aluminum foil. Cut the bell pepper in half lengthwise, core, and seed. Place on the rack, cut side down, 2 to 3 inches from the heat source. Broil for about 5 minutes, until charred. Remove the pepper carefully with tongs and seal in an airtight plastic bag. Let cool for about 10 minutes.

Peel the beets and cut them into cubes. (You should have about 1 cup cubed beets.) Transfer the cubes to a saucepan.

Remove the pepper from the plastic bag, rub off the skin, and chop. (This should render about ¼ cup.) Add to the beets. Add the ginger and water. Bring to a boil over medium heat, lower the heat to a bare simmer, and cook for 10 minutes uncovered.

Puree the soup in a food processor or blender for 1 minute, then transfer it to a mixing bowl. Whisk in the lemon juice, sugar, and yogurt. Cover and refrigerate for at least 2 hours to chill.

Garnish each serving with a dollop of yogurt and a sprinkling of chives.

Yield—4 servings
Fat per serving—0.17 g.

Roasted Vegetable Soup

3 medium yellow onions (about 1
   pound total), quartered
1 whole, unpeeled head garlic, top trimmed
1 pound unpeeled banana squash, cut
   into large chunks

1 sprig fresh thyme (optional)
2⅔ cups 99% Fat-Free Chicken Stock
   (page 10)
½ cup water
1 cup evaporated skim milk

Preheat the oven to 300 degrees.

Put the onions, garlic, squash, and thyme into a glass baking dish. Add 1 cup of the chicken stock and bake, uncovered, for 1½ hours.

Remove the dish from the oven and allow to cool for about 1 hour.

Remove the squash from the baking dish, peel, and place in the bowl of a blender. Add the onion. Separate the garlic cloves and squeeze the meats from their peels into the blender. Pour in the cooking stock. Add the water to the emptied baking dish, swirl to combine with any residual stock, and add to the ingredients in the blender. Puree to a smooth consistency. (This should yield about 2½ cups of puree.)

Transfer the puree to a large saucepan or stockpot. Stir in the remaining 1⅔ cups of chicken stock and the evaporated milk. Cook over medium heat for 5 minutes. Serve immediately.

Yield—6 servings
Fat per serving—0.43 g.

Delicate and silky in texture, this soup has a complex flavor derived from the combination of three distinctive vegetables. An equal amount of parsnip can be substituted for the sometimes-hard-to-find banana squash—the result will be just as good.

4

SALADS

Ann's Hash Brown Potato Salad

1 pound unpeeled new red potatoes
Light vegetable oil cooking spray
½ teaspoon mustard seed
¼ cup cider vinegar
½ cup diced red onion
½ cup plain nonfat yogurt

1 teaspoon Dijon mustard
¼ cup chopped flat-leaf parsley
2 teaspoons finely chopped fresh rosemary
¼ teaspoon freshly ground black pepper
1 cup halved red cherry tomatoes
    (about ½ pound tomatoes)

Preheat the oven to 350 degrees.

Fill the bottom of a steamer with water and bring to a boil. Place the potatoes in the steamer basket, cover, and steam for about 10 minutes, until fork tender. Cool for about 5 minutes and cut into ¼-inch-thick slices.

Spray a cookie or baking sheet twice lightly with the vegetable oil spray and distribute the oil evenly over the surface. Place the potato slices on the sheet in a single layer. Bake for about 15 minutes, turning the slices after 8 minutes, until golden brown. Remove from the oven and set aside.

Put the mustard seed into a cast-iron frying pan, covered, over high heat. As soon as the seeds begin to pop (like popcorn), add the vinegar, re-cover, and remove from the heat.

Combine the onion, yogurt, Dijon mustard, parsley, rosemary, and pepper in a large serving bowl. Mix well. Stir in the popped mustard seed. Add the potato slices, then the tomatoes, tossing to coat.

Yield—6 servings
Fat per serving—0.78 g.

We named this salad for our talented friend Ann Bloomstrand, whose thoughtful suggestions and critical palate helped shape our salad-making endeavors.

Roasted Eggplant Pasta Salad

This stylized treatment of pasta salad orchestrates the intense but complementary tastes of roasted eggplant, roasted zucchini, and roasted pepper.

2 Chinese eggplants (about 1 pound total), cut into ¼-inch rounds
2 teaspoons coarse kosher salt
Light vegetable oil cooking spray
4 small zucchini (about 1 pound total), cut into ¼-inch rounds
One 4-ounce red bell pepper
1 cup cooked pasta (see Pantry)
2 tablespoons diced green bell pepper
2 tablespoons trimmed and chopped scallion (about 2 scallions)
2 tablespoons chopped fresh curly-leaf parsley

DRESSING:
½ cup plain nonfat yogurt
1 clove garlic
2 tablespoons chopped fresh basil

Put the eggplant in a colander. Sprinkle with the salt, and toss to coat. Set aside for 30 minutes. Rinse the eggplant and pat dry.

Meanwhile, preheat the oven to 350 degrees.

Spray a nonstick baking sheet twice lightly with the vegetable oil spray and smooth the oil evenly the over surface. Spread the eggplant and zucchini slices on the sheet in a single layer. Spray twice lightly over the vegetables with the vegetable oil spray. Bake for 25 to 30 minutes, turning the slices after 10 minutes, until golden brown.

Remove from the oven and turn the heat up to broil. Line the broiler rack with aluminum foil.

Cut the red bell pepper in half lengthwise, core, and seed.

Place it on the rack, cut side down, 2 to 3 inches from the heat source. Broil for about 5 minutes, until charred. Remove carefully and seal in an airtight plastic bag. Let cool for about 10 minutes.

Remove from the plastic bag, rub off the skin, and chop the pepper. (This should render about ¼ cup chopped pepper.)

Combine the eggplant, zucchini, roasted red pepper, pasta, green pepper, scallion, and parsley in a large serving bowl and mix well.

For the dressing, press the garlic into the yogurt. Stir in the basil. Pour over the pasta salad and toss well to coat.

Yield — 6 servings
Fat per serving — 0.98 g.

Papaya and Watercress Salad

A cool and refreshing last-course salad to follow a spicy entrée, this is also visually stunning, with a fan of papaya emerging from a base of watercress on the plate.

One 1-pound papaya, peeled, seeded, and
  cut lengthwise into thin slices
4 ounces watercress, trimmed

⅓ cup julienned red onion
¼ cup Honey-Ginger Dressing
  (page 187)

Fan an equal amount of papaya on each of 4 plates. Mound the watercress at the base of the fan and sprinkle the onion on top of the papaya. Use 1 tablespoon of dressing for each serving.

Yield — 4 servings
Fat per serving — 0.14 g. (including dressing)

Composed Fruit Salad

4 niño (or finger) bananas (about 8
 ounces total)
1 tablespoon freshly squeezed lemon juice
8 ounces whole strawberries (do not hull)
2 cups trimmed, very thinly sliced spinach
 (about 4 ounces)
2 kiwis (about 8 ounces total), peeled
 and sliced

DRESSING:
2 tablespoons freshly squeezed lemon juice
½ teaspoon grated lemon rind
½ teaspoon poppy seed
¼ cup plain nonfat yogurt
4 teaspoons light corn syrup

Peel the bananas and cut them in half lengthwise. Combine with the 1 tablespoon lemon juice and mix to coat.

Partially slice the strawberries lengthwise to create fans.

To compose the salads, mound the spinach on the top half of each of 4 plates. Overlap kiwi slices on the lefthand side of the bottom half of the plate. Place the fanned strawberries on the righthand side, with 2 banana slices in the middle. Cover the plates with plastic wrap and refrigerate the salads for at least 1 hour before serving.

For the dressing, combine all the ingredients, whisk thoroughly, and drizzle over the salads.

Yield—4 servings
Fat per serving—0.88 g.

Warm Cassoulet Salad

A light rendition of the traditional cassoulet, perfect for Sunday suppers or the buffet. All this needs is a loaf of crusty bread (try the French Country Round on page 134) and a bottle of good dry white wine.

1 cup thinly sliced white onion (about 1 medium onion)
5 tablespoons white wine
2 teaspoons finely chopped garlic (about 3 cloves)
4 ounces skinless smoked turkey breast, shredded
1 small head Napa cabbage (about 1¼ pounds), thinly sliced

2 cups cooked Great Northern beans
1 cup 99% Fat-Free Smoked Turkey Stock (page 8)
1 teaspoon ground sage
½ teaspoon dried thyme
½ teaspoon salt

Combine the onion and 1 tablespoon of the wine in a saucepan and cook for about 3 minutes over low heat, until the onion is wilted. Add the garlic and cook for another minute.

Add the turkey, cabbage, beans, stock, spices, and the rest of the wine. Cover and cook for 2 minutes. Stir, and cook for about 2 minutes more, uncovered, until the cabbage begins to wilt. Serve warm.

Yield — 8 servings
Fat per serving — 0.86 g.

Wild Rice Salad

1 cup cooked wild rice
¼ cup diced red bell pepper
2 large radishes, halved lengthwise and
    thinly sliced across (about ¼ cup slices)
1½ tablespoons trimmed, chopped scallion
    (about 1 scallion)

DRESSING:
½ tablespoon prepared white horseradish
½ tablespoon Dijon mustard
2 tablespoons white wine vinegar

Put the wild rice, bell pepper, radishes, and scallion in a salad bowl and mix together well.

For the dressing, combine all the ingredients in a small bowl and whisk thoroughly. Pour over the salad, toss, and serve.

Yield — 4 servings
Fat per serving — 0.33 g.

Red and White Cabbage Slaw

We added the crunch of caraway to this colorful medley and took away the fatty mayonnaise dressing that drowns the typical coleslaw.

1 cup shredded red cabbage
1 cup shredded white cabbage
½ cup peeled, shredded carrot
   (about 1 carrot)
¼ cup finely chopped white onion
½ cup seeded, chopped yellow bell pepper
½ tablespoon caraway seed

DRESSING:
1 tablespoon stone-ground mustard
½ tablespoon freshly squeezed lemon juice
⅓ cup plain nonfat yogurt
¼ teaspoon sugar
¼ teaspoon salt

Combine the vegetables and caraway in a large serving bowl and mix well.

For the dressing, whisk the mustard and lemon juice together in a small bowl. Whisk in the yogurt, then the sugar and salt. Pour over the cabbage mixture and toss thoroughly.

Serve room temperature or chilled.

Yield — 4 servings
Fat per serving — 0.55 g.

Diced Cucumber and Roasted Beet Salad

2 large beets (about 1 pound total)
1 cup peeled, seeded, and diced cucumber
½ cup diced red onion

DRESSING:
½ cup plain nonfat yogurt
3 tablespoons chopped fresh dill
1 tablespoon freshly squeezed lemon juice
½ teaspoon salt
¼ teaspoon white pepper

Preheat the oven to 350 degrees.

Wrap the beets securely in a double thickness of aluminum foil and roast in the oven for 1½ hours.

Remove from the oven, open the foil, and set aside for about 10 minutes to allow the beets to cool. Peel and dice the cooled beets.

Combine the diced beets, cucumber, and onion in a serving bowl.

For the dressing, whisk together the ingredients. Pour the dressing over the diced vegetables, and toss to coat thoroughly. Chill for at least 1 hour in the refrigerator before serving.

Yield — 6 servings
Fat per serving — 0.12 g.

Roasting the beets provides a novel twist to this traditional Swedish smorgasbord fare.

Tossed Jicama and Snap-Pea Salad

4 ounces sugar snap peas, trimmed
½ pound romaine lettuce, torn into
    bite-sized pieces
4 ounces jicama, peeled and cut into
    matchstick slices (about ⅔ cup
    sliced jicama)

¼ cup julienned red onion
¼ cup Honey-Mustard Dressing
    (page 185)

Fill a saucepan at least halfway with water and bring to a boil. Blanch the peas by dropping them into the boiling water and immediately removing the pan from the heat. Drain and rinse at once under cold running water.

Combine the blanched peas, romaine lettuce, jicama, and onion in a serving bowl. Combine with the dressing, toss, and serve.

Yield—4 servings
Fat per serving—0.58 g. (including dressing)

Black Bean Garden Salad

1 cup cooked black beans
½ cup husked, sliced tomatillos
   (about 2 tomatillos)
½ cup seeded, chopped red bell pepper
½ cup seeded, chopped yellow bell pepper
1 cup peeled, seeded, and cubed cucumber
   (about 1 medium cucumber)
½ medium red onion, sliced into half
   rounds (about 1 cup)
½ cup julienned jicama
1 cup seeded, chopped tomato (about
   1 large tomato)
1 cup chopped fresh cilantro
8 large leaves red-leaf lettuce, chilled
Snipped fresh chives, for garnish

DRESSING:
½ tablespoon Dijon mustard
1 tablespoon raspberry vinegar
¾ cup apricot nectar
½ teaspoon salt
½ teaspoon freshly ground black pepper
¼ teaspoon crushed red pepper flakes

Combine the black beans, vegetables, and cilantro in a large salad bowl and mix well.

For the dressing, whisk together the ingredients in a small bowl.

Pour the dressing over the salad and toss thoroughly. Cover and chill for at least 1 hour before serving. When you refrigerate the salad, also put 8 salad plates in to chill.

Line each plate with a chilled lettuce leaf, top with a serving of salad, and garnish with a bit of snipped chives.

Yield — 8 servings
Fat per serving — 0.69 g.

Vibrant sprays of colorful crisp vegetables permeate the salad bowl. This is a substantial salad that can also serve as a full summertime meal.

Minted Fruit Salad

Refreshing mint and creamy sherried yogurt impart unexpected verve to this fruit salad. Pair it with a Pasta Frittata (page 90) to complete our update of the classic quiche and fruit plate.

8 ounces strawberries, hulled
3 ounces blueberries, picked over
One 3-ounce plum, pitted, thinly sliced
8 cantaloupe balls (about 4 ounces)
8 honeydew balls
1 teaspoon sugar
2 tablespoons freshly squeezed
    orange juice
1 tablespoon chopped fresh mint, plus
    additional for garnish

DRESSING:
½ cup nonfat vanilla yogurt
1 tablespoon sherry

Combine the fruit in a large mixing bowl. Add the sugar, orange juice, and mint. Mix to coat evenly.

For the dressing, whisk the sherry into the yogurt.

Distribute fruit salad among 4 individual serving bowls. Top each portion with 2 tablespoons of the sherried yogurt and garnish with chopped mint. Refrigerate for 1 hour to chill before serving.

Yield — 4 servings
Fat per serving — 0.54 g.

Orange-Watercress Salad

16 leaves Belgian endive (about 8 ounces)
2 cups trimmed watercress
   (about 6 ounces)
2 navel oranges (about 1 pound total),
   peeled and cut into segments

⅓ cup pomegranate seeds (about 5 ounces)
6 tablespoons Orange-Honey Dressing
   (page 189)

To assemble the salads, fan 4 leaves of endive on each of 4 salad plates, with the bottom of the leaves meeting about two-thirds of the way down from the top of the plate. Mound ½ cup watercress at the juncture, and arrange 5 orange segments on the bottom third of the plate. Sprinkle the pomegranate seeds over each salad. Top each serving with 1½ tablespoons of the dressing.

Yield — 4 servings
Fat per serving — 0.32 g. (including dressing)

A smashing accompaniment to the Curried Lobster Risotto (page 106).

Radish Sprout and Lentil Salad

The crunchy lentils provide a distinctive contrast, and the cool watercress a taming edge, to the pungent bite of radish sprouts in this salad.

1 cup dried lentils
3 cups water
1 shallot
1 clove garlic
1 bay leaf
1 cup radish sprouts
½ cup chopped watercress

DRESSING:
¼ cup freshly squeezed orange juice
1 teaspoon Dijon mustard
1 tablespoon white wine vinegar
⅛ teaspoon freshly ground black pepper
¼ teaspoon salt

Rinse, drain, and set aside the lentils.

Put the water and shallot in a saucepan over medium heat and bring to a boil. Add the garlic, bay leaf, and lentils. Reduce the heat and simmer for 15 minutes, uncovered. Do not overcook; the lentils should have a crunch. Drain the lentils, discarding the shallot, garlic, and bay leaf.

For the dressing, combine the ingredients in a small bowl and whisk to blend.

Mix the lentils, sprouts, and watercress in a salad bowl. Add the dressing and toss to combine. Cover and refrigerate the salad for 2 to 3 hours before serving.

Yield—6 servings
Fat per serving—0.57 g.

Colin's Roasted Ginger-Beet Salad

2 large beets (about 1 pound total)
4 slices fresh ginger, each the size
    of a quarter
8 leaves green-leaf lettuce
2 ounces white flowering kale
2 navel oranges (about 1 pound total),
    peeled and cut into segments
2 tablespoons trimmed and chopped
    scallions (about 2 scallions)

DRESSING:

2 tablespoons freshly squeezed
    orange juice
¼ teaspoon freshly grated ginger
Dash of white pepper
¼ teaspoon light corn syrup

Preheat the oven to 350 degrees.

Wrap the beets and sliced ginger securely in a double thickness of aluminum foil. Roast in the oven for 1½ hours.

Remove the beets and turn up the oven to preheat the broiler (if you will be broiling rather than grilling the beets).

Open the foil and allow the beets to cool for 10 minutes. Discard the ginger, peel the beets, and cut them into ¼-inch slices. Grill or broil the beet slices for about 3 minutes per side, until browned.

Place 2 lettuce leaves in the upper left quarter of each salad plate. Place 2 medium-sized kale leaves in the upper right quarter. Overlap 3 roasted beet slices and 4 orange segments on the bottom half of the plate, sprinkling ½ tablespoon of scallion on top.

For the dressing, whisk together the ingredients in a small bowl and spoon the dressing evenly over the entire salad.

Yield—4 servings
Fat per serving—0.38 g.

Caterer and food consultant Colin Reeves lent his dramatic flair to the creation of this elegant composed salad, which juxtaposes dark roasted beets with white flowering kale.

Grilled Potato Salad

For added texture, we like to prepare the potatoes on a stove-top grill, but they can be done in the broiler as well.

1 red bell pepper (about 6 ounces)
1 pound new white potatoes
4 ounces arugula
¼ cup Mustard-Buttermilk Dressing
    (page 184)

4 teaspoons snipped fresh chives,
    for garnish

Preheat the broiler and line the rack with aluminum foil.

Halve, seed, and core the pepper. Broil, cut sides down, 2 to 3 inches from the heat source, for about 5 minutes, until charred. Remove carefully and seal in an airtight plastic bag to cool for about 10 minutes. Do not turn off the broiler. When cool, rub off the skin and cut the pepper into thin strips.

Meanwhile, fill the bottom of a steamer with water and bring to a boil. Put the potatoes into the steamer basket, cover, and steam for about 10 minutes, until fork tender.

Cut the potatoes into ¼-inch-thick slices, scatter them on a baking sheet, and grill or broil for about 2 minutes per side, until brown.

To compose the salads, cover the top half of each salad plate with arugula. On the bottom half, place a quarter of the potato slices. Lay strips of roasted pepper across the potato. Drizzle 1 tablespoon of dressing over the entire arrangement, and sprinkle about a teaspoon of chives on top.

Yield—4 servings
Fat per serving—0.43 g. (including dressing)

5

Main
COURSES

Crab and Tomato Broth Couscous

1½ pounds plum tomatoes (about 10
   tomatoes), cored and quartered
2 tablespoons chopped fresh basil
3 tablespoons chopped fresh flat-leaf
   parsley
1 tablespoon chopped fresh thyme

2 tablespoons chopped fresh tarragon
2 tablespoons chopped shallot
1 cup uncooked couscous
5 ounces uncooked crabmeat, cartilage and
   shells removed, rinsed

Puree the tomatoes in a food processor or blender.

Combine the pureed tomato, the basil, 2 tablespoons of the parsley, the thyme and tarragon in a small saucepan. Bring to a boil over medium heat and remove from the heat immediately. Work the puree through a food mill, producing a thin broth. Return it to the saucepan and bring to a simmer over low heat.

Preheat a cast-iron skillet over medium heat. Add the shallot and couscous. Cook for about 2 minutes over the medium heat, until the couscous is toasted. Stir in the hot tomato broth. Cook for about 2 minutes more, stirring constantly, until the broth has been absorbed.

Stir in the crabmeat, remove from the heat, and let sit for 2 minutes. Before serving, top with the remaining 1 tablespoon parsley.

Yield—4 servings (6 servings as a first course)
Fat per serving—0.98 g. (0.65 g. as first course)

Steeping the couscous in rich, mellow tomato broth enhances the flavor of this special dish and adds a rosy luster.

Red Snapper and Black Bean Chili

No one will believe this rich snapper and black bean concoction has been prepared without the level of fat that usually sends chili off the meter! It took a long time to perfect this recipe, but we think it was worth the effort. The smoky taste is derived from adding a little bacon to the water below the basket in which the fish steams.

7¼ cups water
1½ cups dried black beans
1 small fresh poblano chile pepper (about 1½ ounces)
¾ cup finely chopped white onion (about 1 small onion)
¾ cup trimmed and finely chopped celery (about 2 stalks)
¾ cup peeled, finely chopped carrot (about 1 large carrot)
½ tablespoon chopped garlic (about 2 cloves)
2 tablespoons chopped fresh oregano
2 tablespoons chopped fresh thyme
1 bay leaf
2 teaspoons ground cumin

½ teaspoon freshly ground black pepper
One 28-ounce can peeled Italian-style plum tomatoes, with their juice
4 cups 99% Fat-Free Smoked Turkey Stock (page 8)
1 tablespoon red wine vinegar
½ teaspoon salt
¼ cup chopped fresh cilantro, plus additional for garnish
⅛ teaspoon cayenne pepper
2 tablespoons freshly squeezed lime juice (about 1 lime)
4 slices smoked bacon, cut into cubes (see Pantry)
7 ounces uncooked red snapper fillet
¼ teaspoon hot sauce (optional)

Preheat the broiler.

Bring 6 cups of the water to a boil in a 3-quart saucepan. Add the beans, bring back to a boil, and continue to boil for 5 minutes. Cover, remove from the heat, and let sit for 1 hour.

Broil the poblano chile, rotating it to char evenly on all sides, about 10 minutes. Remove from the oven and seal in an airtight plastic bag to cool for about 10 minutes. Then peel the pepper and remove the seeds, stem, and veins. Chop it fine and set aside.

Combine the onion, celery, carrot, garlic, and ¼ cup of the water in a large, heavy kettle or Dutch oven. Stir in the seasonings. Cover and cook for 7 minutes over low heat.

Meanwhile, drain the tomatoes, reserving the juice. Seed and coarsely chop the tomatoes, leaving a few large chunks intact.

Drain and rinse the beans. Stir into the kettle, along with the poblano, tomato and reserved juice, the turkey stock, vinegar, salt, and ½ cup of the water.

Raise the heat to medium and bring to a boil, then reduce the heat and simmer for 2½ hours, uncovered, stirring occasionally.

Stir in the cilantro, cayenne pepper, and the lime juice. Cover, turn off heat, and let sit to meld the flavors.

If preparing the chili a day in advance, cool it to room temperature, cover, and refrigerate. Remove from the refrigerator about 1 hour before serving and leave it at room temperature for 30 minutes before resuming the recipe.

Combine the bacon with enough water to fill the bottom of a steamer, but not enough to boil up through the holes into the steamer basket. Bring to a boil, put the snapper in the steamer basket, cover, and steam for 10 minutes. Remove and cool a bit. Peel the skin from the fish and cut the flesh into large bite-sized chunks.

Put the chili kettle back on medium-low heat. Stir in the remaining ½ cup of water and the optional hot sauce. Bring to a simmer and stir in the snapper. Cook for 5 minutes more. Garnish with cilantro if desired.

Yield—8 servings
Fat per serving—0.99 g.

Chive Polenta with Mushroom Ragout

When we're lucky enough to find the extra-large variety of portobello mushrooms, we grill them to serve atop this dish.

CHIVE POLENTA:
2⅔ cups skim milk
⅓ cup buttermilk
1 teaspoon sugar
¼ teaspoon salt
1 cup yellow cornmeal
1 tablespoon snipped fresh chives

MUSHROOM RAGOUT:
2 tablespoons water
1 cup chopped white onion
  (about 1 medium onion)
½ tablespoon chopped garlic
  (about 2 cloves)
8 ounces shiitake mushrooms, stemmed
  and chunked
8 ounces portobello mushrooms, stemmed
  and chunked
1 tablespoon dried oregano
1 tablespoon chopped fresh basil
½ cup dry white wine
One 28-ounce can peeled Italian-style
  plum tomatoes
½ teaspoon salt

For the polenta, combine the milks, sugar, and salt in a saucepan and bring to a simmer over medium heat. Slowly whisk in the cornmeal. Reduce the heat to low and continue to cook for about 5 minutes, stirring constantly with a wooden spoon, until the mixture is thick, smooth, and comes away easily from the sides of the pan. Remove from the heat and whisk in the chives. Pour into a 4-cup nonstick loaf pan, cover, and refrigerate for 1 hour.

Preheat the grill or broiler.

To make the ragout, put the water into a large, deep-sided nonstick frying pan over medium heat. Add the onion and garlic. Cook for about 4 minutes, stirring occasionally, until the onion is translucent. Reduce the heat slightly and add the mushrooms, oregano, basil, and ¼ cup of the wine. Stir, cover, and cook for 2 minutes.

Add the tomatoes, breaking them in half to release their juice, the remaining ¼ cup of wine, and the salt. Bring to a boil, lower the heat to a simmer, and cook, uncovered, for 20 minutes, stirring occasionally to prevent sticking.

Remove the polenta from the loaf pan and cut it into 12 slices. Grill or broil the slices for 2 to 3 minutes on each side, until brown, taking care not to burn them.

For each portion, serve about ⅔ cup of ragout atop 2 slices of toasted polenta.

Yield — 6 servings
Fat per serving — 0.96 g.

Crab and Chicken Gumbo

This marvelously robust gumbo is derived from a dry, fat-free roux, which turns a rich, Cajun dark brown upon addition of the stock.

¼ cup all-purpose flour
2 strips smoked bacon, cut into cubes (see Pantry)
7 ounces skinless, boneless chicken breast
1 cup chopped white onion (about 1 onion)
½ cup seeded, chopped green bell pepper
½ cup seeded, chopped red bell pepper
¼ cup chopped celery
7 ounces okra, sliced into rounds (about ¾ cup)
½ tablespoon finely minced garlic (about 2 cloves)

1 bay leaf
¼ teaspoon freshly ground black pepper
⅛ teaspoon cayenne pepper
¼ teaspoon ground cumin
¼ teaspoon dried thyme
2 cups 99% Fat-Free Smoked Turkey Stock (page 8)
2 cups water
1 cup fresh crabmeat (about 5 ounces), cartilage and shell removed, rinsed
2½–3 cups cooked white rice
Chopped fresh parsley, for garnish

Put the flour into a small cast-iron or other heavy frying pan. Cook over medium heat, stirring constantly, for about 10 minutes, until the flour begins to turn an even dark tan. Take off the heat and remove the flour from the pan.

Fill the bottom of a steamer with enough water to cover, but not to boil up through the bottom of the steamer basket. Add the bacon and bring the water to a boil. If the chicken breast is whole, cut it into 3 or 4 pieces. When the water boils, put the chicken in the steamer basket, cover, and steam for 15 minutes. Remove the chicken and cut it into ½-inch cubes.

Combine the onion, peppers, celery, okra, and garlic in a heavy saucepan or Dutch oven. Cook for 5 minutes over medium-low heat, stirring constantly, until the vegetables become limp. Mix in all the seasonings. Stir in flour with a wooden spoon. While stirring, add the turkey stock and 2 cups water. Bring to a boil, reduce the heat to low, and throw in the chicken and crabmeat. Cover and simmer for 20 minutes.

Remove the bay leaf. Ladle about 1 cup of the gumbo into each bowl, adding about ½ cup tightly packed cooked rice to the center. (If serving as a soup course, use about ¾ cup gumbo topped with ⅓ cup rice.) Garnish with the parsley.

Yield—6 servings (8 servings as soup course)
Fat per serving—0.95 g. (0.71 g. as soup course)

This is elegant
dinner-party fare.
Spoon the coulis
beneath or on top of
the medallions, or
compose the plate
artistically. We like this
accompanied by
Steamed Bitter Greens
(page112).

Turkey Medallions Stuffed with Mushroom Duxelle and Wild Rice on Cranberry-Orange Coulis

TURKEY MEDALLIONS:
2 cups finely chopped white button
    mushrooms (about ½ pound)
1 tablespoon freshly squeezed lemon juice
2 tablespoons water
⅛ teaspoon white pepper
1 teaspoon chopped fresh thyme
½ cup cooked wild rice
1 tablespoon skim milk
1 tablespoon nonfat cream cheese
Four uncooked 4-ounce slices skinless
    turkey breast

CRANBERRY-ORANGE COULIS:
1 medium navel orange (about 8 ounces),
    quartered and seeded
2 cups cranberries
½ cup orange juice
½ teaspoon sugar

Combine the mushrooms, lemon juice, and water in a saucepan.
Simmer for 10 minutes over low heat, uncovered, stirring occasionally. Raise the heat to medium and boil until most of the liquid in
the pan has evaporated, about 5 minutes. Whisk in the white pepper and thyme. Add the wild rice, milk, and cream cheese. Mix until thoroughly blended and remove from the heat.

Place each turkey slice between 2 sheets of wax paper approximately twice its size. Using a meat tenderizer, a rolling pin, or a
rubber mallet, pound the turkey slices to about half their original
thickness. Remove the top layer of wax paper.

On each slice, spread a quarter of the mushroom–wild rice filling, leaving a ¼-inch border all around. Lift a long edge and roll the turkey over onto itself into a cylinder. Tuck the ends under. Place the turkey roll on a square of aluminum foil, roll it closed, and twist the ends of the foil securely. Repeat this procedure for each of the remaining slices.

Fill a wide-bottomed sauté pan about halfway up with water and bring to a boil. Place the foil-encased turkey rolls into the boiling water and simmer, uncovered, for about 15 minutes over medium heat. The turkey rolls will be done when a metal cake tester or skewer inserted into the top of each roll comes out hot to the touch. Turn off heat and let the turkey rolls sit in the water.

For the coulis, combine the orange quarters with the cranberries in a food processor or blender and chop coarsely.

Transfer the mixture to a saucepan, add the orange juice, and bring to a boil over medium heat. Boil for 5 minutes, then add the sugar. Reduce the heat to low and simmer, uncovered, for about 15 minutes, until thick. Do not overcook.

Remove the turkey rolls from their foil wrappers and slice each on the diagonal into 6 medallions. Serve 4 medallions per person set on or around the coulis.

Yield — 6 servings
Fat per serving — 0.97 g.

Turkey Moussaka in an Eggplant Boat

Although we use the more recognizable Greek name for this recipe, we have actually seasoned it in the style of the Turkish dish, *oturema*. Whereas the traditional preparation calls for beef or lamb, we have used turkey.

3 large baby eggplants (about 8 ounces each)
1½ teaspoons coarse kosher salt
1½ cups chopped yellow onion (about 1 large onion)
½ cup seeded, chopped green bell pepper
¼ cup water
12 ounces skinless turkey breast, ground (see Pantry)

1½ pounds peeled, diced fresh tomatoes (about 2 tomatoes)
2 teaspoons ground cinnamon
1 teaspoon ground allspice
1 tablespoon finely chopped dried apricot
½ cup chopped flat-leaf parsley

Slice the eggplants in half lengthwise. Sprinkle the cut sides with the coarse salt. Place in a colander, salted sides against the holes. Drain in the sink for 1 hour. Rinse and pat dry.

Preheat the broiler.

Place the eggplants in the broiler, cut sides up, about 5 inches from the heat source. Broil for 5 minutes, turn, and broil for about 8 minutes more on the skin side, until easily pierced with a fork. Remove and set aside.

Reset the oven to 400 degrees and allow it to cool.

Meanwhile, combine the onion, bell pepper, and water in a large nonstick frying pan. Cook over medium heat for about 6 minutes, stirring constantly, until the onion is translucent and the green pepper soft. Add the turkey and cook for about 5 minutes longer, stirring and crushing the meat with the back of a wooden spoon until it appears cooked but not browned. Add all the remaining ingredients except the parsley. Cook for another 7 to 8 minutes, stirring occasionally, until the liquid in the pan has evaporated and the mixture seems cohesive. Remove from the heat and stir in the parsley.

Place the eggplants, cut side up, in a foil-lined baking dish. Press down with a spoon to create a shallow well in each, and mound equal amounts of the turkey mixture into the wells. Bake for 15 minutes, then serve immediately.

Yield — 6 servings
Fat per serving — 1.0 g.

Gnocchi with
Tomato-Basil Sauce

These tiny Italian dumplings, presented here in a simple tomato sauce, are as light as the pillows they resemble.

GNOCCHI:
1 pound Yukon Gold potatoes
   (about 3 potatoes)
5 cups cold water
1 large egg, white only
3/4 cup all-purpose flour

TOMATO-BASIL SAUCE:
One 28-ounce can peeled Italian-style
   plum tomatoes, with juice
1/2 cup chopped white onion
   (about 1 small onion)
1 clove garlic, finely chopped
1 tablespoon finely chopped fresh basil,
   plus additional for garnish
Dash of salt and freshly ground black
   pepper, to taste

To make the gnocchi, put the potatoes and water in a saucepan and cook for 30 minutes, uncovered, over medium heat. Drain and remove the potato skins while still hot by rubbing with a clean dish towel. Rice the peeled potatoes and let cool for 2 to 3 minutes. Add the egg white and flour and, with lightly floured hands, mix just until a cohesive soft dough is formed.

Break off small sections of dough and roll them out into 1-inch-thick ropes. Cut the ropes on the diagonal into 1/2-inch sections. Using a sharp pointed knife, make a partial incision in the middle of each gnocchi.

For the sauce, seed and finely chop the tomatoes, making sure to reserve the juice separately.

Combine the onion and 2 tablespoons of the juice from the tomatoes in a heavy saucepan. Cook over low heat for about 5 minutes, stirring occasionally, until the onion is soft. Add the garlic and cook for 2 minutes, stirring. Add the tomatoes and cook for 5 minutes, until the tomato starts to give off water. Add the basil, another 8 tablespoons of the reserved tomato juice, and a little salt and pepper, if desired. Simmer for 20 minutes, uncovered, until the sauce thickens.

Meanwhile, bring a large pot of water to a boil. Salt it lightly and lower the heat to a gentle simmer. Drop in 8 to 10 gnocchi at a time and cook for about 3 minutes. The gnocchi are done as soon as they rise to the top of the boiling water. Remove them with a slotted spoon and continue until all the gnocchi are done.

Serve about 12 gnocchi on each plate, topped with some tomato-basil sauce and a sprinkling of fresh basil.

Yield — 4 servings
Fat per serving — 0.30 g.

Pasta Frittata

A great buffet item, this can be served warm or room temperature. It goes well with the crusty French Country Round (page 134).

5 sun-dried tomatoes (see Pantry)
1 clove garlic, minced
⅜ cup boiling water
1 cup nonfat liquid egg substitute
⅓ cup skim milk
¼ cup nonfat sour cream
½ tablespoon chopped fresh chives
1 tablespoon chopped fresh basil

1 cup cooked thin-strand pasta
  (see Pantry)
⅓ cup julienned zucchini
  (about 1 small zucchini)
⅓ cup seeded, julienned red bell pepper
½ tablespoon coarse kosher salt
¼ teaspoon freshly ground black pepper
Light vegetable oil spray

Preheat the oven to 300 degrees.

Combine the sun-dried tomatoes, garlic, and boiling water in a small bowl and set aside for about 10 minutes to reconstitute.

Whisk the egg substitute, milk, and sour cream together. Add the herbs and mix in the cooked pasta, zucchini, bell pepper, and seasonings. Drain the tomatoes, discarding the garlic. Slice the tomatoes thinly and add to the mixture.

Preheat a well-seasoned 9-inch cast-iron skillet. Spray once lightly with the vegetable oil spray and pour in the frittata batter. Place in the oven and bake for 20 to 25 minutes, until the edges are set and the frittata is slightly brown. Remove from the oven and cool for 10 to 15 minutes before slicing into 6 portions.

Yield — 6 servings
Fat per serving — 0.34 g.

Fish and Vegetable Kebabs

8 ounces uncooked cod fillet, cut into
  1-inch chunks
2 tablespoons freshly squeezed lemon juice
¼ cup tarragon vinegar
⅓ cup trimmed and chopped scallions
  (3–4 scallions)
⅛ teaspoon white pepper
1 large red bell pepper (7–8 ounces),
  seeded and cut into 1-inch cubes

1 large green bell pepper, seeded and cut
  into 1-inch cubes
1 large white onion (about 8 ounces), cut
  into 1-inch cubes
Four 8-inch wooden skewers
2 cups cooked white rice

Combine the cod, lemon juice, vinegar, scallions, and white pepper in a nonreactive bowl, mixing to coat the fish well. Cover and marinate for 30 minutes in the refrigerator. Drain and pat the fish dry.

Preheat the broiler.

Thread an assortment of fish, peppers, and onion onto each skewer. (Placing the firm peppers at both ends will help hold the kebabs together.) Broil the kebabs for 6 minutes, turning once to brown evenly. Serve with the rice.

Yield—4 servings
Fat per serving—0.71 g.

A fat-free rendition of the classic kebab. It also pairs well with Saffron Rice or Wild Rice Risotto (page 125 or 130).

Perfect for a homey Sunday brunch. To make an elegant presentation, wrap each casserole in a napkin and set it on an ornate old dinner plate.

Individual Chicken Potpies

DOUGH:
1½ cups all-purpose flour
½ teaspoon salt
1 tablespoon chopped fresh dill
7 tablespoons plain nonfat yogurt
3 tablespoons buttermilk
1 tablespoon water

FILLING:
6 sprigs fresh dill
4 ounces uncooked skinless, boneless
   chicken breast
2 carrots, peeled and thinly sliced on the
   diagonal (about 1 cup sliced carrots)
6 ounces whole white pearl onions,
   unpeeled

¾ cup canned or frozen corn kernels
¾ cup canned or frozen peas
2 tablespoons chopped fresh oregano
2 tablespoons chopped fresh rosemary
Dash of salt and freshly ground black
   pepper, to taste
2 cups 99% Fat-Free Chicken Stock
   (page 10)
2 tablespoons all-purpose flour

GLAZE:
1 large egg, white only
½ tablespoon water

To make the dough, combine the flour, salt, and dill in a bowl and mix well with a fork. Add 4 tablespoons of the yogurt and mix to a sandy consistency. Repeat with the remaining yogurt. Add the buttermilk and water. Using a wooden spoon, blend just until a ball of dough is formed. Wrap the dough in plastic wrap, flatten it slightly into a patty, and refrigerate for 1 hour.

To make the filling, add the dill sprigs to water sufficient to fill the bottom of a steamer and bring to a boil over medium heat. Place the chicken in the steamer basket, cover, and steam for 15 minutes. Remove the chicken, replace with the carrots, re-cover, and steam for 5 minutes. Dice the steamed chicken into ¼-inch cubes.

Fill a small saucepan with water, bring to a boil, drop in the pearl onions, and cook for 3 minutes. Rinse the onions in cold water. Trim the root on each onion, then grasp the root end and gently squeeze toward the stem until the onion slips out of its skin.

Combine the corn kernels and peas in a small bowl.

Into each of four 10-ounce casseroles, put ⅜ cup corn-and-pea mixture, ¼ cup carrot, and about ⅛ cup pearl onions. Divide the cubed chicken among the 4 casseroles (about ⅛ cup each). Add ½ tablespoon oregano and ½ tablespoon rosemary to each. Dust with salt and freshly ground black pepper to taste, mix each casserole well, and set aside.

Roll out the dough on a lightly floured surface with a lightly floured rolling pin, to a 10-inch circle about ¼ inch thick. Form 4 small circles in the dough, using the top of a clean 10-ounce casserole as a guide, and cut them out with a knife.

Preheat the oven to 400 degrees.

Bring the chicken stock to a simmer in a saucepan over medium heat. While continuing to simmer, remove 2 tablespoons of the stock to a small bowl, add the flour, and stir until smooth. Add another 2 tablespoons of stock and stir to a thin paste. Remove the remaining stock from the heat and whisk in the paste until the mixture is smooth and free of lumps. Return to the heat and continue to simmer, stirring occasionally, just until thickened, about 5 minutes.

Place the casseroles on a baking sheet. Spoon ½ cup of the chicken stock mixture over each, and divide any remaining stock equally. Top each casserole with a dough round. Beat the egg white until frothy with the ½ tablespoon water and paint the dough with this mixture. Bake for 20 to 25 minutes, until golden and bubbly.

Yield — 4 servings
Fat per serving — 1.0 g.

Shrimp Jambalaya

We think you will find this jambalaya every bit as good as the New Orleans version that inspired it—it has all of the taste with none of the fat.

1 cup chopped white onion (about 1 medium onion)
⅓ cup seeded, chopped green bell pepper
⅓ cup seeded, chopped red bell pepper
1 tablespoon minced garlic (3–4 cloves)
1 cup seeded, chopped fresh tomato (about 1 large tomato)

½ teaspoon dried thyme
Up to ⅛ teaspoon cayenne pepper, to taste
2 cups 99% Fat-Free Chicken Stock (page 10)
1 cup uncooked long-grain white rice
4 ounces uncooked medium shrimp, peeled, deveined, and halved

Combine the onion, bell peppers, and garlic in a deep-sided non-stick frying pan. Cook for about 5 minutes over medium heat, stirring frequently, until the onion begins to turn golden. Stir in the tomato, thyme, and cayenne pepper. Add the stock, raise the heat to medium, and bring to a boil.

Add the rice and shrimp. Cover, reduce the heat to low, and simmer for 20 minutes. Serve hot.

Yield—4 servings
Fat per serving—0.78 g.

Chinese Noodles with Shrimp and Chicken

1 ounce dried shiitake mushrooms
   (6–8 mushrooms)
1 cup boiling water
8 cups plus 3 tablespoons cold water
4 ounces nouilles batons (Chinese dried
   noodle sticks)
½ cup sliced white onion
1 teaspoon chopped garlic (1–1½ cloves)

1 teaspoon freshly grated ginger
3 ounces uncooked medium shrimp, peeled,
   deveined, and halved
3 ounces skinless smoked chicken breast,
   shredded
½ cup 99% Fat-Free Chicken Stock
   (page 10)
3 tablespoons soy sauce

In a small bowl, combine the dried mushrooms and boiling water. Set aside to soak for about 5 minutes.

In a pot, bring the 2 quarts cold water to a boil, add the noodles, and cook for 3 minutes. Drain the noodles in a colander and rinse under cold running water.

Remove the mushrooms from the soaking water, squeezing out any excess moisture. Stem and slice.

Combine the onion, garlic, and the 3 tablespoons cold water in a large, heavy frying pan. Cook for about 5 minutes over low heat, stirring often, until the onion turns limp. Add the ginger and shrimp and cook for about 2 minutes more, until the shrimp just begin to turn pink. Stir in the chicken, add the noodles, and toss. Stir in the chicken stock and soy sauce. Cook for an additional 30 seconds to 1 minute, until all the ingredients are incorporated. Serve immediately.

Yield—6 servings
Fat per serving—0.88 g.

Brimming with shiitake mushrooms, smoked chicken, and shrimp, redolent of fresh ginger—and tossed with delicate Chinese noodles—this is a stylish, light dinner that can be prepared in minutes.

This recipe is based upon one of our favorite dishes, developed by food columnist William Rice. To make it fat free, we removed the vegetable oil and replaced the ham with smoked turkey.

Almost Bill's Rice-and-Bean Special

2 cups Spanish talosano beans or pinto beans, rinsed and picked over
2 small dried hot chile peppers
3 sprigs fresh thyme, plus ½ teaspoon minced fresh thyme
2 bay leaves
1 cup uncooked long-grain white rice
6 slices smoked bacon, cubed (see Pantry)
12 ounces uncooked skinless, boneless turkey breast
3 tablespoons water
1 cup chopped white onion (about 1 medium onion)

1 tablespoon minced garlic (about 3 cloves)
⅛ teaspoon ground allspice
⅛ teaspoon ground cinnamon
⅛ teaspoon ground nutmeg
1 cup cooked, coarsely chopped spinach
1 tablespoon wine vinegar, plus additional as condiment
Dash of freshly ground black pepper, to taste
Hot sauce, as condiment

Put the beans in a large saucepan and cover with water by 2 to 3 inches. Bring to a boil over medium heat. Remove from the heat. Drain and rinse the beans.

Return the beans to the pan and cover with 2 to 3 inches of fresh water. Add the dried chile peppers, the sprigs of thyme, and the bay leaves. Cover and simmer for 40 to 45 minutes.

About 20 minutes before the beans are done, cook the rice according to the package directions.

Fill the bottom of a steamer with water, add the bacon and bring to a boil. Make sure there is not enough water to boil up through the holes in the bottom of the steamer basket. If the turkey breast is whole, cut it into 3 to 4 pieces. When the water is boiling, place the turkey in the basket, cover, and steam for 15 minutes. Remove and chop.

Combine the 3 tablespoons water and the onion in a large skillet. Cook for about 5 minutes over medium heat, stirring, until the onion is soft. Add the garlic, minced thyme, and spices. Cook for 2 minutes more, stirring often. Add the chopped turkey and the spinach and heat through (about 5 minutes).

Stir the contents of the skillet into the cooked beans. Add the tablespoon of vinegar and a bit of pepper, if desired, and stir. If the mixture seems dry, add some water or stock.

Serve the beans over the cooked rice with hot sauce and vinegar on the side.

Yield — 8 servings
Fat per serving — 0.94 g.

Scallops with Red Lentil Pilaf

The pale apricot of the cooked lentils contrasts strikingly with the pure white scallops, while the crunch of the lentils is juxtaposed against the smooth-textured shellfish.

LENTIL PILAF:
2 tablespoons trimmed and chopped
  scallions (2–3 scallions)
⅛ cup seeded, diced green bell pepper
⅓ cup peeled, diced carrot (about 1 carrot)
½ cup peeled, diced zucchini (about 1
  small zucchini)
½ cup dried red lentils
1 cup 99% Fat-Free Chicken Stock
  (page 10)

½ teaspoon minced garlic
Dash of freshly ground black pepper,
  to taste
2 tablespoons chopped fresh parsley

SCALLOPS:
12 ounces uncooked bay scallops
½ cup dry white wine
Snipped fresh chives, for garnish

To make the pilaf, combine the vegetables in a heavy frying pan. Cook for about 5 minutes over low heat, stirring constantly, until the scallion wilts.

Add the lentils, chicken stock, and garlic. Stir. Bring to a boil over medium heat, then lower the heat, cover, and simmer for 10 minutes. Stir in the black pepper and parsley. Take care not to overcook; the lentils should have a crunch.

While the lentils simmer, bring to a boil enough water to fill a shallow, flat-bottomed baking dish about halfway.

When the pilaf if done, transfer it to four 4-ounce custard cups. Place the cups in the baking dish to keep warm in the hot water while you cook the scallops.

Preheat a nonstick frying pan over medium heat. Add the scallops and cook for 30 seconds, stirring constantly. Add the wine and cook for another 2 minutes.

To serve, unmold each cup of pilaf in the center of a dinner plate. Encircle it with scallops and garnish with chives.

Yield—4 servings
Fat per serving—0.92 g.

Pasta with Smoked Chicken and Pea Pods

9 ounces uncooked thin-strand pasta
(see Pantry)
1 cup thinly sliced white onion (about
1 medium onion)
1 tablespoon water
1 tablespoon coarsely chopped garlic
(about 3 cloves)
4 ounces red bell pepper, seeded and thinly
sliced

4 ounces Chinese pea pods
3 ounces skinless smoked chicken breast,
thinly sliced
1/4 cup shredded fresh basil
1/8 teaspoon salt
1/8 teaspoon freshly ground black pepper
1 cup 99% Fat-Free Chicken Stock
(page 10)

Cook the pasta in a large pot of boiling water over high heat to desired tenderness (3 to 4 minutes for homemade or other fresh pasta, 8 to 10 minutes for dry). Drain and set aside.

Combine the onion and water in a nonstick frying pan. Cook for about 4 minutes over medium-low heat, shaking the pan a little, until the onion is wilted. Add the garlic, bell pepper, and pea pods. Cover and cook for 2 minutes. Add the chicken and seasonings, cover, and cook for another 5 minutes.

While this mixture is cooking, return the pasta to the pot and add the chicken stock. Cook over medium-low to medium heat, stirring, until most of the stock has been absorbed. Turn off the heat, add the chicken mixture, toss, and serve.

Yield — 6 servings
Fat per serving — 0.83 g.

A satisfying dish with Chinese overtones. Its rich, smoky flavor demonstrates how much can be achieved with the addition of just a little smoked poultry.

Spicy Turkey Chili

This is a unique chili, set apart both by its firm, almost crunchy texture and by the inclusion of turkey meatballs.

12 ounces skinless turkey breast, ground (see Pantry)
2 tablespoons water
1 cup chopped white onion (about 1 medium onion)
¼ cup seeded, chopped green bell pepper
¼ cup seeded, chopped red bell pepper
½ tablespoon minced garlic (about 2 cloves)
One 28-ounce can peeled Italian-style plum tomatoes, with their juice

2 tablespoons white wine vinegar
2 tablespoons chopped fresh oregano
¼ cup chopped fresh cilantro, plus additional for garnish
1 teaspoon hot chili powder
1 teaspoon ground cumin
½ teaspoon cayenne pepper
⅛ teaspoon salt
1½ cups cooked white beans
6 tablespoons peeled, diced cucumber, for garnish

Roll the ground turkey into meatballs, using about 2 tablespoons for each meatball.

Put the meatballs into a heavy nonstick frying pan over medium-low heat. Shake the pan periodically to ensure that the meatballs cook evenly. Cook for about 5 minutes, just enough for the meatballs to brown lightly and form a slight crust, which will help them hold their shape. Transfer the meatballs to a heavy kettle or Dutch oven.

Combine the water, onion, bell peppers, and garlic in the frying pan. Cook for about 6 minutes over low heat, stirring frequently, until the onion is wilted and the pepper soft. Add the cooked vegetables to the turkey.

Add the tomatoes and their juice to the kettle, crushing the tomatoes slightly with the side of a spoon. Add all the remaining ingredients except the beans and cucumber; stir. Cover partially and simmer for 20 minutes over medium-low heat. Stir in the beans and simmer, uncovered, for 10 minutes more.

Garnish each serving with a little chopped cilantro and a tablespoon of diced cucumber.

Yield — 6 servings
Fat per serving — 0.95 g.

Pasta in Garlic Sauce with Shrimp and Broccoli

10 cloves garlic
1 cup 99% Fat Free Chicken Stock
  (page 10)
7 ounces uncooked thin-strand pasta
  (see Pantry)
2 tablespoons water
1 pound broccoli flowerets (about
  1 large head)

½ cup sliced white onion (about
  1 small onion)
½ pound uncooked medium shrimp (about
  24), peeled, deveined, and halved
½ cup chopped fresh dill
⅛ teaspoon red pepper flakes
Dash of salt and freshly ground black
  pepper, to taste

This clear, thin garlic sauce is a noteworthy change from the heavy mound under which pasta typically is buried. It lends both a permeating flavor and a gloss to the pasta, set off by flecks of seafood and vegetables.

Put the garlic and stock in a small nonreactive saucepan and bring to a boil over medium heat. Reduce the heat to low and cover. Simmer for about 20 minutes, until the garlic is soft and easily mashed with a fork. Transfer the contents of the pan to a food processor or blender and puree until smooth. Set aside.

Bring a large pot of water to a boil. Add the pasta, stirring to make sure the strands don't stick together, and cook over high heat to desired tenderness (3 to 4 minutes for homemade or other fresh pasta, 8 to 10 minutes for dry).

Meanwhile, put 1 tablespoon of the water in a nonstick frying pan and bring to a boil over medium heat. Add the broccoli and onion, reduce the heat to low, cover, and cook for 3 minutes. Add the shrimp, dill, and the remaining tablespoon of water. Stir, re-cover, and cook for 4 to 5 minutes more, until the shrimp turn pink. Remove from the heat.

When the pasta is done, drain it in a colander and return it to the pot over very low heat. Add the garlic puree and mix well to coat the pasta. Add the broccoli-shrimp mixture and the seasonings. Toss together until well blended and serve immediately.

Yield — 6 servings
Fat per serving — 1.0 g.

Cumin Noodles

This dish combines culinary influences from the American Southwest and the Pacific rim to create an interesting medley of flavors.

2 tablespoons soy sauce
6 ounces uncooked skinless, boneless chicken breast, thinly sliced
12 ounces soba noodles (Japanese buckwheat noodles)
2 tablespoons water
4 ounces snow peas, trimmed and quartered

1 teaspoon chopped garlic (1–1½ cloves)
¾ cup 99% Fat-Free Chicken Stock (page 10)
1½ teaspoons ground cumin
2 tablespoons chopped fresh cilantro
3 scallions (about 3 ounces total), trimmed and julienned
½ teaspoon freshly ground black pepper

Fill a large saucepan with water and bring to a boil.

Meanwhile, combine ½ tablespoon of the soy sauce with the sliced chicken and mix to coat the chicken well. Set aside.

When the water boils, add the noodles and cook for 2 minutes over high heat. Drain and rinse under cold running water.

Put the 2 tablespoons of water into a deep-sided nonstick frying pan over low heat. When warm, add the chicken and the snow peas and cook for 3 minutes, stirring constantly. Add the garlic and cook for 1 minute more.

Raise the heat to medium. Add the drained noodles, the chicken stock, the remaining 1½ tablespoons soy sauce, and the cumin. Toss. Add the cilantro, scallions, and pepper. Cook for another 2 minutes, again stirring constantly. Serve immediately.

Yield — 6 servings
Fat per serving — 0.97 g.

Chicken Vesuvio

6 ounces uncooked skinless, boneless
    chicken breast
2 medium red potatoes (about 5 ounces
    each), cut into 8 spears each
¼ pound white button mushrooms,
    stemmed and cut into large chunks
One 14-ounce can artichoke bottoms,
    drained and halved

2 tablespoons freshly squeezed lemon juice
2 tablespoons pear nectar
½ tablespoon chopped garlic (about
    2 cloves)
½ tablespoon chopped fresh rosemary

Trim any excess fat from the chicken breast and cut the breast into 2-inch cubes.

Combine the chicken cubes, potato spears, mushrooms, and artichokes in a very large bowl.

Mix the remaining ingredients thoroughly and pour on top. Toss to coat well. Cover and marinate in the refrigerator for at least 30 minutes.

Preheat the oven to 450 degrees.

Transfer the mixture to a baking dish large enough to hold all the ingredients in a single layer. Bake for 20 minutes.

Yield — 4 servings
Fat per serving — 0.93 g.

We replaced oil with pear nectar for this old Chicago favorite, which is a garlic lover's delight. Our version comes out crisp and imbued with a subtle hue from the nectar.

We serve these tacos soft, in the traditional Mexican manner, rather than frying the tortillas before stuffing them. The cool salsa, thick and filled with jicama chunks, provides a nice contrast in temperature and texture.

Chicken Tacos with Jicama Salsa

Eight 7-inch corn tortillas

FILLING:
6 slices smoked bacon, cut into cubes (see Pantry)
6 ounces uncooked skinless, boneless chicken breast
1½ tablespoons chopped fresh cilantro
2 tablespoons water
½ teaspoon seeded, finely chopped fresh jalapeño pepper
1 cup chopped spinach (chop spinach in strips crosswise)

JICAMA SALSA:
1 cup seeded, chopped yellow tomato (about 1 tomato)
1 cup peeled, finely diced jicama
¼ cup coarsely chopped red onion
2 tablespoons seeded, coarsely chopped fresh jalapeño pepper (about 1 small jalapeño)
½ tablespoon finely chopped garlic (about 2 cloves)
2 teaspoons freshly squeezed lime juice
2 tablespoons chopped fresh cilantro

Preheat the oven to its lowest setting.

Wrap the tortillas in a clean kitchen towel and place them in the oven to keep warm.

Fill the bottom of a steamer with water and add the bacon. Bring to a boil, making sure there is not enough water to boil up through the holes in the bottom of the steamer basket. If the chicken breast is whole, cut it into 3 or 4 pieces. When the water is boiling, place the chicken in the basket, cover, and steam for 15 minutes. Remove and shred the chicken.

To make the salsa, mix the tomato, jicama, and onion well. Mix in the remaining salsa ingredients and set aside.

Place 4 dinner plates in the oven to warm.

To make the filling, combine the shredded chicken, water, cilantro, and jalapeño pepper in a small nonstick frying pan over medium heat. Cook for 1 to 2 minutes, stirring constantly, just to heat through (be careful not to dry out the chicken).

Remove the tortillas and dinner plates from the oven. Assemble the tacos by spreading a little spinach in the center of each and topping it with the chicken mixture. Roll each one into a cylinder and place 2 tacos on each warmed dinner plate. Surround with the salsa and serve immediately.

Yield — 4 servings
Fat per serving — 0.86 g.

Curried Lobster Risotto

This dish is made for entertaining. Everyone loves lobster. We keep lobster tails on hand in the freezer so that we can put this together on barely a moment's notice. The preparation time for a thick, creamy risotto is brief. You can even put your guests to work stirring the rice.

5 cups 99% Fat-Free Chicken Stock (page 10)
4 ounces snow peas, trimmed and cut into quarters on the diagonal
Six 3-ounce uncooked warm-water lobster tails (such as rock lobster)
⅓ cup chopped shallots (about 2 large shallots)

½ tablespoon minced garlic (about 2 cloves)
2 tablespoons water
1½ cups uncooked arborio rice
½ cup chopped fresh parsley, loosely packed
½ tablespoon curry powder

Bring the chicken stock to a boil, lower the heat, and maintain at a simmer.

Fill a small saucepan about three quarters full with water and bring to a boil over high heat. Add the snow peas and blanch for 20 seconds. Immediately drain and rinse under cold water. Set aside.

Fill the bottom of a steamer with water and bring to a boil. Add the lobster, cover, and steam for about 5 minutes, until the shells turn red. Cool a bit, then cut the soft white underside with scissors, remove the meat, and slice it into medallions.

Combine the shallots, garlic, and water in a heavy-bottomed saucepan. Cook for 4 minutes over low heat, stirring constantly. Add the rice and cook, stirring, for another 3 minutes.

Slowly add ½ cup of the hot stock, stirring constantly. Allow to come to a simmer. Once the stock has been absorbed, add another ½ cup of stock and bring back to a simmer, always stirring.

Continue adding hot stock, ½ cup at a time. When only about 1 cup of stock remains to be added, stir the snow peas, lobster, parsley, and curry powder into the rice, then add ½ cup of chicken stock and stir until absorbed. Add the remaining ½ cup of stock and stir until all the stock is absorbed and the rice is creamy. Preparation of this risotto should take 15 to 20 minutes from the first addition of stock. Serve immediately.

Yield—6 servings
Fat per serving—0.97 g.

Shrimp and Leek Risotto

The quality of the rice is critical to any risotto; it's best made from arborio. We seal the kernels by adding them to the hot pan in which the vegetables have been prepared, rather than coating them with butter. The whole dish can be made in less than half an hour, but vigilance and careful attention to stirring the rice are crucial.

6 cups 99% Fat-Free Chicken Stock (page 10)
1 cup trimmed, sliced leek, white and light green parts only (about 4 ounces trimmed)
2 cups uncooked arborio rice
1 cup dry white wine

½ pound uncooked medium shrimp, peeled, deveined, and cut into chunks
Dash of salt and freshly ground black pepper, to taste
4 teaspoons freshly grated Parmesan cheese

Bring the stock to a boil over medium heat. Lower the heat and keep at a constant simmer.

Put the leek in a heavy saucepan and sauté dry over low heat for about 5 minutes, stirring constantly, until soft. Add the rice and cook, stirring constantly, for 2 minutes.

Slowly add 1½ cups of the hot stock, stirring constantly. Allow the liquid to come to a simmer. Once the stock has been absorbed, add another 1½ cups and bring the mixture back to a simmer, stirring constantly. When this additional stock has been absorbed, stir in the wine and shrimp.

Continue adding hot stock, ½ cup at a time, until absorbed, stirring constantly, until the risotto is tender and creamy. The entire process, from addition of the first 1½ cups of stock, should take 20 to 25 minutes.

Stir in a dash of salt and pepper, along with the grated cheese. Serve immediately.

Yield—8 servings
Fat per serving—0.79 g.

6

Side
DISHES

Gratin of Root Vegetables

9 ounces rutabaga, peeled
12 ounces sweet potato, peeled
6 ounces parsnip, peeled
2 ounces parsley root, peeled
1 teaspoon ground nutmeg

Dash of salt and freshly ground black
  pepper, to taste
9 ounces leek, trimmed and thinly sliced
1 cup buttermilk

Preheat the oven to 400 degrees.

Very thinly slice the rutabaga, sweet potato, parsnip, and parsley root with a mandoline cutter.

Layer the rutabaga slices on the bottom of a gratin dish. Sprinkle about ¼ teaspoon of the nutmeg on top and lightly dust with salt and pepper. Top with layers of sweet potato and parsnip, sprinkling ¼ teaspoon of nutmeg and a dash of salt and pepper between each layer. Layer the leek on top, leaving an open circle in the center. Place the parsley root in the circle. Dust the top with salt, pepper, and the remaining nutmeg. Carefully pour the buttermilk down the sides and into the center of the dish.

Bake for 30 to 35 minutes, until the top has browned.

Yield — 8 servings
Fat per serving — 0.69 g.

This is the most complex of our gratins. The flavors of the root vegetables, sliced paper thin and layered, intermingle with the creamy buttermilk and the hint of sweetness provided by the nutmeg.

Steamed Bitter Greens

This is basic and satisfying fare that goes well with such poultry dishes as Turkey Medallions (page 84).

4 ounces turnip greens, trimmed
4 ounces mustard greens, trimmed
4 ounces spinach, trimmed

4 strips smoked bacon, cut into cubes
   (see Pantry)
1 teaspoon rice wine vinegar

Tear the mustard greens and spinach leaves in half, the turnip greens in thirds. Rinse thoroughly under cold running water, taking care to pick out any residual grit. Set aside to drain.

Fill the bottom of a steamer with water and add the bacon. Bring to a boil, taking care that the water level is not high enough to boil up through the holes in the bottom of the steamer basket. Put the greens in the steamer basket, cover, and steam for about 3 minutes, until wilted.

Toss in the vinegar before serving.

Yield — 4 servings
Fat per serving — 0.18 g.

Couscous with Vegetables

1½ cups 99% Fat-Free Chicken Stock
   (page 10)
1 cup uncooked couscous
One 8-ounce can garbanzo beans, rinsed
   and drained
1 teaspoon chopped garlic (about 1 clove)
½ cup finely chopped yellow onion
⅔ cup seeded, roughly chopped yellow
   bell pepper
½ cup trimmed and chopped celery
   (about 1 stalk)

½ cup peeled, finely chopped carrot
   (about 1 small carrot)
¼ cup water
2 tablespoons sherry
¼ teaspoon freshly ground black pepper
¼ teaspoon ground allspice
⅛ teaspoon ground mace
½ teaspoon salt

Bring the stock to boil in a saucepan. Stir in the couscous, cover, and remove from the heat. After 5 minutes, fluff the couscous, re-cover, and set aside.

Combine the garbanzo beans, garlic, vegetables, water, and sherry in a nonstick frying pan. Cover and cook for 10 minutes over medium heat. Add the seasonings and stir.

To serve, ring the couscous around a platter and mound the vegetable mixture in the center.

Yield — 6 servings
Fat per serving — 0.43 g.

Stuffed Zucchini

One 4-ounce red bell pepper
4 baby zucchini (about 1 pound total),
 trimmed
¼ cup plus 2 tablespoons water
¼ cup chopped white onion
1 teaspoon finely chopped garlic
 (about 1 clove)
½ cup seeded, finely chopped tomato
Dash of freshly ground black pepper,
 to taste

1 teaspoon dried fines herbes (a French
 seasoning mixture, available in most
 supermarkets)
½ teaspoon coarse kosher salt
⅓ cup cooked pearled barley
½ teaspoon freshly grated Parmesan
 cheese

Preheat the broiler and line the rack with aluminum foil.

Cut the bell pepper in half lengthwise, core, and seed.

Place the pepper on the rack, cut side down, 2 to 3 inches from the heat source. Broil for about 5 minutes, until charred. Remove the pepper carefully, leaving the broiler on.

Seal the pepper in an airtight plastic bag and let cool for about 10 minutes. Remove from the plastic bag, rub off the skin, and chop. (This should yield about ¼ cup chopped pepper.)

Cut a thin slice off the entire top length of each zucchini, and a partial slice in the center of the bottom side, just enough to allow the zucchini to set flat. Hollow out the zucchini by making a rectangular incision around the top, leaving a ¼-inch outer border. Scoop out, chop, and reserve the meat.

Place the zucchini, hollowed side down, in a small nonstick frying pan. Add the ¼ cup water and cook for 5 minutes over medium heat.

Meanwhile, combine the chopped zucchini, onion, garlic, tomato, black pepper to taste, chopped roasted bell pepper, and the 2 tablespoons water in another small pan. Cook, uncovered, for about 7 minutes over medium-low heat, until all the liquid in the pan (including that given off by the vegetables) has evaporated.

Transfer the mixture to a bowl and add the fine herbes, salt, and barley. Mix well and spoon into the hollow cavities of the zucchini. Sprinkle with the Parmesan cheese. Place on a foil-lined shallow baking dish and broil for about 2 minutes, until the tops of the stuffed zucchini are browned and crusty.

Yield—4 servings
Fat per serving—0.51 g.

Horseradish Mashed Potatoes

Celery root and parsley root add character to this unusual variation on the once basic mashed potato. The addition of horseradish gives the combination a special zest.

4 ounces celery root, peeled and cut into chunks
8 ounces red potatoes (about 2 medium potatoes), peeled and cut into chunks
¼ cup peeled, chopped parsley root

½ teaspoon chopped garlic
1 teaspoon prepared white horseradish
⅛ teaspoon white pepper
¼ teaspoon coarse kosher salt
¼ cup buttermilk

Bring a saucepan of water to a boil over high heat. Add the celery root and cook for 5 minutes, uncovered. Add the potatoes and parsley root. Cook for another 15 minutes, then drain.

Put the mixture through a ricer into a serving bowl. Add the remaining ingredients, stir with a fork, and serve.

Yield — 4 servings
Fat per serving — 0.29 g.

Cajun Red Beans and Rice

1 cup chopped white onion
(about 1 medium onion)
¼ cup trimmed, chopped scallions
(2–3 scallions)
½ tablespoon minced garlic
(about 2 cloves)
⅔ cup seeded, chopped yellow bell pepper
Two 15-ounce cans red kidney beans,
drained and rinsed

3½ ounces skinless smoked turkey breast,
chopped
2 cups 99% Fat-Free Smoked Turkey
Stock (page 8)
2 cups cooked white rice
¼ teaspoon freshly ground black pepper
½ teaspoon dried thyme
1 bay leaf
½ teaspoon salt

Combine the onion, scallions, garlic, and bell pepper in a saucepan. Cook for about 5 minutes over medium-low heat, until the onion turns translucent.

Add all the remaining ingredients. Bring to a boil over medium heat, cover, reduce the heat, and simmer for 30 minutes.

Yield—6 servings (4 servings as main course)
Fat per serving—0.64 g. (0.96 g. as main course)

Turnip Gratin

1 tablespoon chopped garlic (3–4 cloves)
1 pound turnips (3–4 turnips), peeled and
cut into ⅛-inch slices
2 teaspoons dried fines herbes (a French
seasoning mixture, available in most
supermarkets)
Dash of salt and freshly ground black
pepper, to taste

½ pound red potatoes (about 2 small
potatoes), peeled and sliced ⅛ inch thick
½ cup buttermilk
½ cup homemade bread crumbs
(see Pantry)

Preheat the oven to 400 degrees.

Sprinkle 1 teaspoon of the garlic on the bottom of a gratin dish. Layer with about half the turnip slices. Sprinkle with half the fines herbes and a dash of salt and pepper.

Scatter a second teaspoon of garlic over the seasoned turnip slices, then add a layer of potato slices. Top with the remaining fines herbes, another dusting of salt and pepper, and the rest of the garlic.

Arrange the final layer of turnip slices on top, pour the buttermilk over all, and top with the bread crumbs.

Bake for 35 to 40 minutes, until the bread crumbs are brown.

Yield—6 servings
Fat per serving—0.31 g.

Smoked Okra

4 slices smoked bacon, cut into cubes
   (see Pantry)

1 pound small okra pods, trimmed
¼ cup rice wine vinegar

Fill the bottom of a steamer with water, add the bacon, and bring to a boil, making sure there is not enough water to boil up through the holes in the bottom of the steamer basket. Put the okra into the basket, cover, and steam for 3 to 4 minutes, until fork tender.

Turn immediately into a warm serving dish, toss with the vinegar, and serve.

Yield — 4 servings
Fat per serving — 0.10 g.

Everything old is new again. Long in culinary limbo, okra has been rediscovered by a new generation of home cooks. This pleasantly smoky update eschews the fats of traditional Southern cooking and renders the pods drier and crisper. A great alternative to string beans.

Turnip and Onion Puree

A robust side dish that presents classic root vegetables in a new manner.

10 ounces turnip, peeled and cut into
    eighths (about 1 large turnip)
10 ounces white onion, quartered
    (about 1 medium onion)
2 ounces new red potato, peeled and halved
    (about 1 small potato)

⅛ teaspoon ground nutmeg
⅛ teaspoon freshly ground black pepper
¼ cup buttermilk

Combine the turnip, onion, and potato in a saucepan and add water to cover. Bring to a boil over medium heat, cover, and cook for about 20 minutes, until the vegetables are fork tender.

Drain and transfer the vegetables to a food processor or blender. Add the nutmeg and pepper. Puree to a smooth consistency, while gradually adding the buttermilk.

Return the puree to the saucepan and bring to a boil over medium heat. Stir and serve immediately.

Yield — 4 servings
Fat per serving — 0.36 g.

Cumin Rice with Black Beans

½ cup peeled, chopped carrot (about
   1 small carrot)
½ cup chopped white onion
1 teaspoon chopped garlic (about 1 clove)
½ teaspoon chopped fresh thyme
1 teaspoon ground cumin
¼ teaspoon dried coriander

½ teaspoon salt
1 cup uncooked long-grain white rice
1 cup cooked black beans
1²/₃ cups 99% Fat-Free Chicken Stock
   (page 10)
2 tablespoons chopped fresh cilantro
1 tablespoon freshly squeezed lime juice

Combine the carrot, onion, and garlic in a saucepan and cook for 5 minutes over low heat, until the onion is wilted, stirring constantly. Add the thyme, cumin, coriander, and salt, then stir in the rice. Add the beans and stock, raise the heat to medium-high, and bring to a boil. Cover, lower the heat, and simmer for 15 minutes.

Stir in the cilantro and lime juice and serve.

Yield—4 servings
Fat per serving—0.44 g.

We made this dish, which was inspired by Cuban black beans and rice, healthier and thicker in texture, adding some new seasoning twists in the process.

Corn and Carrot Puree

1 cup peeled, chunked carrots (about 2 carrots)
½ cup corn kernels (about 1 small ear)
½ cup water

¼ cup buttermilk
⅛ teaspoon freshly ground black pepper
⅛ teaspoon ground nutmeg
Snipped fresh chives, for garnish

Combine the carrots, corn, and water in a small, heavy-bottomed saucepan. Bring to a boil over medium heat, taking care not to boil off the water. Cover, reduce the heat, and simmer for about 10 minutes, until the carrots are fork tender.

Drain and transfer the solid ingredients to a food processor or blender and puree to a smooth consistency. Return the puree to the pan, and whisk in the buttermilk, pepper, and nutmeg. Warm for about 1 minute over low heat. Sprinkle with the chives and serve.

Yield—4 servings
Fat per serving—0.45 g.

Oven-Baked Potato Chips

2 medium red potatoes (about 10
  ounces total)

Light vegetable oil cooking spray
1 teaspoon celery salt

Preheat the oven to 350 degrees.

Slice the potatoes very thin, using a mandoline slicer.

Lightly spray a nonstick baking sheet twice with the vegetable oil spray and distribute the oil evenly over the surface.

Arrange the potato slices in a single layer on the baking sheet. Bake for 5 minutes, then turn the slices over. After another 5 minutes, sprinkle with about half the celery salt, flip again, and sprinkle the other side with the remaining salt. Bake for 5 minutes more, until crisp and browned.

Yield—4 servings
Fat per serving—0.65 g. (about 15 chips)

Simple, healthful, and quite satisfying, oven-baked potatoes can stand alone as a light snack or accompany a salad, sandwiches, or soup. Heap them in a colorfully lined, decorative wicker basket.

Minted Pea Puree

¼ cup chopped fresh mint
1 cup shelled peas (about 1 pound pods)
¾ cup water

1 tablespoon skim milk
⅛ teaspoon freshly ground black pepper

Put the mint, peas, and water in a small saucepan and bring to a boil over medium heat. Simmer for 10 to 15 minutes, uncovered, until the peas are easily mashed with a fork.

Drain and transfer the solid ingredients to the bowl of a food processor or blender and puree until smooth.

Return the mixture to the saucepan over low heat. Whisk in the milk and pepper and heat through, about 1 minute. Serve immediately.

Yield—4 servings
Fat per serving—0.28 g.

Saffron Rice

½ cup diced yellow onion (about
    1 small onion)
½ cup seeded, diced red bell pepper
1 teaspoon finely chopped garlic
    (about 1 clove)
2 tablespoons water
1 cup uncooked long-grain white rice
½ cup shelled peas (about 8 ounces pods)

Scant ⅛ teaspoon saffron threads
1¼ cups 99% Fat-Free Chicken Stock
    (page 10)
¼ teaspoon salt
⅛ teaspoon freshly ground black pepper
¼ teaspoon dried thyme
¼ teaspoon dried oregano
Chopped fresh parsley, for garnish

Combine the onion, bell pepper, garlic, and water in a saucepan. Cook for 4 minutes over medium-low heat, stirring occasionally. Add the rice, peas, and saffron. Cook for 30 seconds, stirring constantly. Stir in the stock and seasonings. Raise the heat to medium and bring to a boil. Cover, lower the heat, and simmer for 15 minutes.

Garnish with parsley before serving.

Yield—4 servings
Fat per serving—0.16 g.

This vibrant yellow rice, which derives its distinctive color from the saffron, will be instantly recognizable to devotees of Spanish cuisine as the basis for paella.

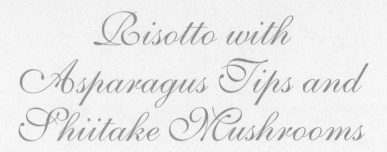

Risotto with Asparagus Tips and Shiitake Mushrooms

We think risotto is just about perfect for any occasion—it can serve as hearty and homey comfort food or stylish party fare equally well. It's extraordinarily simple once you get the hang of the stirring, and it can be made in a matter of minutes.

4 large dried shiitake mushrooms (about ¾ ounce)
2 cups hot water
1½ cups trimmed asparagus tips (about 8 ounces)
2½ cups 99% Fat-Free Chicken Stock (page 10)

1 cup uncooked arborio rice
½ cup dry white wine
Dash of salt and freshly ground black pepper, to taste
1 tablespoon chopped flat-leaf parsley
3 teaspoons freshly grated Parmesan cheese

Place the mushrooms in the hot water and soak for 15 minutes.

Microwave the asparagus tips for 1 minute at full power and set aside.

Put the chicken stock in a small saucepan and bring to a boil over medium heat. Lower the heat and maintain at a simmer.

Remove the mushrooms from their soaking liquid. Strain 1 cup of the liquid into a measuring cup and reserve it. Cut away the woody stems of the mushrooms and slice them into matchsticks.

Put the rice in a heavy saucepan and warm it over low heat, stirring constantly, for 1 minute. While continuing to stir, slowly add 1 cup of the hot stock. Bring to a simmer, and, when the stock has been absorbed into the rice, stir in the reserved cup of strained mushroom water and bring back to a simmer. When this liquid has been absorbed, stir in the mushrooms, asparagus, and wine.

Continue to add stock, ½ cup at a time, stirring constantly, until the rice is creamy and tender. The total cooking time from addition of the first cup of stock is 15 to 20 minutes.

Stir in the salt and pepper, if desired, and the parsley. Sprinkle ½ teaspoon of Parmesan cheese over each portion and serve immediately.

Yield — 6 servings
Fat per serving — 0.40 g.

Mushroom Basmati

We've limited the ingredients in this dish to showcase the hearty, aromatic personality of the domestic brown rice.

½ cup trimmed and chopped celery (about 1 stalk)
½ cup chopped yellow onion (about 1 small onion)
1 teaspoon chopped garlic (about 1 clove)
1 teaspoon chopped fresh thyme
¼ teaspoon ground sage
1 cup sliced white button mushrooms (about 4 ounces)

½ teaspoon salt
⅛ teaspoon freshly ground black pepper
1 cup uncooked domestic basmati brown rice
2 cups 99% Fat-Free Chicken Stock (page 10)

Combine the celery, onion, and garlic in a saucepan and cook for 5 minutes over low heat, stirring constantly. Stir in the thyme and sage. Add the mushrooms and stir. Stir in the salt and pepper. Add the rice, mix for 30 seconds, then add the stock. Raise the heat and bring to a boil. Stir, cover, lower the heat, and simmer for 45 minutes.

Remove from the heat and set aside, covered, for 5 minutes more before serving.

Yield—4 servings
Fat per serving—0.16 g.

Potato and Squash Gratin

10 ounces red potatoes (about 2 potatoes), peeled

1 pound acorn squash (about 1 medium squash), peeled and seeded

1 pound butternut squash (about ½ medium squash), peeled and seeded

Dash of salt and freshly ground black pepper, to taste

½ cup buttermilk

Preheat the oven to 350 degrees.

Slice the potatoes and squash very thin using a mandoline slicer.

Layer about half the potato slices on the bottom of a gratin dish. Lightly dust with salt and pepper. Top with layers of butternut squash, acorn squash, and a final layer of potato, lightly dusting each layer with salt and pepper to taste. Pour the buttermilk over and around the contents of the dish.

Bake for 30 to 35 minutes, until the top has browned.

Yield — 6 servings
Fat per serving — 0.32 g.

Wild Rice Risotto

The nutty crunchiness of the wild rice contrasts with the smooth, creamy arborio.

5 cups 99% Fat-Free Chicken Stock (page 10)
⅓ cup chopped shallots (about 2 large shallots)
½ tablespoon minced garlic (about 2 cloves)

2 tablespoons water
½ cup uncooked wild rice
1 cup uncooked arborio rice
½ cup seeded, diced red bell pepper
¾ cup corn kernels (about 1 ear)
⅓ cup chopped flat-leaf parsley

Bring the chicken stock to a boil, lower the heat, and maintain at a simmer.

Combine the shallots, garlic, and water in a heavy-bottomed saucepan. Cook for 4 minutes over low heat, stirring constantly. Add the wild rice, stir, and cook for 15 seconds. Add ¾ cup of the chicken stock, cover, and simmer for 15 minutes.

Add the arborio rice and slowly stir in another ¾ cup of the stock. Bring to a simmer. When the stock has been completely absorbed, add another ½ cup, stirring constantly, and bring back to a simmer.

Continue adding hot stock, ½ cup at a time. With the last addition, stir in the bell pepper and corn. Cook, stirring constantly, until all the stock is absorbed and the rice is creamy. The preparation should take 15 to 20 minutes from the addition of the arborio rice. Stir in the parsley and serve immediately.

Yield — 8 servings
Fat per serving — 0.36 g.

7

BREADS

Hearty Stout Bread

¼ cup buttermilk
¼ cup sugar
2 cups all-purpose flour
1 cup stone-ground rye flour
½ teaspoon baking soda

1 teaspoon baking powder
½ teaspoon salt
½ teaspoon caraway seeds
12 ounces dark, heavy-bodied stout
Light vegetable oil cooking spray

A dense, coarse bread that goes well with soups, stews, and chilies.

Preheat the oven to 350 degrees.

Put the buttermilk in a small bowl and whisk in the sugar until dissolved. Set aside.

Combine the dry ingredients in a large mixing bowl and form a well in the center. Pour in the buttermilk mixture and the stout. Stir with a wooden spoon just until blended.

Spray a 9¼-inch loaf pan once lightly with vegetable oil spray and distribute the oil evenly over the surface of the pan. Pour in the batter. Bake for 40 to 45 minutes, until the loaf begins to separate from the edges of the pan and a tester inserted into the center comes out clean.

Yield — 16 slices
Fat per slice — 0.35 g.

French Country Round

This crusty bread is extremely versatile. We serve it whole for dinner, slice it for sandwiches, and use it for croutons and bread crumbs.

1½ cups skim milk
2½ teaspoons active dry yeast (1 packet)
2 teaspoons salt
1 teaspoon sugar
3 cups all-purpose flour, plus a little
    extra for flouring during preparation

1 tablespoon cornmeal (if using a
    baking sheet)
4 ice cubes

Put the milk in a saucepan and scald over medium heat just until bubbly around the edges, making sure not to bring to a full boil. Remove from the heat and cool for a few minutes to lukewarm (105 to 115 degrees on an instant-read thermometer).

Combine ¾ cup of the lukewarm milk and the yeast in a small bowl and set aside for about 10 minutes to proof. (The mixture will begin to bubble.)

Combine the salt and sugar in a large mixing bowl. Mix in the proofed yeast and the remaining ¾ cup of milk. Continue to mix until well combined. Using a wooden spoon, gently mix in the flour, 1 cup at a time, until completely incorporated.

Transfer the dough to a lightly floured surface and gently knead for about 8 minutes, until it is smooth and elastic, and springs back to the touch. Form into a ball, flour lightly, and place in a warm, ungreased bowl. Cover with a damp cloth and set aside until the dough has doubled in size. (This should take about 2 hours in a warm kitchen.)

Punch the dough down to flatten it and remove it from the bowl. Form into a round loaf and place on a baking sheet sprinkled with cornmeal or on a baking stone. Cover and allow the dough to double a second time, about 1 hour.

Preheat the oven to 400 degrees.

Cut an "X" on the top of the loaf with a sharp knife. Place the baking sheet or baking stone on the middle rack and ice cubes on the bottom of the oven to create vapor. Bake for 30 to 40 minutes, until lightly brown. The loaf is done if it sounds hollow when lightly tapped on the bottom.

Yield — 12 slices
Fat per slice — 0.31 g.

Herbed Sandwich Braid

1½ cups lukewarm water (105 to 115 degrees on an instant-read thermometer)
2½ teaspoons active dry yeast (1 packet)
½ teaspoon salt
½ tablespoon chopped fresh dill

1 teaspoon sugar
3 cups bread flour, plus a little extra for flouring during preparation
1 tablespoon cornmeal (if using a baking sheet)
2 ice cubes

Combine ¾ cup of the lukewarm water and the yeast in a small bowl and set aside for about 10 minutes to proof. (The mixture will begin to bubble.)

Combine the salt, dill, and sugar in a large mixing bowl. Mix in the proofed yeast and the remaining ¾ cup of water. Mix well. Using a wooden spoon, gently mix in the flour, 1 cup at a time, until completely incorporated.

Transfer the dough to a lightly floured surface and knead gently for about 8 minutes, until the dough is smooth and elastic, and springs back to the touch. Form into a ball, flour lightly, and place in a warm, ungreased bowl. Cover with a damp cloth and set aside for about 2 hours in a warm place, until the dough has doubled in size.

Punch the dough down to flatten it and remove it from the bowl. Divide the dough into 3 equal portions. Flour your hands lightly and work each portion into a long thin rope about 1 inch in diameter.

Lay the strips side by side about ½ inch apart on a lightly floured surface. Crimp them together at one end and braid the strips, tucking the ends under. Carefully transfer the braided loaf to a baking sheet sprinkled with cornmeal or to a baking stone. Cover and set aside for about 1 hour, until doubled in size.

Preheat the oven to 400 degrees.

Place the baking sheet or baking stone on the middle rack and the ice cubes on the bottom of the oven to create vapor. Bake for 30 to 40 minutes, until lightly browned. The loaf is done if it sounds hollow when lightly tapped on the bottom.

Yield — 24 slices
Fat per slice — 0.26 g.

Earl Grey Dinner Rolls

1½ cups boiling water
2 Earl Grey tea bags
2½ teaspoons active dry yeast
   (1 packet)
2 teaspoons salt
1 teaspoon sugar

3 cups all-purpose flour, plus a little extra
   for flouring during preparation
1 tablespoon cornmeal
3 ice cubes

The Earl Grey tea imparts a rich, browned appearance usually achieved by painting rolls with egg yolk. It also lends a flavor redolent of cardamom.

Combine the boiling water and tea bags in a bowl and set aside to steep for a few minutes, until tea cools to lukewarm (105 to 115 degrees on an instant-read thermometer).

Remove ¾ cup of the lukewarm tea to a small bowl. Add the yeast and set aside for about 10 minutes to proof. (The mixture will begin to bubble.)

Combine the salt and sugar in a large mixing bowl. Mix in the proofed yeast and the remaining ¾ cup of tea. Continue to mix until well combined. Using a wooden spoon, gently mix in the flour, 1 cup at a time, until completely incorporated.

Transfer the dough to a lightly floured surface and knead gently for about 8 minutes, until the dough is smooth and elastic, and springs back to the touch. Form it into a ball, flour lightly, and place in a warm, ungreased bowl. Cover with a damp cloth and set aside for about 2 hours, until the dough has doubled in size.

Punch the dough down to flatten it and remove it from the bowl. Cut the dough into 12 equal pieces, shape each piece into an oval, and place the ovals on a heavy cookie sheet sprinkled with cornmeal. Cover, and allow the dough to double a second time, about 1 hour.

Preheat the oven to 400 degrees.

Cut a slit down the center on the top of each oval with a sharp knife. Place the baking sheet on the middle rack of the oven and the ice cubes on the bottom to create vapor. Bake the rolls for 20 to 25 minutes, until lightly browned. The rolls are done if they sound hollow when lightly tapped on the bottom.

Yield — 12 rolls
Fat per roll — 0.26 g.

Chocolate-Cherry Bread

The addition of cocoa adds richness and complexity to this bread, not sweetness. It's a singular dinner bread with a heartiness and texture seldom found in nonyeast breads.

¼ pound dried sour cherries
¼ cup boiling water
1¼ cups medium rye flour
1¾ cups plus ½ teaspoon all-purpose flour
1½ teaspoons baking powder
1 teaspoon baking soda
1 teaspoon salt
3 tablespoons unsweetened Dutch-processed cocoa powder
3 tablespoons nonfat liquid egg substitute
¼ cup honey
2 tablespoons natural unsweetened applesauce
¾ teaspoon vanilla extract
1 cup buttermilk
1 tablespoon cornmeal

Preheat the oven to 375 degrees.

Mix the cherries and boiling water in a small bowl and set aside.

Sift the rye flour, 1½ cups of the all-purpose flour, the baking powder, baking soda, salt, and cocoa powder together into a large mixing bowl.

In a separate bowl, beat the liquid egg substitute until frothy with an electric mixer. Add the honey, applesauce, vanilla extract, and buttermilk. Beat to mix.

Add the egg mixture to the flour mixture and blend with a wooden spoon just until the flour is absorbed. Drain the cherries and stir them into the mixture. Sprinkle ¼ cup of all-purpose flour over the top and work by hand into a dough ball. Let the dough sit in the bowl for 5 minutes.

Transfer the dough to a nonstick cookie sheet sprinkled with the cornmeal. Using a sieve, dust the top of the dough with the remaining ½ teaspoon flour. With a sharp knife that has been dipped in flour, cut an "X" in the center of the bread.

Bake for 40 to 50 minutes, until a tester inserted into the center comes out clean.

Yield—12 slices
Fat per slice—0.61 g.

Orange-Bran Muffins

2 cups all-purpose flour
2½ teaspoons baking powder
1 teaspoon baking soda
¼ teaspoon salt
½ teaspoon ground cloves
½ teaspoon ground nutmeg
¼ teaspoon ground cinnamon
¾ cup honey
1½ cups orange juice

2 cups oat bran
¼ cup buttermilk
¼ cup dark unsulphured molasses
¾ cup peeled, shredded carrot
   (1–2 carrots)
¾ cup golden raisins
¼ cup plain nonfat yogurt
Light vegetable oil cooking spray

Preheat the oven to 375 degrees.

Sift the flour, baking powder, baking soda, salt, and spices together and set aside.

Whisk the honey and orange juice to blend. Add the oat bran and whisk thoroughly.

Combine the buttermilk and molasses in a large mixing bowl and whisk well. Thoroughly mix in the carrot, then the oat bran mixture.

Add the raisins to the flour mixture and stir into the oat bran–buttermilk mixture with a wooden spoon. Fold in the yogurt.

Spray vegetable oil spray over the surface of 12 large muffin tin cups for about 3 seconds, covering as much of the exposed surface as possible. Spread the oil evenly into the wells with your fingers. Fill the wells to the top with batter. Bake for 25 to 30 minutes, until a tester inserted into the center of a muffin comes out clean.

Yield — 12 oversized muffins
Fat per muffin — 0.83 g.

In this recipe, we use a baker's paper liner to eliminate the need to oil the loaf pan to prevent sticking. The paper liners are available in most kitchenware stores.

Good Morning Zucchini Muffins

2 cups all-purpose flour
2 teaspoons baking powder
¼ teaspoon baking soda
½ teaspoon salt
6 tablespoons nonfat liquid egg substitute
1 teaspoon grated orange rind
⅓ cup light corn syrup
6 tablespoons dark brown sugar,
   firmly packed

½ teaspoon ground allspice
1¼ teaspoons ground cinnamon
¼ teaspoon ground cloves
1 cup peeled, shredded zucchini
   (about 12 ounces)
½ cup seedless raisins
Light vegetable oil cooking spray

Preheat the oven to 400 degrees.

Sift the flour, baking powder, baking soda, and salt together and set aside.

Put the egg substitute into a large mixing bowl and whisk for about 30 seconds, until frothy. Whisk in the orange rind and corn syrup. Add the sugar and spices and whisk. Whisk in the zucchini, then the raisins.

Dump this into the flour mixture and combine with a wooden spoon, just until blended.

Spray the vegetable oil spray over the surface of 12 muffin tin cups for about 3 seconds, covering as much of the exposed surface as possible. Spread the oil evenly into the wells with your fingers. Fill the wells about two-thirds full with batter. Bake for 15 minutes, until the muffins begin to separate from the sides of the tin and a tester inserted into the center of a muffin comes out clean.

Store in an airtight container.

Yield—12 muffins
Fat per muffin—0.47 g.

Banana Tea Bread

2 cups all-purpose flour
½ teaspoon baking soda
2 teaspoons baking powder
½ teaspoon salt
1¼ teaspoons ground cinnamon
¼ teaspoon ground nutmeg
⅛ teaspoon ground allspice

2 large eggs, whites only
⅔ cup buttermilk
⅔ cup light brown sugar, firmly packed
1 teaspoon vanilla extract
1⅓ cups mashed very ripe banana
   (3–4 bananas)
¼ cup light corn syrup

Preheat the oven to 375 degrees.

Sift the flour, baking soda, baking powder, salt, and spices together and set aside.

In a large mixing bowl, combine the egg whites and ⅓ cup of the buttermilk. Beat with an electric mixer at high speed for about 2 minutes, until frothy. At low speed, beat in the remaining ⅓ cup of buttermilk, the brown sugar, and the vanilla extract. Beat in the banana until well blended, then the corn syrup. Add the dry ingredients and mix with a wooden spoon just until blended.

Insert a paper liner into an 8½-inch loaf pan and pour in the batter. Bake for about 50 minutes, until the edges of the loaf begin to separate from the pan and a tester inserted into the center of the loaf comes out clean.

Yield — 16 slices
Fat per slice — 0.32 g.

Strawberry-Apple Quick Bread

1½ cups all-purpose flour
2 teaspoons baking powder
½ teaspoon salt
½ cup sugar
½ cup natural unsweetened applesauce
6 tablespoons nonfat strawberry yogurt
1 teaspoon vanilla extract

1½ teaspoons ground cinnamon
¼ teaspoon ground nutmeg
¼ cup dark brown sugar, firmly packed
¼ cup rolled oats
1¼ cups mashed very ripe banana (about
    3 medium bananas)

Preheat the oven to 375 degrees.

Sift the flour, baking powder, salt, and sugar together into a bowl.

In a large mixing bowl, combine the applesauce and yogurt. Add the vanilla, cinnamon, and nutmeg, mixing well. Beat in the brown sugar. Stir in the oats. Add the banana and mix well. Add the flour mixture and blend well with a wooden spoon.

Pour the batter into a nonstick 9¼-inch loaf pan. Bake for 40 to 50 minutes, until the loaf begins to separate from the edges of the pan and a tester inserted in the center comes out clean. Remove from the oven, cool a few minutes in the pan, then turn the loaf out onto a rack.

Yield—16 slices
Fat per slice—0.27 g.

Skillet Corn Bread

1⅓ cups yellow cornmeal
⅔ cup all-purpose flour
1 teaspoon baking powder
1 teaspoon baking soda
1 teaspoon salt
1½ cups buttermilk

¼ cup light corn syrup
2 tablespoons skim milk
5 tablespoons plain nonfat yogurt
2 large eggs, whites only
Light vegetable oil cooking spray

Put a large, heavy, well-seasoned cast-iron skillet into an oven pre-heated to 450 degrees.

Sift the dry ingredients together into a large mixing bowl. Set aside.

In another bowl, whisk together the buttermilk and corn syrup until well blended and frothy. Add the skim milk and whisk again. Whisk in the yogurt until just dissolved.

Beat the egg whites with an electric mixer until they form stiff peaks.

Pour the buttermilk mixture into the flour and blend well, using a wooden spoon. Gently fold in the beaten egg whites.

Remove the skillet from the oven and spray it 3 times lightly with vegetable oil spray. Pour in the batter, return the pan to the oven, and bake the corn bread for about 15 minutes, until the edges brown. Serve immediately.

Yield — 10 wedges
Fat per wedge — 0.87 g.

In this recipe, we have removed the fat from our favorite corn bread — a light, fluffy version with a crusty bottom derived from skillet baking.

8

DESSERTS

Flourless Chocolate Cake

2 ounces whole dried apricots
   (about 6 apricots)
½ cup cold water
¼ cup boiling water
8 large eggs, whites only (do not combine)

1 cup sugar
½ cup unsweetened Dutch-processed
   cocoa powder
1 cup Grape-Nuts cereal
Light vegetable oil cooking spray

Preheat the oven to 350 degrees.

Combine the dried apricots and the cold water in a small saucepan and bring to a boil over medium heat. Cover, reduce the heat to low, and simmer for 20 minutes.

Remove from the heat and pour into the bowl of a food processor or blender. Add the boiling water and puree until smooth. (You should have about 3 tablespoons of apricot puree.)

Combine the puree, 2 of the egg whites, the sugar, and the cocoa powder in a large mixing bowl. Whisk together well. Add the Grape-Nuts and mix with a wooden spoon.

Using an electric mixer (preferably the heavy, stationary type), beat the 6 remaining egg whites at medium speed until they form stiff, dry peaks.

Add a third of the beaten egg whites to the apricot-cocoa mixture and stir with a wooden spoon until thoroughly incorporated. Add the remaining egg whites. Fold gently with a slotted spoon until completely incorporated.

Spray the bottom and sides of a 9-inch springform pan once lightly with the vegetable oil spray. Spread the oil evenly over the surface of the pan with your fingers.

Slowly pour in the batter, shaking the pan gently to even the top. Bake for about 25 minutes, until the cake is firm to the touch in the center and the sides begin to pull away from the pan.

Remove from the oven, place the pan on a rack, and cool thoroughly. The cake will shrink some as it cools.

Yield — 10 servings
Fat per serving — 0.65 g.

This is an elegant finale to the most stylish of meals, one that will humble more fatty desserts by comparison. Don't be put off by the use of Grape-Nuts, which provide all the taste and texture of real nuts with none of the guilt. Keep in mind that the trick to making this flourless cake is taking care not to overbeat the egg whites.

Let the cake stand on its own: Finish it with a sprinkling of powdered sugar, or fan a strawberry on each slice. We also like it topped with the Roasted Banana Sauce or Mixed Berry Sauce (page 177 or 180).

Pumpkin Swirl Cheesecake

The eye-catching swirl will add a festive accent to your dessert board. This cheesecake derives its buttery texture from the inclusion of pumpkin puree.

CRUST:

1¼ cups rolled oats
2 tablespoons dark brown sugar, firmly packed
2 tablespoons all-purpose flour
¼ cup pear nectar
Light vegetable oil cooking spray

FILLING:

1½ cups Yogurt Cheese (see Pantry)
¼ cup plain nonfat yogurt
¾ cup granulated sugar
1 teaspoon vanilla extract
6 tablespoons nonfat liquid egg substitute
1 teaspoon Frangelico liqueur
1 cup pumpkin puree
¾ teaspoon ground cinnamon
¼ teaspoon ground nutmeg

Preheat the oven to 350 degrees.

To make the crust, combine the rolled oats, brown sugar, flour, and pear nectar and mix well.

Lightly spray a 9-inch springform pan once with the vegetable oil spray and evenly distribute it with your fingers over the inner surface of the pan. Scrape the batter (which will be very thick) into the pan. Pat the top to even it, by hand or using the back of a soup spoon, and bake for 15 minutes. Remove from the oven to cool. Leave the oven on.

For the cake, using an electric mixer at medium speed, beat the yogurt cheese, yogurt, ½ cup of the sugar, and the vanilla extract until well blended. Add the egg substitute, 2 tablespoons at a time, mixing well after each addition. Remove 1 cup of the mixture and set aside.

To the mixing bowl, add the remaining ¼ cup of granulated sugar, the Frangelico, pumpkin puree, and the spices. Mix well with an electric mixer until all the ingredients are well incorporated.

Pour atop one side of the crust. Pour the reserved cup of yogurt mixture on the other side. Shake lightly to even the top. With a dinner knife, cut through both batters several times in a circular motion to create a marbleized effect. Bake for 1 hour, until firm.

Remove from the oven and place on a rack. Run a knife around the sides of the pan to loosen the cake. Cool for 30 to 40 minutes in the pan, then remove the sides. Chill in the refrigerator for 2 to 3 hours before serving.

Yield — 12 servings
Fat per serving — 0.77 g.

Cocoa Cheesecake

This is a very special chocolate treat. Most people we've served it to have been so intrigued by the notion that a dessert with this intense chocolate flavor can be virtually fat free that they don't even notice the more basic alchemy at work here—the substitution of Yogurt Cheese for cream cheese and sour cream in the base.

CRUST:

3 tablespoons light corn syrup
¼ cup sugar
3 tablespoons nonfat liquid egg substitute
⅔ cup all-purpose flour
1½ tablespoons unsweetened Dutch-processed cocoa powder
Light vegetable oil cooking spray

FILLING:

½ cup dried apple chunks (about 2 ounces)
⅓ cup cold water
10 tablespoons boiling water
¼ cup light corn syrup
¾ cup unsweetened Dutch-processed cocoa powder
1¾ cups Yogurt Cheese (see Pantry)
⅔ cup sugar
6 tablespoons nonfat liquid egg substitute
½ tablespoon vanilla extract

Preheat the oven to 450 degrees.

To make the crust, beat the corn syrup and sugar with an electric mixer until the sugar is dissolved and the mixture is slightly frothy. Beat in the egg substitute.

Add the flour and cocoa powder. Mix well with a wooden spoon.

Spray a 9-inch springform pan once lightly with vegetable oil spray and evenly distribute the oil around the inside surface of the pan with your fingers.

Scrape the batter (which will be very thick) evenly into the pan with a spatula. Bake for 10 minutes and remove from the oven.

Lower the oven temperature to 350 degrees.

For the filling, bring the dried apple and cold water to a boil in a small saucepan. Cover, lower the heat, and simmer for 20 minutes.

Transfer to a food processor or blender and puree while slowly adding 6 tablespoons of the boiling water.

Place 6 tablespoons of the puree into a bowl (discard any left over). Add the corn syrup and cocoa powder. Mix well. Continue to mix while adding the remaining 4 tablespoons boiling water. The mixture should be smooth and glossy, resembling melted chocolate. Set it aside.

In another bowl, combine the yogurt cheese and the sugar. Using an electric mixer, beat at medium speed until well blended. Add the liquid egg substitute, 2 tablespoons at a time, beating well after each addition.

Scrape in the chocolate mixture and add the vanilla extract. Blend well with a spatula. Pour into the crust. Bake for 45 minutes, until firm.

Remove from the oven and place on a rack. Run a dinner knife around the sides of the pan to loosen the cake. Cool for 30 to 40 minutes in the pan, then remove the sides and chill in the refrigerator for at least 2 hours before serving.

Yield — 12 servings
Fat per serving — 0.40 g.

Individual Peach and Sour Cherry Strudel

This is best made in late summer, when the peaches are at their prime. The quality of this strudel is truly dependent on the quality of the peaches used. You can, however, substitute natural unsweetened peach nectar for the juice component if you don't have an extractor. For an added touch, spoon a little Cinnamon Cream Topping (page 179) over the strudel.

4 ripe peaches (about 22 ounces total), halved and stoned
6 tablespoons granulated sugar
2 tablespoons ground cinnamon
6 sheets phyllo dough (about 4½ ounces)
¼ cup dried sour cherries
1 teaspoon confectioners sugar

Preheat the oven to 450 degrees.

Put 2 peaches through a juice extractor. (This should yield about ½ cup juice.)

Cut the remaining peaches lengthwise into ¼-inch slices.

Combine the sugar and cinnamon in a small bowl.

Layer 3 sheets of phyllo dough on top of each other, painting the top of each one with peach juice as you assemble them. Sprinkle about half the sugar and cinnamon mixture over the top sheet. Layer another 3 sheets, painting between them but not on top of the last sheet. Sprinkle with the remaining sugar and cinnamon.

Cut the layered sheets into quarters. Mound an equal amount of peaches along one short side of each quarter, leaving an exposed border on 3 sides. Spoon 1 tablespoon of dried cherries over and alongside the peaches. Raise the border next to the filling and roll the dough continuously over onto itself to form a log. Crimp the open ends to seal.

Transfer the logs to a parchment-lined baking sheet and brush the exposed dough with peach juice. Bake for about 6 minutes, until the logs are golden brown.

Remove from the oven. With a serrated knife, trim the crimped ends to expose the filling and sprinkle the tops with the confectioners sugar.

Yield—4 servings
Fat per serving—0.65 g.

Banana-Chocolate Rice Pudding

One 8-ounce banana, unpeeled
6 tablespoons nonfat liquid egg substitute
⅔ cup buttermilk
1 tablespoon unsweetened Dutch-processed cocoa powder

¼ cup light brown sugar, firmly packed
½ teaspoon vanilla extract
1 cup cooked white rice, packed
Light vegetable oil cooking spray

Preheat the oven to 350 degrees.

Put the banana in the oven and roast for about 15 minutes, until it turns black and soft.

Remove the banana and lower the oven temperature to 325 degrees.

Let the banana sit until cool enough to handle. Peel, transfer the flesh to a small bowl, and mash it with a fork. Set aside.

Put the egg substitute into a mixing bowl and whisk until frothy. Whisk in the buttermilk. Add the cocoa powder, brown sugar, vanilla extract, mashed banana, and cooked rice, whisking after each addition.

Spray a 1-quart glass casserole once lightly with vegetable oil spray, and distribute the oil evenly over the surface. Transfer the pudding mixture to the casserole and bake for 45 minutes.

Remove the pudding from the oven and let it sit for about 10 minutes before serving. The pudding can be served warm or at room temperature.

Yield — 4 servings
Fat per serving — 0.90 g.

The richness in this version of the traditional rice pudding is derived from banana and buttermilk instead of butter and cream. Warm, succulent, and good for the soul.

Apple Upside-Down Cake

This recipe is a fat-free rendition of a wonderful Rosh Hashanah cake created by our friend Jill Van Cleave for her Chicago bakery. It's a very moist cake that stands on its own but also works well with Cinnamon Cream Topping (page 179).

¼ cup honey
¼ cup dark brown sugar, firmly packed
2 Granny Smith apples (about 1 pound total), peeled, cored, and cut into ¼-inch slices (should yield about 2½ cups sliced apples)
Light vegetable oil cooking spray
¾ cup granulated sugar
½ cup light corn syrup

1 large egg, white only
1 cup natural unsweetened applesauce
½ cup buttermilk
1 teaspoon baking soda
1½ teaspoons ground cinnamon
¼ teaspoon freshly grated nutmeg
½ teaspoon salt
2¼ cups all-purpose flour

Preheat the oven to 350 degrees.

Combine the honey and brown sugar in a nonstick frying pan. Cook over medium heat until the sugar dissolves, 2 to 3 minutes. Add the apples and continue to cook for about 4 minutes, stirring often, until the apples begin to soften. Remove from the heat.

Wrap the bottom and outer sides of a 9-inch springform pan with aluminum foil. Lightly spray the inside surface once with vegetable oil spray, distributing the oil evenly with your fingers. Transfer the apple mixture to the pan and arrange the slices into an even layer on the bottom.

Put the granulated sugar and corn syrup into a large bowl and beat with an electric mixer at medium speed until blended. Add the egg white and beat at high speed until the mixture is smooth. Beat in the applesauce and buttermilk and continue beating at high speed for 1 minute. The mixture should have a slight froth.

Combine the remaining ingredients then add to the batter in the large bowl and mix until smooth.

Spread the batter evenly over the apples. Place the pan on a baking sheet and bake on the middle rack of the oven for 40 to 45 minutes, until a tester inserted into the center of the cake's top comes out clean.

Remove from the oven and cool in the pan, on a rack, for 15 minutes. Run a dinner knife around the inner edges of the pan and invert the cake onto a serving platter. Replace any apple slices that may have dislodged from the top of the cake.

Yield — 10 servings
Fat per serving — 0.61 g.

Linzertorte

We have substituted apricot for the more traditional raspberry filling, because it provides a nice, smooth contrast to the nutty texture of the dough. The torte can be served individually in wedges, or chilled and sliced as you would a bar cookie for a buffet presentation.

1¼ cups Grape-Nuts cereal
1½ cups all-purpose flour
¾ cup granulated sugar
1 teaspoon ground cinnamon
¼ teaspoon ground cloves
1¼ teaspoons baking powder
¾ cup natural unsweetened applesauce
3 tablespoons plain nonfat yogurt

Light vegetable oil cooking spray
⅞ cup apricot spreadable fruit
 (about one 10-ounce jar)
1 large egg, white only
1 teaspoon skim milk
½ teaspoon confectioners sugar,
 for topping

Put the cereal into the bowl of a food processor or blender and process to the consistency of finely ground nuts.

Transfer to a large mixing bowl. Add the dry ingredients. Mix together with a fork, making sure to blend well. Add the applesauce and yogurt. Stir until the mixture is smooth and all the dry ingredients have been incorporated. Form into a ball by hand, enclose the dough in plastic wrap, and refrigerate for 1 hour.

Preheat the oven to 350 degrees.

Spray the bottom of a 9-inch springform pan once lightly with the vegetable oil spray and distribute the oil evenly over the surface of the pan with your fingers.

Remove the dough from the refrigerator and cut it in half. Place half the dough in the pan and press it out evenly to cover the entire bottom surface. Cover the dough evenly with the spreadable fruit, leaving a ½-inch border.

Cut the remaining dough into long thin slices. Lightly flour your hands and work each slice into a thin cigar-shaped rope. Lay 4 evenly spaced ropes in each direction across the top of the spreadable fruit in a lattice pattern. Work any excess dough into a long rope to encircle the outer border (This border can be made up of shorter dough ropes crimped together.)

Mix the egg white and skim milk together well. Using a pastry brush, paint the exposed surface of the dough with the mixture.

Bake for 35 to 40 minutes, until the dough is uniformly golden brown and firm to the touch. Transfer to a rack and cool in the pan. Remove the sides and sift the confectioners sugar over the top of the torte.

Yield — 10 servings
Fat per serving — 0.27 g.

Spice Cake with Lemon Glaze

This is based on a recipe from World War II, when eggs and butter were hard to come by. The holes poked in the cake before glazing allow the topping to penetrate, adding moisture and a pervading lemon aroma. Apply the glaze repeatedly, allowing the cake to absorb the liquid between each application.

SPICE CAKE:
2 cups boiling water
1 cup dried currants
2½ cups all-purpose flour
6 tablespoons cornstarch
2 teaspoons baking soda
1 teaspoon baking powder
1½ teaspoons ground cinnamon
1 teaspoon ground allspice
½ teaspoon ground cloves
½ teaspoon salt
1½ cups dark brown sugar, firmly packed
⅔ cup light corn syrup
2 teaspoons vanilla extract
2 tablespoons freshly squeezed lemon juice
Light vegetable oil cooking spray

LEMON GLAZE:
1 cup plain nonfat yogurt
1 cup confectioners sugar
2 teaspoons freshly squeezed lemon juice

Preheat the oven to 350 degrees.

For the cake, mix the boiling water and currants in a small bowl and set aside.

Sift flour, cornstarch, baking soda, baking powder, and spices together.

Cream the brown sugar, corn syrup, vanilla extract, and lemon juice in a large mixing bowl, using a wire whisk.

Whisk in about a third of the dry ingredients, then half of the water-currant mixture. Whisk in another third of the dry ingredients, followed by the remainder of the water-currant mixture and, finally, the remaining third of the dry ingredients.

Lightly spray a 12-cup tube pan once with the vegetable oil spray, spreading the oil evenly over the inside surface with your fingers. Pour in the batter.

Bake for 45 to 50 minutes, until a tester comes out clean. Cool for 10 minutes in the pan on a rack. Run a dinner knife around the edges of the cake to loosen it. Remove the cake from the pan, set it on a rack, and prick a number of holes in the top and sides with a toothpick.

Combine all the glaze ingredients and mix with a whisk until smooth and blended.

Spread some of the glaze evenly over the top of the cake, allowing it to drip down the sides. Periodically add more glaze as the cake cools.

Yield — 24 servings
Fat per serving — 0.17 g.

Persimmon Mousse

The "late-blooming" persimmon has lent a hint of summer-past to many a year-end meal. Just when it seems the harvest is long gone, this refreshing fruit comes into season.

1 pound ripe persimmon (about 2 large
    persimmons), trimmed and peeled
¼ cup granulated sugar
2 tablespoons unflavored gelatin
    (1 packet)

¼ cup water
1 teaspoon plus 2 tablespoons light rum
½ cup evaporated skim milk, well chilled
2 tablespoons confectioners sugar

Puree the persimmon in a food processor or blender to a smooth consistency. (You should have about 1½ cups puree.)

Put the granulated sugar and gelatin in a small saucepan. Stir in the water and let sit for 1 minute. Turn on low heat and cook for about 3 minutes, stirring constantly, until the sugar and gelatin have completely dissolved. Remove from the heat.

Combine the gelatin mixture with 1 cup of the persimmon puree and 1 teaspoon of the rum in a bowl and stir to blend completely. Cover tightly and refrigerate until chilled and thick, about 45 minutes. When you put this mixture into the refrigerator, place a metal mixing bowl and the beaters from an electric mixer into the freezer.

After 45 minutes, put the evaporated milk into the chilled bowl. Beat on high with the chilled beaters just until stiff (taking care not to overbeat). Beat in the chilled mixture, and spoon into 4-ounce parfait glasses.

For the sauce, mix the remaining ½ cup of persimmon puree with the 2 tablespoons rum and the confectioners sugar. Spoon a little over each serving.

Yield—6 servings
Fat per serving—0.28 g.

Poached Pears with Port Sauce

POACHED PEARS:

1 cup white wine

⅔ cup water

⅓ cup sugar

2½ ounces navel orange, peeled, seeded, and thinly sliced

6 firm Bartlett pears (about 2½ pounds total), peeled, stems left intact

2 tablespoons freshly grated ginger

PORT SAUCE:

3 tablespoons port wine

½ cup plain nonfat yogurt

For variety, we sometimes replace the port sauce with Mixed Berry Sauce (page 180).

To poach the pears, combine the wine, water, and sugar in a large saucepan or pot. Bring to a boil over medium heat, reduce the heat, and simmer for 5 minutes. Add the orange slices, pears and ginger. Cover partially and cook for 45 minutes to 1 hour, until the pears are fork tender.

Remove from the heat and allow the pears to cool in the pan. Transfer the cooled pears to a bowl and pour the poaching liquid on top. Cover and refrigerate for 2 to 3 hours, until well chilled.

For the sauce, whisk the port into the yogurt until well blended.

To serve, roll each pear in the chilled poaching liquid just to coat it and transfer with a slotted spoon to a small plate. (The pear should stand upright on the plate.) Top with a little sauce and serve immediately.

Yield — 6 servings
Fat per serving — 0.73 g.

Chocolate-Hazelnut Biscotti

The classic Italian dunking cookie. The last step of the recipe should really be to submerge the biscotti briefly into a steaming cup of espresso or cappuccino.

½ cup honey
1 tablespoon instant coffee granules
½ cup granulated sugar
½ cup dark brown sugar, firmly packed
¼ cup Frangelico liqueur
10 tablespoons nonfat liquid egg substitute

3 cups all-purpose flour, plus a little extra for flouring during preparation
⅓ cup unsweetened Dutch-processed cocoa powder
2 teaspoons baking powder
¼ teaspoon salt

Preheat the oven to 350 degrees.

Put the honey and coffee granules in a small saucepan and warm for about 2 minutes over low heat, until the granules dissolve. (Or combine in a small bowl and microwave for about 20 seconds at full power.)

In a large mixing bowl, combine the coffee mixture with the sugars, liqueur, and egg substitute. Whisk until well blended. Sift the remaining ingredients together into the mixture. Stir to combine thoroughly.

Turn the dough out onto a lightly floured surface and gently knead for about 30 seconds, until the dough holds together. Work it into a loaf about 16 inches long by 4 inches wide. Place the loaf on a baking sheet lined with baker's parchment, and bake for about 25 minutes, until firm.

Remove from the oven and lower the temperature to 275 degrees.

Transfer the loaf to a rack and cool for 15 minutes, then put it on a cutting board. Using a serrated knife, cut the loaf into ½-inch slices on the diagonal. Remove the parchment from the cookie sheet and place the slices on the sheet, with one of the cut sides of each slice exposed. Bake for 30 to 35 minutes, turning after 15 minutes to expose the other cut side of each slice. The biscotti should be done when they look dry and toasted. Remove from the oven and allow to cool and crisp.

Yield — 22 biscotti
Fat per biscotti — 0.27 g.

Orange-Buttermilk Ice Cream

This is our updated rendition of the traditional Pennsylvania Dutch buttermilk ice cream. We suggest pairing it with either the chilled Mixed Berry Sauce or the warm Rum-Raisin Sauce (page 180 or 178).

2 cups buttermilk
⅓ cup confectioners sugar

1 tablespoon Triple Sec liqueur

Combine the buttermilk and sugar and beat with an electric mixer until the sugar has dissolved and the mixture is frothy. Beat in the liqueur. Chill for 1 hour in the freezer.

Process in an ice cream maker according to the manufacturer's instructions.

Yield—4 servings
Fat per serving—1.0 g.

Champagne Sorbet with Apricot Sauce

CHAMPAGNE SORBET:
2 cups water
1 cup sugar
1 cup brut champagne

APRICOT SAUCE:
6 medium apricots (about 8 ounces total)
1 teaspoon freshly squeezed lemon juice
2 teaspoons sugar

To make the sorbet, combine the water and the sugar in a saucepan and bring to a boil over medium heat. Lower the heat and simmer for 5 minutes. Remove from the heat, stir in the champagne, and cool to room temperature. Allow to chill in the refrigerator for 1 hour, then process in an ice cream maker according to the manufacturer's instructions.

To make the sauce, bring a large saucepan or pot of water to a boil. Make an "X" on the skin of each apricot. Drop the apricots into the boiling water and bring back to a boil. Remove and peel, pit, and chop the apricots.

Combine the chopped apricots, lemon juice, and sugar in a food processor and puree until smooth.

Serve a heaping scoop of sorbet either set on top of the sauce or with the sauce drizzled over and around the sorbet.

Yield — 6 servings
Fat per serving — 0.10 g.

A light and refreshing palate cleanser that is the perfect thing to serve after such hearty dishes as chili or gumbo. We suggest preparing it a couple of hours in advance (or the day before serving) and storing it in the freezer, because homemade sorbets and ice creams that include alcohol usually take longer to solidify. The thick apricot sauce can be spooned onto the dessert plate as a base or drizzled over the sorbet.

Honeydew Granita with Melon Balls

A novel change from the more common smooth sorbet, this frozen dessert has a coarse, granular texture. We've found it to be a memorable way to conclude a long, leisurely brunch.

One 4-pound honeydew melon
2 tablespoons freshly squeezed lemon juice

2 tablespoons chopped fresh mint, plus 4 sprigs for garnish

Remove the rind and seeds from the melon. Cube about half (to yield 3 cups cubed melon) and reserve the rest.

Combine the cubed honeydew, lemon juice, and chopped mint in a food processor or blender and puree until very smooth. Transfer to a bowl and freeze for 3 hours.

Scoop 20 honeydew balls from the reserved melon with a melon-ball cutter. Remove the granita from the freezer and chop it into rough crystals.

Place 5 honeydew balls in each of 4 balloon glasses. Top with granita and garnish with a sprig of mint.

Yield — 4 servings
Fat per serving — 0.15 g.

Lemon Madeleines

1 large egg, white only
2½ tablespoons sugar
1 tablespoon light corn syrup

1½ tablespoons all-purpose flour
1 teaspoon finely grated lemon rind
Light vegetable oil cooking spray

Preheat the oven to 350 degrees.

Put the egg white into a mixing bowl and beat until frothy. Add the sugar and corn syrup. Stir in the flour and lemon rind, mixing until completely blended.

Lightly spray vegetable oil twice on a madeleine tin, and distribute it evenly over the surface of the molds using your fingers. Scoop 1 tablespoon of batter into each mold. Bake for about 11 minutes, until the edges of the cakes are golden brown.

Place a sheet of baker's parchment on top of a wire rack. Remove the madeleine tin from the oven, invert, and lightly tap to release the madeleines onto the parchment to cool. Serve the same day.

Yield — 6 madeleines
Fat per madeleine — 0.35 g.

This simple version of the small French sponge cake is a smashing accompaniment to the Honeydew Granita (see page 168). Madeleine tins are available from most kitchenware stores.

Ginger Madeleines

We like to serve ginger madeleines with Champagne Sorbet (page 167).

2½ tablespoons sugar
1 tablespoon light corn syrup
1 large egg, white only, beaten until
    frothy

1½ tablespoons all-purpose flour
1 teaspoon grated fresh ginger
Light vegetable oil cooking spray

Preheat the oven to 350 degrees.

Add the sugar and corn syrup to the beaten egg white. Stir in the flour and ginger until completely blended.

Lightly spray vegetable oil twice on a madeleine tin, spreading it into all the crevices of the molds with your fingers. Scoop 1 tablespoon of batter into each mold. Bake for about 11 minutes, until the edges of the cakes are golden brown.

Remove from the oven and invert the madeleines onto a sheet of baker's parchment set atop a cooling rack. Serve the same day.

Yield — 6 madeleines
Fat per madeleine — 0.35 g.

Chocolate-Apricot Madeleines

1 ounce whole dried apricots
   (about 3 apricots)
¼ cup cold water
2 tablespoons boiling water
1 large egg, white only

3 tablespoons sugar
1 teaspoon unsweetened Dutch-processed
   cocoa powder
1½ tablespoons all-purpose flour

Preheat the oven to 350 degrees.

Combine the dried apricots and the cold water in a small saucepan and bring to a boil over medium heat. Cover, reduce the heat to low, and simmer for 20 minutes.

Remove from the heat and pour into the bowl of a food processor or blender. Add the boiling water and puree until smooth.

Put the egg white into a mixing bowl and beat until frothy. Add the sugar and 1 tablespoon of the apricot puree (discard any left over). Stir in the cocoa powder and flour, mixing until completely blended.

Lightly spray the vegetable oil twice on a madeleine tin, and spread it evenly over the surface of the molds using your fingers. Scoop 1 tablespoon of batter into each mold. Bake until the edges of the cakes are golden brown, about 11 minutes.

Place a sheet of baker's parchment on top of a wire rack. Remove the tin from the oven, invert, and lightly tap to release the madeleines onto the parchment to cool. Serve the same day.

Yield — 6 madeleines
Fat per madeleine — 0.41 g.

Great with the Orange-Buttermilk Ice Cream (page 166). Serve the pale ice cream in a balloon glass, with a dark, rich madeleine impaled on the rim for a striking visual contrast.

Strawberry-Rhubarb Crumble

This is a fat-free comfort food, similar to an old-fashioned Brown Betty. Bake in a casserole, rather than in a broader, shallower baking dish, if you like a thicker layer of crumble on top of each portion.

2 ounces whole dried apricots
   (about 6 apricots)
½ cup cold water
¼ cup boiling water
½ cup all-purpose flour
¼ cup dark brown sugar, firmly packed
¼ cup granulated sugar
¼ teaspoon salt
⅛ teaspoon ground ginger
⅛ teaspoon freshly grated nutmeg

FILLING:

1 pound firm fresh rhubarb
12 ounces strawberries, hulled
⅓ cup granulated sugar
3 tablespoons all-purpose flour
½ teaspoon grated lemon rind

Preheat the oven to 400 degrees.

For the crumble, combine the dried apricots and the cold water in a small saucepan and bring to a boil over medium heat. Cover, reduce the heat to low, and simmer for 20 minutes.

Remove from the heat and pour into the bowl of a food processor or blender. Add the boiling water and puree until smooth. (You should have about 3 tablespoons apricot puree.)

Combine the remaining dry ingredients in a bowl and mix thoroughly. Add the apricot puree and mix with a fork to the texture of coarse meal. Set aside.

For the filling, trim the rhubarb and cut it into ¼-inch chunks. Put the chunks into a 1-quart casserole or an 8-by-8-inch nonstick baking pan. Cut the strawberries in half and add to the rhubarb. Add the sugar, flour, and lemon rind and mix thoroughly with a spatula.

Sprinkle the crumble over the fruit filling and bake for 25 to 30 minutes, until the top is browned and the edges are bubbly. Remove from the oven and let sit for 10 minutes before serving.

Yield—4 servings
Fat per serving—0.71 g.

Soft Chewy Oatmeal Cookies

1½ cups rolled oats
1 cup all-purpose flour
½ teaspoon baking soda
½ teaspoon baking powder
½ teaspoon salt
¾ cup natural unsweetened applesauce

½ cup dark brown sugar, firmly packed
¼ cup light corn syrup
1 large egg, white only, beaten
1 teaspoon vanilla extract
¾ teaspoon ground cinnamon
1 cup seedless raisins

Preheat the oven to 350 degrees.

Put the oats, flour, baking soda, baking powder, and salt into a bowl, mix thoroughly, and set aside.

In a large mixing bowl, combine the applesauce, brown sugar, and corn syrup. Mix until the sugar is completely dissolved. Stir in the beaten egg white, then the vanilla extract. Add the cinnamon and the rolled oat mixture. Stir well. Fold in the raisins.

With a ¼-cup measure, scoop level measures of dough onto an ungreased cookie sheet, leaving 2 inches of space between each. Bake for about 15 minutes, until the edges turn golden brown.

Remove the cookie sheet from the oven and cool for about 1 minute, then transfer the cookies to a rack and cool for 10 to 15 minutes longer.

Yield—Fourteen 3½-inch cookies
Fat per cookie—0.55 g.

We created this fat-free goodie in response to the challenge set down by our literary agent, Susan Ramer, who has very demanding standards for "the perfect oatmeal cookie." It wasn't easy, but Susan says we succeeded.

Old-Fashioned Cocoa Brownies

The all-time ultimate, moist, chewy, chocolate brownie, with a minuscule fraction of the fat found in any other brownie. Treat the yogurt as if it were egg white, gently folding, rather than stirring it into the batter.

1 cup unsweetened Dutch-processed cocoa powder
¾ teaspoon baking soda
½ teaspoon salt
½ cup double-strength hot brewed coffee
¼ cup light corn syrup

1 cup natural unsweetened applesauce
2 cups sugar
1 teaspoon vanilla extract
1½ cups all-purpose flour
½ cup plain nonfat yogurt

Preheat the oven to 350 degrees.

Sift the cocoa powder, baking soda, and salt together into a large bowl. Add the coffee and corn syrup. Blend with a wire whisk until the mixture is smooth and glossy. Add the applesauce, sugar, and vanilla extract. Whisk until completely blended. Add the flour. Fold in the yogurt with a wooden spoon just until it is incorporated.

Fold the batter into an 8-by-8-inch nonstick baking pan. Bake for about 30 minutes, until the mixture is just beginning to separate from the edges of the pan and is firm to the touch in the center.

Remove from the oven, place on a rack, and cool completely in the pan, about 2 hours.

Yield—20 brownies
Fat per brownie—0.30 g.

9

Sauces,
DRESSINGS,
and Condiments

Sauces

Roasted Banana Sauce

One 8-ounce banana, unpeeled   2 teaspoons light rum
½ teaspoon freshly squeezed lemon juice

Preheat the oven to 350 degrees.

Roast the banana in the oven until it softens and turns black, about 15 minutes.

When cool enough to handle, peel the banana and mash the flesh with a fork. Beat in the lemon juice and rum.

Serve immediately.

Yield — ½ cup
Fat per tablespoon — 0.09 g.

The pale hue of roasted bananas is dramatic atop our deep, dark Flourless Chocolate Cake (page 149).

Rum-Raisin Sauce

Goes well with Orange-Buttermilk Ice Cream (page 166).

¼ cup seedless raisins
¾ cup water
1 tablespoon light corn syrup

¼ cup light rum
1 teaspoon cornstarch dissolved in
2 teaspoons water

Combine the raisins and the water in a small saucepan. Bring to a boil over medium heat. Lower the heat and simmer for about 20 minutes, uncovered, until the raisins are plump and soft.

Whisk in the corn syrup and bring back to a simmer, which should take about 1 minute. Whisk in the rum and the cornstarch mixture. Continue to cook, whisking constantly, for about 1 minute more, until the sauce is clear and thick. Do not allow it to come to a boil.

Serve warm.

Yield — ⅔ cup
Fat per tablespoon — Less than 0.01 g.

Cinnamon Cream Topping

½ cup nonfat vanilla yogurt
¼ cup evaporated skim milk, chilled

½ teaspoon ground cinnamon
2 tablespoons confectioners sugar

Combine the yogurt, evaporated milk, and cinnamon in a mixing bowl. Beat for about 1 minute with an electric mixer at medium speed. Gradually beat in the sugar.

Serve at room temperature or chilled.

Yield—1 cup
Fat per tablespoon—0.02 g.

We like this silky sauce on Apple Upside-Down Cake or Individual Peach and Sour Cherry Strudel (page 156 or 154).

Mixed Berry Sauce

Serve this on Flourless Chocolate Cake, Poached Pears, or Orange-Buttermilk Ice Cream (page 177, 163, or 166).

⅔ cup hulled, quartered strawberries
    (about 4 ounces)
⅔ cup raspberries (about 4 ounces)

½ teaspoon freshly squeezed lemon juice
1½ tablespoons confectioners sugar

Combine all the ingredients in a blender or food processor and puree.

Yield — ¾ cup
Fat per tablespoon — 0.08 g.

Garlic Sauce

1 cup 99% Fat-Free Chicken Stock
   (page 10)
10 cloves garlic (about 2 ounces)

½ cup buttermilk
1 teaspoon cornstarch
2 teaspoons water

Combine the chicken stock and garlic in a saucepan and bring to a boil over medium heat. Lower the heat, cover, and simmer for about 25 minutes, until the garlic is soft.

Transfer to a food processor or blender and puree to a smooth consistency.

Return the puree to the saucepan over low heat. Whisk in the buttermilk and cook for 1 to 2 minutes, just until the mixture begins to bubble around the edges. Remove from the heat.

Whisk the cornstarch and water together in a small bowl and then whisk into the garlic sauce.

Return to the heat and cook for 2 to 3 minutes longer, until the sauce thickens. Serve hot.

Yield — ¾ cup
Fat per tablespoon — 0.10 g.

An intense sauce that complements smoked poultry.

Celery Sauce

This works well with Fish Sausage (page 18), as an alternative to the fennel sauce.

1¾ pounds celery, trimmed
¼ cup peeled, shredded celery root
6 teaspoons water
1 tablespoon cornstarch

1 teaspoon freshly squeezed lemon juice
½ teaspoon ground cardamom
⅛ teaspoon white pepper

Put the celery through a juice extractor. (This should yield about 2 cups juice.)

Combine the celery juice and celery root in a small saucepan and bring to a boil over low heat.

Meanwhile, whisk the water and cornstarch together.

When the juice comes to a boil, whisk in the lemon juice and spices. Remove from the heat and whisk in the cornstarch mixture. Return to heat and bring back just to a boil. Serve immediately.

Yield—2 cups
Fat per tablespoon—0.04 g.

Spicy Carrot Sauce

2 pounds carrots (about 6 large carrots), trimmed
2 teaspoons freshly squeezed orange juice
1 teaspoon freshly grated ginger

2 teaspoons cornstarch
4 teaspoons water
Pinch of cayenne pepper
1 tablespoon chopped fresh cilantro

Put the carrots through a juice extractor. (This should yield about 2 cups of carrot juice.)

Combine the carrot juice, orange juice, and ginger in a saucepan and bring just to a boil over low heat. This should take about 5 minutes.

Meanwhile, whisk the cornstarch and water together in a small bowl.

When the juice comes to a boil, remove it from the heat and whisk in the cornstarch mixture. Return to the heat and continue to whisk until bubbly. Whisk in the cayenne pepper and cilantro and cook for 1 minute more. Serve hot.

Yield—2 cups
Fat per tablespoon—0.06 g.

Works well with shellfish, especially shrimp and scallops.

This works extremely well on Grilled Potato Salad (page 74).

Dressings
Mustard-Buttermilk Dressing

½ cup buttermilk
1 teaspoon light corn syrup
1 tablespoon white wine vinegar
½ tablespoon freshly squeezed lemon juice

1 clove garlic, halved
½ teaspoon mustard powder
¼ teaspoon salt
⅛ teaspoon freshly ground black pepper

Combine all the ingredients in a blender and puree to a smooth consistency.

Yield — ½ cup
Fat per tablespoon — 0.19 g.

Honey-Mustard Dressing

2 teaspoons Dijon mustard
2 tablespoons honey

½ cup apple juice
1 teaspoon chopped fresh thyme

Combine all the ingredients and mix until well blended.

Yield — ½ cup
Fat per tablespoon — 0.13 g.

Try this on Tossed Jicama and Snap-Pea Salad (page 68).

Zucchini Dressing

Serve on sliced tomatoes, a medley of thinly sliced squashes, or green salads.

2 medium zucchini (about 1 pound total), peeled and quartered lengthwise
½ cup buttermilk
2 teaspoons light corn syrup
1 teaspoon finely chopped garlic (1–1½ cloves)

1 teaspoon dried oregano
⅛ teaspoon freshly ground black pepper
¼ teaspoon salt

Put the zucchini through a juice extractor. (This should yield about 1 cup juice.)

Combine the zucchini juice with the remaining ingredients and mix until thoroughly blended.

Yield — 1½ cups
Fat per tablespoon — 0.07 g.

Honey-Ginger Dressing

½ cup honey
1 teaspoon freshly grated ginger
2 tablespoons apple juice

1 tablespoon freshly squeezed lemon juice
2 teaspoons finely chopped fresh mint

Combine all the ingredients and whisk thoroughly.

Yield — ¾ cup
Fat per tablespoon — Less than 0.01 g.

Try this on Papaya and Watercress Salad (page 62).

Southwestern Ranch Dressing

Use this spicy dressing with your favorite leafy green salad.

1 cup buttermilk
2 teaspoons light corn syrup
2 tablespoons freshly squeezed lemon juice
2 tablespoons chopped fresh cilantro

1 teaspoon chili powder
1/8 teaspoon white pepper
Dash of salt
4 drops of hot sauce

Combine all the ingredients and whisk thoroughly.

Yield—1 cup
Fat per tablespoon—0.09 g.

Orange-Honey Dressing

½ cup freshly squeezed orange juice
2 tablespoons honey
1 tablespoon champagne vinegar

1 teaspoon light corn syrup
½ teaspoon coarse kosher salt
½ teaspoon freshly ground black pepper

Combine all the ingredients and whisk thoroughly.

Yield—¾ cup
Fat per tablespoon—0.04 g.

Pair this dressing with Orange-Watercress Salad (page 71).

Spicy Pumpkin Catsup

This is based on the Victorian "catsups," which were savory spreads bearing little resemblance to today's commercial tomato catsup. The spicy pumpkin flavor blends exceptionally well with cold turkey or chicken. Bottled onion juice is available for those without juice extractors.

One 6-ounce white onion, quartered
1 cup pure pumpkin puree
   (not pie filling)
½ cup water
¼ cup apple cider vinegar
2 tablespoons apple juice
1½ tablespoons honey

⅛ teaspoon freshly grated ginger
¼ teaspoon ground cloves
½ teaspoon curry powder
⅛ teaspoon ground allspice
¼ teaspoon salt
⅛ teaspoon cayenne pepper

Put the onion through a juice extractor. (This should yield about ¼ cup onion juice.)

Put the pumpkin in a small saucepan. Whisk in the water, onion juice, vinegar, and apple juice. Add all the remaining ingredients, stir, and simmer for about 20 minutes, uncovered. The mixture will be done when the water doesn't separate from a small portion removed to a plate.

Use hot as a sauce or refrigerate for 1 to 2 hours to thicken and serve chilled as a catsup. The catsup will keep for about a week in the refrigerator.

Yield — 1½ cups
Fat per tablespoon — 0.02 g.

Sweet and Sour Red Onions

½ cup balsamic vinegar
½ cup sugar
1 cup thinly sliced red onion
   (about 1 small onion)

⅓ cup seeded, thinly sliced green bell pepper
½ cup seeded, thinly sliced yellow bell
   pepper

Combine the vinegar and sugar in a saucepan and bring to a boil over medium heat. Lower the heat and simmer for 5 minutes. Remove from the heat and cool for 10 minutes.

Combine the onion and peppers in a bowl. Pour the vinegar and sugar mixture over them. Leave at room temperature for 20 minutes, stirring occasionally, then refrigerate for at least 1 hour. Drain most of the liquid before serving.

Yield — 1½ cups
Fat per tablespoon — 0.02 g.

A pungent, chunky, homemade condiment. Try it with Potato Cakes (page 30) in lieu of the red pepper cream.

Tarragon-Peach Chutney

A savory and slightly tart accompaniment to chicken or shrimp.

1½ cups unpeeled chopped peaches (about 2 medium peaches)
¾ cup peeled, chopped pear
¾ cup peeled, chopped Granny Smith apple
1 tablespoon freshly squeezed lemon juice
¼ teaspoon grated lemon rind
¾ teaspoon finely grated fresh ginger

¼ cup tarragon vinegar
¼ cup dark brown sugar, firmly packed
¼ cup golden raisins
1 tablespoon chopped fresh parsley
¼ teaspoon dried tarragon
⅛ teaspoon ground cloves
⅛ teaspoon ground nutmeg
⅛ teaspoon ground allspice

Combine all the ingredients in a large heavy saucepan and mix well. Bring to a boil over medium heat. Reduce the heat and simmer for 30 to 35 minutes, uncovered, stirring frequently, until the chutney is thick.

Remove from the heat and cool. Serve chilled or at room temperature.

Yield — 1¼ cups
Fat per tablespoon — 0.08 g.

Glazed Pearl Onions

12 ounces pearl onions   ½ cup red wine vinegar
6 tablespoons honey

Bring a saucepan of water to a boil, add the onions, and boil for 3 minutes. Rinse under cold running water.

Trim the root on each onion. Grasp the root end and gently squeeze toward the stem until the onion slips out of its skin.

When the onions are peeled, put the honey in a small saucepan and cook for about 1 minute over low heat, until it liquefies. Stir in the vinegar. Cook, stirring, until well mixed, about 1 minute more.

Remove from the heat and stir in the onions. Cool to room temperature, then chill in the refrigerator for 2 to 3 hours.

Yield — 6 servings
Fat per serving — 0.09 g.

A chilled condiment that is best the day after it's made.

A cool and refreshing summertime condiment that can also be added to leafy green salads.

½ cup halved red cherry tomatoes
  (about 4 ounces)
½ cup halved yellow cherry tomatoes
1 cup quartered tomatillos (about
  4 tomatillos)
⅓ cup basil vinegar (see Pantry)

⅓ cup water
½ tablespoon coarse kosher salt
6 leaves fresh basil
2 thin lemon slices
1 clove garlic

Combine the tomatoes and tomatillos in a mixing bowl.

Put the basil vinegar, water, and salt in a saucepan over high heat. Bring to a boil, then remove from the heat and set aside to cool.

Stack the basil leaves on top of each other, roll into a long cylinder, and slice thin. Add the sliced basil and the lemon to the tomato mixture, then press in the garlic.

Pour the cooled vinegar liquid over the tomato mixture and toss to coat. Marinate for 2 hours at room temperature before refrigerating. Serve chilled.

Yield — 8 servings
Fat per serving — 0.16 g.

Index

Flourless chocolate cake, 149
French country round bread,
    134–35
Frittata, pasta, 90
Fruit
    salad
        minted, 70
        with spinach, 63
    See also names of fruit
Frying, *xvi*

G

Garlic
    and polenta crostini with bell
        peppers, 14–15
    sauce, 181
    soup, cream of, 43
Ginger (fresh)
    and honey dressing, 187
    madeleines, 170
Glistening, *xvi–xvii*
Gnocchi with tomato-basil sauce,
    88–89
Good morning zucchini muffins,
    142
Granita, honeydew, with melon
    balls, 168
Gratin
    potato and squash, 129
    of root vegetables, 111
    turnip, 118
Greens, bitter, steamed, 112
Gumbo, crab and chicken, 82–83

H

Hash brown potato salad, 59

Hazelnut-chocolate biscotti,
    164–65
Hearty stout bread, 133
Herbed sandwich braid, 136–37
Honeydew melon
    granita, with melon balls, 168
    soup, 49
Honey dressing
    with ginger, 187
    with mustard, 185
    with orange juice, 189
Horseradish-washed potatoes, 116
Hummus with sweet potato chips,
    21

I

Ice cream, orange-buttermilk, 166

J

Jambalaya, shrimp, 94
Jicama
    salsa with chicken tacos, 104–5
    and snap-pea salad, tossed, 68

K

Kebabs, fish and vegetable, 91

L

Leek
    and shrimp risotto, 108
    soup, creamy, 38
Lemon

-glazed spice cake, 160–61
    madeleines, 169
Lentil(s)
    and radish sprout salad, 72
    red, pilaf, with scallops, 98
Linzertorte, 158–59
Lobster
    risotto, curried, 106–7
    tostadas, 22

M

Madeleines
    chocolate-apricot, 171
    ginger, 170
    lemon, 169
Main courses
    chicken
        potpies, individual, 92–93
        tacos with jicama salsa, 104–5
        Vesuvio, 103
    chive polenta and mushroom
        ragout, 80–81
    couscous, crab and tomato
        broth, *77*
    fish
        cod and vegetable kebabs, 91
        red snapper and black bean
        chili, 78–79
    gnocchi with tomato-basil sauce,
        88–89
    gumbo, crab and chicken, 82–83
    noodles
        Chinese, with shrimp and
        chicken, 95
        with cumin, 102
    pasta
        frittata, 90

P9-BUH-169

Hands*On Healing Remedies

150 Recipes for Herbal Balms, Salves, Oils, Liniments & Other Topical Therapies

Stephanie L. Tourles

Illustrations by Samantha Hahn

Storey Publishing

**The mission of Storey Publishing is to serve our customers by
publishing practical information that encourages
personal independence in harmony with the environment.**

Edited by Deborah Balmuth and Lisa H. Hiley
Art direction and book design by Mary Winkelman Velgos
Text production by Liseann Karandisecky

Illustrations by © Samantha Hahn, except for page 17 by Alison Kolesar
Author's photograph by © Debra Bell

Indexed by Andrea Chesman

© 2012 by Stephanie L. Tourles

All rights reserved. No part of this book may be reproduced without written permission from the publisher, except by a reviewer who may quote brief passages or reproduce illustrations in a review with appropriate credits; nor may any part of this book be reproduced, stored in a retrieval system, or transmitted in any form or by any means — electronic, mechanical, photocopying, recording, or other — without written permission from the publisher.

The information in this book is true and complete to the best of our knowledge. All recommendations are made without guarantee on the part of the author or Storey Publishing. The author and publisher disclaim any liability in connection with the use of this information.

Storey books are available for special premium and promotional uses and for customized editions. For further information, please call 1-800-793-9396.

Storey Publishing
210 MASS MoCA Way
North Adams, MA 01247
www.storey.com

Printed in the United States by R.R. Donnelley
10 9 8 7 6 5 4 3 2 1

Library of Congress Cataloging-in-Publication Data

Tourles, Stephanie L., 1962–
 Hands-on healing remedies / by Stephanie L. Tourles.
   p. cm.
 Includes bibliographical references and index.
 ISBN 978-1-61212-006-5 (pbk. : alk. paper)
 ISBN 978-1-60342-877-4 (e-book)
 1. Materia medica, Vegetable. 2. Naturopathy. I. Title.
RS164.T684 2012
615.5'35—dc23
                    2012027705

To my dearest Bill — my husband, partner, and best friend. Your never-ending energy, independent spirit, support, and encouragement uplift me in all that I do. I treasure the boulder-lined garden you created for me, filled with incredibly deep, dark, fertile, crumbly soil. It's a garden beyond my wildest dreams. My culinary and healing herbs thrive, the vegetable plants strain under their heavy yields, and the flowers explode with vibrant colors . . . eliciting curiosity from the neighbors, causing them to wonder if I have magical, quick-fingered plant fairies who work in and maintain my massive "jungle of a garden" under the cloak of darkness. It makes me chuckle. I cherish every moment we have together on this incredible journey we call life, my dear Willy.

And in memory of "Mainie," my 20-pound, middle-aged, semi-wild Maine Coon cat who loved to sleep in my chamomile patch on warm late-spring afternoons. When sick or injured, he'd let me feed him dropper after dropper of chamomile tea, which zonked him right out and usually had him feeling better within a matter of days. "Mainie" definitely chose German chamomile as his herbal ally; unfortunately, it couldn't protect him from cars.

acknowledgments

In writing this book, I'm indebted to the great herbal teachers and elders who have shaped my "green education" over the years: Mrs. Ottie Faye Ashe and Mrs. Eveline Pilkington, for sharing their handwritten herbal formulas with me, many of which date back to the mid-nineteenth century; my grandfather Earl C. Ashe, who initiated me into this healing world of herbalism; and my grandmother Phenie S. Ashe, the possessor of the greenest thumb on earth. Much gratitude goes out to Candis Cantin, Anne McIntyre, Rosemary Gladstar, Deb Soule, and Michael Tierra, teachers with whom I've had a chance to study varying traditions of herbal wisdom, namely Ayurvedic, Western, and Chinese.

I've been researching and formulating topical, plant-based healing recipes for the past three decades, and I am indeed grateful to all of you who have volunteered to be my "guinea pigs," my live subjects on whom I was allowed to test my herbal formulations and receive much valued feedback. And lastly, thanks to Deborah Balmuth, my longtime, beloved editor, for giving me the opportunity to share these healing remedies with you, my dear readers.

Contents

Introduction

It was the early 1900s, and like other self-reliant folk in the Great Smoky Mountains region of North Carolina, my great-grandmother, Maude Ashe, practiced the basic yet effective traditional healing arts of her ancestors, supplemented by a few remedies acquired from the local Cherokee Indians, in order to care for her family's ills. She, like so many other housewives of the day, was expected to be the family doctor, if need be. Making effective, gentle medicine generally wasn't a complicated affair. If an infant had colic, you fed him a little warm catnip, chamomile, or calendula tea and bathed him in a linden flower or catnip tea bath. If you had a bad cough, you could make a fine soothing medicine from honey, strong black cherry bark tea, and real apple cider vinegar. My great-grandmother, along with her many children, explored the hollows and hills of impoverished Appalachia, learning to identify the local flora and fauna, and collected beneficial herbs to use as healing medicines. Whether intentioned or not, she passed this knowledge down to my grandfather, Earl C. Ashe.

I never planned on becoming an herbalist, a lover of the plant kingdom, a creator of healing formulas. I think it was — and is — my destiny. I inherited my "I can grow anything" green thumb and green blood from my grandmother, Phenie Sims Ashe, and my initiation into herbalism came under the tutelage of my grandfather.

Several times a year, my family would make the two-hour drive north from our suburban home in Stone Mountain, Georgia, to my grandparent's 20-acre country homestead located in Clarkesville. My brother, Shawn, and I loved to visit the country — so many things to see and do. Shawn liked to go visit the cows out in the back pasture and tour the barn, and I was drawn to the gardens, fields, woods, and streams. We liked to walk and explore with my grandfather as he did his chores. On one particular walk, my grandfather and I were hiking through cattle pastures and woods — his big, rough farmer hand holding my soft little girl hand — and I can remember him telling me,

"Where we grew up, we didn't go to doctors unless it was a dire emergency. We didn't have the money. Our mother made medicine from the local herbs and she dosed us with that, whether we liked it or not. The stuff you had to swallow often didn't taste good. The medicines that got rubbed into your skin, like the herbal salves, thickened with local beeswax, lard, or lanolin, and the brownish-green colored liniments made with homemade grape wine or corn whiskey, were used to prevent infections, relieve stuffiness, help you sleep, or make your muscles feel better after a long day at work. Those things worked real nice and most times smelled pretty good, too." I was intrigued.

Thus began my "training." From then on, sensing my interest, my grandfather turned our walks into "botany and chemistry classes" — so to speak. He taught me the names of the trees and the green plants, the uses and medicinal properties of tree bark, acorns, pine sap, roots, leaves, flowers, and even the gray-blue clay in the stream banks. I can remember my fourth-grade science teacher being amazed at how much I knew! I learned that these free-for-the-taking "medicines of the earth" could aid the body's natural processes to heal illnesses within and without. I fell in love with the idea that nature could provide just about anything you needed to naturally care for your health and beauty. I was hooked. I was in awe of my grandfather's knowledge and absorbed it like a sponge. Unbeknownst to me, I was a budding herbalist.

Today, as a licensed holistic aesthetician, certified aromatherapist, and community herbalist, I devote my career to plant-based topical remedies and nutritional therapies for skin disorders. I write, formulate remedies, grow herbs, teach, and work as an herbal practitioner. I feel that my grandfather's spirit has literally pushed me into spreading the word about the healing benefits of herbs. This ancient form of plant medicine, phytotherapy, should stay alive and vibrant.

This book represents the collection of topical herbal healing formulations that, over the past 30 years, I've developed, experimented with, and perfected to the best of my ability. In these pages, I'll share with you my opinions, knowledge, and observations, based upon accumulated wisdom and experience, of how our green neighbors, the herbs, can be effective medicine. I hope you find the instructions easy to follow and the remedies useful; combined with the right lifestyle and diet, they can bring significant relief to common skin conditions and body ailments, plus enhance your well-being and comfort.

May you be happy, healthy, hearty, and whole!

PART 1 *Making Your Own* Healing Formulas

No one knows who the first curious human being was who decided to approach a particular plant, pick a handful of leaves, stems, and flowers, and brew them into a tea in hopes of soothing indigestion. Nor do we know who first chewed on a plantain leaf in order to apply the resultant green "spit paste" to a bee sting, bringing almost immediate pain relief. Who realized that adding cumin seeds to dinner greatly enhanced the flavor and digestibility of the food? Or that infusing olive oil with St. John's wort flowers and leaves resulted in an amazingly bright red oil that works topically to bring relief from muscle soreness, bruises, and the pain and inflammation of nerve damage? Who discovered that elderberries and pokeberries could color cloth a beautiful bluish-purple, or that rose petals, when allowed to macerate in warm, purified fat, make a solid perfume that doubles as an uplifting medicinal aromatic for times of grief, depression, and emotional stress? We'll never know who these individuals were, but thank goodness for them and their inquisitive natures.

Uncomplicated, ardent medicine-making is as fundamental to the art and science of Herbalism as simple passionate cooking is to the art and science of nutrition. High technology has never increased the nutritional power of good food, simply prepared.

—JAMES GREEN, *The Herbal Medicine-Maker's Handbook*

CHAPTER 1

An Introduction to Traditional Healing

The word *phytotherapy* is bandied about quite often these days with regard to the subjects of whole-food nutrition, chemical-free skin care, and natural medicine. But what does it actually mean? *Phyto,* from the Greek word *phyton,* indicates a plant or something that grows, and *therapy,* from the Greek *therapeia,* means treatment of a disease or pathological condition. Thus, *phytotherapy* means using plant-based medicines or remedies to treat disease or discomfort, which is what this book is about — its primary focus being on herbal formulations for topical application.

The use of herbs for healing medicines, personal care, ceremonial purposes, and nutrition dates back to the earliest cultures — and in all probability, since our ancestors first walked the earth. You can delve all the way back to the time of the Neanderthals, in fact, to learn that they used herbs to protect themselves from bug infestations, to help heal infections, and to fortify their body for the journey to the next world, among other things.

Once upon a time, nearly all of the ingredients required for these purposes were harvested from the fields, woods, deserts, water's edge, or swamps and prepared by the local medicine man or woman. Some particular herbs and spices, such as frankincense, myrrh, amber, cinnamon, garlic, anise, sage, coriander, thyme, fennel, hyssop, dill, and cumin, were either wild-harvested or cultivated, and came to be so highly valued for their use in food and medicine that they played an important role in establishing trade routes throughout the Middle East, India, the Orient, and the Mediterranean, thousands of years before the time of Christ.

The Rig Veda, the sacred Hindu book that dates from around 1000 BCE, includes many references to medicinal herbs. Most of the Egyptian remedies recorded in the Ebers Papyrus around 1550 BCE are based on herbs. The ancient Greeks and Romans combined herbal extracts with fresh-pressed olive and sesame oils, animal fats, and beeswax to make ointments, unguents (another term for salves), and balms for health and beauty. And looking back as recently as the late 1800s or so, it's clear that herbs remained an important aspect of everyday life all over the world, used by laypeople and trained herbalists for medicinal purposes as well as enhancement of well-being. They are still used for those purposes in many places, by many people, today.

The Decline of Herbalism

The early 1900s, with its terrible wars and epidemics, saw the favor and practice of medical herbalism fall to near oblivion. It was deemed inadequate, especially for curing raging bacterial infections such as gangrene and swift-moving killers such as meningitis and pneumonia. The infantile but rapidly expanding U.S. pharmaceutical industry, with research grants heavily funded by John D. Rockefeller and Andrew Carnegie, turned its back on the plant world, and was off and racing for synthetically derived chemical medicines that could cure acute infection, among other things, and that could be patented and profitably marketed. Sound familiar? Glamorous synthetic chemicals were the way of the future; herbalism was messy, unscientific, unpatentable, and difficult to reduce to a neat little standardized pill. "Better health and better living through chemistry" was the motto of the twentieth century. Modern society was in awe of the new laboratory-produced "wonder drugs."

Don't get me wrong: I think that we, as a society, are fortunate for the advances that have been made by Western medicine. It truly excels in the treatment of acute trauma and

When I go into my garden with a spade, and dig a bed, I feel such an exhilaration and health that I discover that I have been defrauding myself all this time in letting others do for me what I should have been doing with my own hands.

— Ralph Waldo Emerson

disease. If I break a bone or suffer a heart attack, I want to be transported to an emergency room and put back together or saved from an untimely death by a capable surgeon and medical specialist, that's for sure. But I also think that we have come to rely too heavily on Western medicine for the treatment of diseases that are largely preventable, such as diabetes, heart disease, arthritis, and obesity, and of many non-life-threatening afflictions, such as colds, aches and pains, dermatitis, PMS, and minor cuts and burns, that can be successfully treated at home.

A large percentage of the population is suffering from self-inflicted poor health due to poor dietary habits and a sedentary lifestyle. Many of the ills that we experience today could be prevented or minimized if we only ate a whole-food natural diet, exercised regularly,

There are easy, natural things we can do to promote our health and the well-being of this planet. . . . In most cases, the earth has been a nurturing place for its inhabitants, and it seems logical to turn to plants and natural remedies as a first line of defense in helping our bodies deal with temporary malaise.

— Norma Pasekoff Weinberg,
Natural Hand Care

exposed our bodies to fresh air and a bit of sunshine; had a positive attitude, happy pursuits, and sufficient sleep; and if we once again relied on our plant friends, the herbs, to favorably influence our health and well-being.

Luckily, herbalism is enjoying a remarkable revival. Although modern humans have gradually withdrawn from the natural world and are now bombarded and surrounded by all-things-synthetic, we are still innately nourished, refreshed, and healed by nature. Nature's "life forces" find their most perfect, purest expression in the plant kingdom, which forms the foundation of life on earth. Properly processed and combined, organic plant-derived ingredients lend themselves most beautifully to the creation of nurturing products that deliver effective health care without the potentially negative side effects of allopathic medicines, and, as a bonus, are a pleasure to use.

Why Make Your Own Healing Formulas?

"Know your medicine," I always say. When I use a product, I like to know what I'm absorbing into my person — natural purity being of utmost importance. I know I'm not the only person who wants to know a product's ingredients and their source(s), how the product was made (if that information is available), any possible contraindications, and how it is to be used. Maintaining health and preventing disease is your responsibility. It's serious business. Take your health into your own hands — don't leave it in the hands of others! With the right education, you have the power to care for yourself, your family, and your friends.

Homemade herbal preparations are infused with lots of "healing love energy" — your energy — that will be imparted to the users. Don't take this statement lightly. Grandma's homemade chicken, vegetable, and garlic soup was probably a better remedy for your deep chest cold than that bottle of prescription antibiotic handed to you by an impersonal pharmacist. Not just because the soup was hot, tasty, soothing, and chock-full of antibacterial and antiviral garlic, but because it was also imbued with her love for you and powerful prayers for you to be well and whole again.

Herbal medicine making is part of our cultural heritage, practiced for eons. It's a practice that can reconnect us to Mother Nature. Plus it's simple and fun — it's kind of like cooking, but with different ingredients. Crafting remedies in your home kitchen can become a rather delightful hobby, especially if you like to grow your own herbs, or if you like to hike in the fields and woods and wildcraft herbs (ethically, of course). Even if you're not a gardener or hiker, you can find many resources these days for organically grown, dried herbs and other necessary ingredients (see Resources for a list of my favorite companies).

I encourage you to take responsibility for your own health and healing with the aid of pure, uncomplicated, effective, homemade herbal formulas. Keep reading, and I'll guide you through the process. Perhaps this book will be the starting point for a broader exploration of the healing power of herbs. Let's hope so.

What's in Your Home Medicine Cabinet?

If you've ever looked at the labels of the health-care products you use, there are surely some ingredients that you don't recognize and can't pronounce. You've probably wondered about the questionable toxicity of those artificial fragrances, artificial colors, and synthetic preservatives. Many so-called natural products contain all manner of ingredients that are useless, potentially toxic, cheap, petroleum-derived, or synthetic, mixed with a sprinkling of natural ones that provide a mere smidgen of some true benefit.

It makes sense to evaluate all the products that you currently apply to your skin. Most mass-produced health-care products contain a myriad of synthetic chemicals that have been around for a less than a century. What are their long-term effects on our bodies and environment? No one truly knows . . . yet. On the other hand, herbs and other natural ingredients such as shea butter, essential oils, and distilled alcohol have been effectively and safely used for thousands of years. We know much more about them than their synthetic counterparts.

The skin is the body's largest organ and it absorbs both beneficial and toxic substances, drawing them deep into your tissues. Doesn't it just make good sense to slather your skin with pure products that ensure your health and well-being?

Here are three examples of common, seemingly innocuous, over-the-counter medicinal products that contain deleterious and unnecessary ingredients, with a review of each product and suggested homemade substitutes.

Generic Diaper Rash Ointment

ACTIVE INGREDIENT

Zinc oxide	astringent and antiseptic

INACTIVE INGREDIENTS

Water	
Mineral oil and petrolatum	carrier and skin-conditioning agents; petroleum byproducts that can dry out the skin and leach fat-soluble vitamins
Glyceryl stearate	emulsifier and skin conditioner; fatty acid ester combined with glycerin; frequently synthetic
Tocopherol	synthetic vitamin E
Calendula flower extract	soothing, healing herb
Fragrance	synthetic; a potential irritant
Triethanolamine	dispersion agent, emulsifier, pH adjuster, detergent; a potential skin irritant
Methylparaben	artificial preservative
Yellow #5	artificial color; a potential skin irritant
Titanium dioxide	white mineral tinting powder

I wouldn't apply this to my own derriere, let alone an infant's. There's too much risk of irritation and too many synthetic ingredients. Calendula flower extract should be an active ingredient due to its innate healing and soothing properties. It is naturally deep yellow, so if there were a sufficient, beneficial amount in the product, artificial coloring would not be necessary.

Natural Alternative: The recipe for Smooth-as-a-Baby's-Bottom "Quickie Salve" (page 116) contains organic vegetable shortening and a couple of essential oils. It is pure, has a pleasant fragrance, and will effectively soothe and soften a baby's bottom.

Name-Brand Pain-Relief Ointment

ACTIVE INGREDIENTS

Camphor, menthol, and methyl salicylate	topical analgesics derived from herbs

INACTIVE INGREDIENTS

Carbomer	petroleum-derived thickener, emulsifier, suspension, and dispersion agent; potential skin irritant
Cetyl esters	emollients and texturizers; could be synthetic or natural
Glyceryl stearate	emulsifier and skin conditioner; fatty acid ester combined with glycerin; frequently synthetic
Lanolin	skin softener, emulsifier, and thickener; some people who are allergic to wool may find that it irritates their skin
Polysorbate 80	emulsifier; can be drying to the skin
Potassium hydroxide	caustic potash used as an emulsifier, potential skin irritant
Water	
Stearic acid	white, waxy, emollient fatty acid; used as a pearlizing agent
Triethanolamine	dispersion agent, emulsifier, pH adjuster, detergent; potential skin irritant

Together the active ingredients act as natural analgesics, anti-inflammatory agents, and circulatory stimulants, helping to relieve pain on the surface of the skin as well as in the underlying muscles. The overall effect is felt as a cooling sensation, with an increased sense of comfort. This product does not need the many cheap emulsifiers and other potential irritants.

Natural Alternative: The recipe for Joint-Ease Balm (page 63) contains only shea butter and essential oils. It smells wonderful, soothes sore muscles and stiff joints, and conditions the skin.

Name-Brand Mentholated Vapor Balm

ACTIVE INGREDIENTS

Camphor, menthol	topical analgesics and respiratory stimulants derived from herbs

INACTIVE INGREDIENTS

Fragrance	synthetic; a potential irritant
Petrolatum	carrier and skin-conditioning agents; petroleum byproduct that can dry out the skin and leach fat-soluble vitamins
Titanium dioxide	white mineral tinting powder

The camphor and menthol have really potent aromas, so why does the manufacturer add a synthetic fragrance? And once again there is a cheap petroleum byproduct, offering no real benefit to the skin. I must admit that I grew up with this product and still occasionally use it, as I'm addicted to the fragrance and I enjoy the fond memories of my grandmother caring for me that it evokes.

I do make my own formula with pharmaceutical-grade essential oils, fresh beeswax or shea butter, and organic soybean or almond oil, but it's taken a long time to wean myself off the commercial vapor balm!

Natural Alternative: See the recipe for Eucalyptus, Pine, and Thyme Respiratory Vapors Balm (page 246), which works wonders to open stuffed sinuses.

Your Skin: A Perfect Delivery System

Ingesting herbs or inserting them into the body (via eardrops, for instance) aren't the only methods for administering herbal remedies. Therapeutic preparations can be applied topically as well, using fabulous restorative products such as salves, balms, infused oils, aromatherapeutic oil blends, liniments, clay packs, body powders, hydrosol sprays, and plant juices. In *The Take Charge Beauty Book: The Natural Guide to Beautiful Hair & Skin*, authors Aubrey Hampton, a cosmetic chemist and founder of Aubrey Organics, and Susan Hussey, a nutrition and beauty expert, state:

> Traditional cultures around the world never questioned whether or not substances applied to the skin were absorbed into the body. They knew: whole systems of medicine were organized around effective methods of applying herbal medicines directly to the skin. Thousands of years ago the Chinese were increasing the benefits of acupuncture with moxibustion, the process of applying burning herbs to particular points on the skin, and Native American tribes applied heated herbal poultices to injured areas to increase circulation and absorption.
>
> Yet modern Western medicine has considered the skin impervious to absorption, even as recently as 1957, when Dr. Stephen Rothman, keynote speaker at the 11th International Congress of Dermatology, held in Sweden, asserted that nothing from the outside could penetrate through the skin. Forty years later, absorption is so much taken for granted that today many drugs are administered via skin patches, including nicotine (in antismoking treatments), estrogen, and nitroglycerin.
>
> Unfortunately, much of the current understanding of the skin's permeability (its ability to absorb substances) is due to the damage powerful pesticides and other man-made chemicals have inflicted on exposed workers.

Your skin is your largest organ, covering your body and providing protection from potentially harmful substances. It is often called "the third kidney," as it excretes wastes just like your other excretory organs, namely, the kidneys, bladder, lungs, and colon. But the skin, with its thousands of pores of the sudoriferous (sweat) glands and the hair follicles with their associated sebaceous (oil) glands, is also the perfect delivery vehicle for herbal remedies. It "eats" or absorbs up to 60 percent of what is applied to it! This process, called *transdermal penetration* — which means "to cross over or go through the skin"— enables the skin to transmit both toxins and healing powers into the tissues below.

Any topically applied substance can either penetrate or affect the skin's surface. To what degree depends on the particular substance,

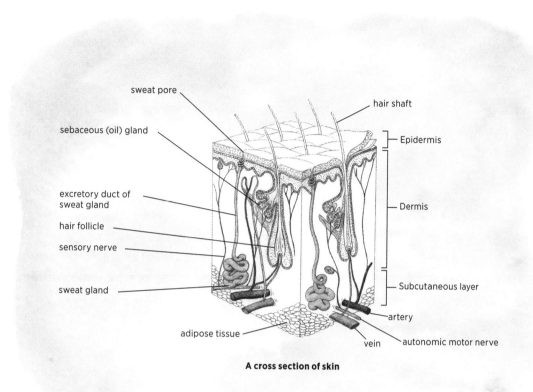

sweat pore

sebaceous (oil) gland

excretory duct of
sweat gland

hair follicle

sensory nerve

sweat gland

adipose tissue

hair shaft

Epidermis

Dermis

Subcutaneous layer

artery

vein   autonomic motor nerve

A cross section of skin

the molecular size of the ingredient(s), the temperature of the skin, and the condition of the skin at the time of contact. Handmade, topical herbal medicines and soothing, comforting remedies prepared at home have four distinct advantages over commercially formulated preparations.

YOU CONTROL EXACTLY WHAT GOES INTO THE END PRODUCT. Because of the skin's powerful absorptive potential, it's good to know what your skin is "eating." By avoiding deleterious and unnecessary ingredients, as well as known personal allergens, I guarantee that your formula will be skin-friendly and deliver desirable results, with little risk of toxicity or irritation.

YOU CAN CUSTOMIZE YOUR PRODUCTS.
An illness can affect different people differently. For example, if your sinuses are blocked, your chest is tight, and you're sweating with a fever, you could create a heavily mentholated, ultra-cooling balm containing peppermint-derived menthol crystals. Smear it on thickly to help open respiratory channels and bring down your fever.

If you have the same sinus and chest symptoms with chills and little or no fever, a warming ginger-infused oil with thyme and cajeput essential oils would make you feel better.
YOU CAN USE LOCAL HERBS, herbs that grow in the same environment in which you live, and that share the same water, mineral-rich soil, climate, seasons, and air. Many herbalists, including myself, believe that medicinal herbs grown in your surrounding area are the most potent, containing the exact substances and energy you need to maintain health. You can grow your own herbs or purchase them at a good farmers' market or local herb supplier.
YOU USE THE WHOLE HERB, with all of its naturally occurring chemical constituents intact. Your remedies will not contain concentrated active ingredients or standardized extracts combined with synthetic substances that may result in undesirable side effects such as breathing difficulties, drowsiness, rapid heart rate, skin rashes, or headaches.

Pure, *nontoxic*, *minimally processed*, and *good for you* should be the requirements of any substances you inhale, ingest, or apply to your body, whether they're nutritional products, personal care products, oral medications, or topical remedies. This is why it's important to read labels and learn what the ingredients are and their designated purpose, especially with regard to the commercial remedies you buy. Better yet, learn to make quite a few of these products at home, guaranteeing purity and genuine benefit. Nature's ingredients, combined properly, will support and holistically work with your own body's innate healing tendencies.

Useful Vocabulary

ALKALOIDS. Biologically active alkaline compounds containing nitrogen that are usually present in plants as groups of chemicals. Their effects on the body can be profound.

ANALGESIC. An agent that reduces pain.

ANTHELMINTIC (also vermifuge). An agent that destroys parasitic worms.

ANTIOXIDANTS. Compounds that protect the body against free radical damage resulting from oxidation. Free radicals are highly reactive compounds that bind to and destroy other molecules.

BALM. A fatty, semisolid mixture of a base oil with beeswax, cocoa butter, and/or shea butter, usually containing essential oils or medicinal herbs and found in make up. Balms and salves are similar but balms are typically more aromatic.

EXTRACT. To draw out the active alcohol-, water-, or oil- soluble, chemical components of an herb into the solvent medium or menstruum.

FLAVONOIDS. A class of plant constituents with potent anti-inflammatory and anti-oxidant properties. They tend to strengthen and protect the integrity of the vascular system, but have a wide variety of actions that include antispasmodics, stimulants, and diuretics.

GLYCOSIDES. Common plant chemicals consisting of a sugar molecule and one or more other products. They can have various properties, such as analgesic, anti-oxidant, laxative, and so on.

HEMOSTATIC. Reduces or stops external bleeding.

INFUSE. To steep plant matter in water, ethyl alcohol, witch hazel, vinegar, or a carrier oil in order to extract the active constituents.

LINIMENT. A solution of herbal constituents that are typically extracted using ethyl alcohol, denatured or isopropyl alcohol, witch hazel, or vinegar as the menstruum. Some herbalists make liniments using oil as the extractive medium. Liniments are used to treat bruises and sore muscles and joints.

MACERATE. To steep an herb in a liquid solvent or extractive medium, such as a base oil, witch hazel, ethyl alcohol, or vinegar, to extract the herb's medicinal properties.

MARC. The solid residue remaining after extracting the soluble components of an herb or herbs with a menstruum or solvent.

MENSTRUUM. A liquid solvent or extractive medium, such as a base oil, ethyl alcohol, witch hazel, or vinegar, used to make herbal extracts (liniments, infused oils, and tinctures).

MUCILAGE. A sticky, gooey, or slimy substance found in some herbal roots, such as comfrey, Solomon's Seal, or marshmallow. It soothes and protects skin tissue.

OLEORESINS. A plant extract containing resins and oil.

SALVE (SEE BALM).

SEBUM. The semi-fluid, fatty or oily secretions of the sebaceous glands.

TANNINS. Plant compounds that shrink swollen tissue, promoting healing and reducing of pain.

TINCTURE. A solution of herb constituents that are typically extracted using ethyl alcohol as the menstruum. Tinctures can be taken orally or applied topically.

VULNERARY. Having tissue-healing properties.

CHAPTER 2

The Herbal Home Apothecary

This chapter introduces you to the ingredients called for in the recipes for herbal medicines in part 2. For your convenience and further education, The Ingredient Dictionary (page 277) describes *all* the herbs, base and essential oils, waxes, and other plant-based constituents used in this book and lists substitutes, when applicable, that can be used when a particular ingredient is unavailable.

If this is your first foray into creating herbal health- and comfort-care products, I can see that your head might be spinning as you flip through the pages of ingredients — some of which may seem foreign to you. "Where the heck do I find this stuff?" you might ask. Don't worry, most of these ingredients are quite readily available.

Your local health food store, food co-op, or whole foods grocer is the first place to check for herbal remedy crafting supplies. Try your local drugstore or a cosmetic supply house; they may carry some of the items you need, such as storage containers, or they may be able to order them for you. The yellow pages are also an excellent place to find ingredients — yes, people still do use the phone book for information. Look under "Apothecaries," "Botanicals," "Beauty Supplies," "Herbs," "Nurseries," "Garden Centers," "Health Food Stores," "Natural Food Stores," "Restaurant Supplies," "Pharmacies," "Spices," and "Oils."

The Internet, of course, is a go-to resource for just about everything you'll need to create all the recipes in this book. I try to grow many of my medicinal herbs, but those that I don't or can't, along with other necessary ingredients, I purchase from mail-order catalogs or Internet sources that I know and trust. I prefer sources that I know have a relatively rapid turnover of stock, so that I can be sure the ingredients I purchase are fresh. (For a listing of tried and trusted ingredient suppliers, see Resources.)

If you have a green thumb and room for a garden, you can grow many of the herbs yourself (depending on your climate). Many herbs are biennials or perennials, providing you with a continued source of medicine, beauty, and nectar for the pollinators. In fact, I strongly recommend that you dedicate some space for the cultivation of medicinal herbs, if possible. Super-fresh, lovingly grown, organic herbs make for potent medicine with powerful healing energy.

You can also *wildcraft* or forage for herbs in the wild. If you decide to go this route, rule number one is always to ask the landowner for permission to enter his or her property with the intention of harvesting wild herbs. Purchase a good herb identification book (preferably with color photos) and educate yourself while hiking through the woods and meadows. A wild plant identification class offered by a local herb school, nature center, county extension service, or adult education program would be well worth the time and expense. You'll be amazed at what natural medicines grow in your environment.

In the summer, a good farmers' market can be a wonderful source for medicinal flowers and herbs such as lavender, calendula, chamomile, yarrow, peppermint, comfrey, rosemary, sage, oregano, and thyme. If you get lucky, you'll find fresh, aromatic beeswax direct from the apiary, which is a real luxury that I like to include in lip treatments, salves, and balms.

If you can locate a local herb farm and apothecary, you'll think you've died and gone to medicine maker's heaven. What a glorious resource for herbs and infused oils, plus many professionally made remedies for you to try. Herb farms often have public "strolling gardens" and offer classes in all manner of herb studies. And when traveling and driving around the countryside, always keep an eye out for purveyors of fresh farm specialties that

---

I just come and talk to the plants, really — very important to talk to them, they respond I find.

— CHARLES, PRINCE OF WALES,
in a 1986 television interview

Home Remedy Starter Kit

Is the crafting of herbal home remedies a new realm of adventure for you? A new hobby you'd like to explore? Learning how to make topical herbal remedies is akin to learning how to cook food, except that instead of making a delicious meal, you'll be using herbs and other natural ingredients to concoct soothing, healing potions that will bring relief to a multitude of discomforts and ailments. And you can use virtually the same basic kitchen tools and skills as you do making dinner for your family.

The recipes below are a good starting place for an aspiring herbalist. They are all easy to craft, plus they share some relatively easy-to-find ingredients and can address a wide range of health complaints, including sunburn and common household skin burns, minor to moderate skin infections, cuts and scrapes, ingrown toenails, rashes, brittle nails and ragged cuticles, blisters, and dry, cracked skin on feet, hands, and lips. A couple of these recipes also aid in relieving anxiety, nervous tension, and insomnia.

From just 6 remedies using 13 basic ingredients, you can produce a lot of useful medicine! I believe that each ingredient and all of the prepared remedies discussed here should be in everyone's home medicine cabinet — you never know when you'll need a helping, healing hand from Mother Nature!

RECIPES

- French Lavender Drops: Serious Blemish Treatment (page 81)
- Quench-the-Heat Aloe Liniment (page 97)
- Quick and "Neat" Insect Bite and Sting Relief (page 210)
- Rain's Rosemary Remembrance Balm (page 221)
- Simple Lavender-Infused Oil (page 58)
- Vegan Lanolin (page 136)

INGREDIENTS

Almond oil

Aloe vera juice

Beeswax

Castor oil

Cocoa butter

German chamomile essential oil

Lavender buds

Lavender essential oil

Rosemary (chemotype *verbenon*) essential oil

Tea tree essential oil

Thyme (chemotype *linalool*) essential oil

Vitamin E oil

Shea butter

could be used in topical herbal remedies. A fresh ingredient is a first-rate ingredient!

You are probably familiar with many of the herbs and other naturally derived components called for in this book. There are six broad categories of remedial-care ingredients, however, that may require a more in-depth introduction: alcohol, clays, base oils, essential oils, infused oils, and herbs. In the next few pages, I cover the specific terminology, quality, storage requirements, harvesting, and preparation techniques for the ingredients in each of these categories. Before you purchase any ingredients and start stirring, straining, pouring, and chanting (yes, if you are a lover of the green world, talking to your herbs will come naturally as part of the process of medicine making—trust me on this), take a few minutes and educate yourself. Remember: a knowledgeable consumer makes the wisest choices and the highest-quality handmade healing preparations.

Ethyl Alcohol

Ethyl alcohol is used by herbalists as a **menstruum** (solvent) for extracting an herb's unique healing chemical components. One hundred percent ethyl alcohol dissolves and extracts the alcohol-soluble constituents in the plant, including resins, essential oils, fats, alkaloids, coloring pigments, acrid and bitter compounds, alkaloidal salts, glycosides, organic acids, chlorophyll, uncrystallized sugars, and waxes.

Eighty- or 100-proof ethyl alcohol, which many herbalists use, contains water so it additionally extracts water-soluble constituents such as gums, mucilage, crystallized sugars, polysaccharides, saponins, tannins, and proteins.

To make an alcoholic extract, the dried or fresh herb is first cut, chopped, mashed, or powdered and then **macerated** (soaked) in the alcohol for 2 to 8 weeks. Tougher materials such as bark, stems, roots, and twigs

Important Warning: For Topical Use Only

The herbal alcohol or tincture formulas in this book are *not designed to be taken orally*, even though they are basically made the same way as an edible medicinal tincture. Herbal alcohol formulas designed to be applied topically are called *liniments* and are used to treat sore or strained muscles, skin infections and inflammations, foot fungus, and arthritis, among other afflictions. They can also serve as the primary base for herbal deodorants and disinfectant cleansers.

It's a good idea to put "For External Use Only" on the label of every container of a topical remedy.

require a longer soaking than more tender plant parts such as flowers, fruit, and leaves. Afterward, the plant material is strained and squeezed out, leaving a **tincture** or herbal alcohol. This liquid is convenient to apply, its particular medicinal properties are easily absorbed, it's generally pleasant to use, and it is possibly (but not always) more concentrated than the unprocessed form of the herb. Those chemicals that cannot be extracted into an alcohol-based solution remain in the **marc** (the strained plant residue), which can be tossed into the compost heap.

Ethyl alcohol is an excellent preservative. Alcohol-based herbal extracts last many years, while water-based "herbal tea" solutions degrade in a matter of days. When making fresh medicinal herbal juice in the blender, I add a small amount of ethyl alcohol to the mix to preserve the juice so that it can be stored in the refrigerator for approximately 2 weeks.

I use 80-proof ethyl alcohol (which is 40% alcohol and 60% water) as the solvent for my healing liniment recipes and deodorant preparations (instead of the more frequently used menstruum *isopropyl alcohol*, which is a petroleum byproduct and highly toxic if ingested even in small quantities). Ethyl alcohol is commonly called "grain" alcohol because it used to be made primarily from fermented corn. It is also made by fermenting rye, wheat, potatoes, molasses, or fruit, in which case it's known as whisky, vodka, rum, brandy, or gin. I always use an inexpensive vodka; no need to waste your money on premium brands!

Clays

Excavated from mines throughout the world, including in North America, clay is rich in minerals derived from plants, animals, water, soil, rocks, and volcanic ash that have been compounded and slowly ground into extremely fine particles. These particles are deposited by rivers and streams in large masses, usually in the banks and beds of lakes and rivers or near underground water channels.

As the clay is formed, it picks up various trace minerals that impart earthy colors such as green, white, yellow, red, brown, black, and gray. Each color signifies the different concentrations of minerals in the clay. Green clay contains high levels of calcium, magnesium, potassium, sodium, iron, silica, and plant materials. Yellow clay contains sulfur; red clay contains iron; brown and black have iron, zinc, and sulfur; and white contains zinc, silica, aluminum, calcium, and magnesium.

Medicinally speaking, clay has been used therapeutically for thousands of years in soothing, semi-liquid mud baths or as thick healing poultices applied directly to the skin.

My own poultice recipes call for powdered clay. When sufficient liquid (water or aloe vera juice or gel, plus a drop or two of a specific essential oil) is added to powdered clay, the result is a soft, smooth, spreadable mass that acts as a drawing agent or highly absorptive agent.

As a thick clay pack dries, it tightens the skin (just as a clay facial mask does), raising the skin's temperature, increasing circulation, and encouraging blood and lymph flow to the affected area. The hardening clay draws toxins from beneath the skin, aiding in the release and removal of plant and insect poisons, minor to moderate infection, small splinters and bee stingers, ingrown hairs, and hardened sebum. After the clay pack is washed off and circulation returns to normal, the affected area feels cooler and more comfortable, and the skin texture is smoother. The process can be repeated if necessary.

My favorite varieties of mineral-rich, healing clay for use in clay packs are bentonite and green clay (sometimes called French green clay), which I prefer to purchase in powdered form, though I'll also buy them in prepared formulas. I also have a handful of medicated herbal powder recipes that use green clay or white cosmetic clay blended with powdered herbs for deodorizing and astringent purposes.

Base Oils

Base oils are chemically classified as fats — they contain fatty acids and glycerin — and are derived from beans, nuts, seeds, fruits, and grains. You may also hear them called unctuous oils, fixed oils, or carrier oils. Base oils are characteristically greasy, slippery, smooth in texture, and lighter than water, with an extremely low evaporation rate.

Base oils, as their name implies, are used as a base or carrying agent to which essential oils, solid fats, herbs, or spices are added to make herb-infused oils, salves, balms, or elixirs. Base oils can be used alone or in combination with other base oils to create massage and skin-conditioning oils. I use only plant-derived fats, never lanolin, lard, cod liver oil, or mineral oil.

When warmed, base oils act as wonderful solvents for extracting and absorbing herbal components such as resins, gums, essential oils, and oleoresins. Mucilage, flavonoids, alkaloids, and other active principles are partially soluble in oil. A wonderful benefit derived from

Using Vitamin E

In many recipes I call for using vitamin E to prolong the shelf life of base oils, usually 1,000 IU of liquid vitamin E oil to every cup (8 ounces) of base oil. Using 500 IU or larger capsules is most convenient; simply pierce the capsules and squeeze the oil out.

using base oils in topical remedies is that as they are absorbed, they leave a protective, skin-conditioning barrier on the surface while delivering the herbal benefits to the tissues below.

The best base oils are those that have been organically grown, naturally extracted, and minimally processed. The key words to look for on the label are *organic*, *cold pressed* or *expeller pressed*, and/or *unrefined* — these guarantee the highest quality. An organic, unrefined oil that was either expeller pressed or cold pressed is the most desirable.

These oils have not been exposed to extraction procedures using petroleum-derived solvents such as hexane or alcohol, nor to extremely high temperatures, bleaching, or deodorizing. These processes can destroy or alter an oil's natural molecular state, thereby affecting aromas, flavors, colors, depth, consistency, antioxidant properties, and vitamin, mineral, and essential fatty acid content.

Extra Virgin Is Better

With regard to olive oil and coconut oil, the term *extra virgin* refers to the first pressing of the fruit, which is the most desirable. Subsequent pressings result in a gradually lower quality of oil, with less flavor, color, and nutrients and a thinner texture.

More gently processed oils are produced by mechanically pressing beans, fruits, nuts, seeds, or grains and straining out any resulting debris. Some heat is naturally generated during the pressing; the oil usually reaches a temperature of between 80°F and 175°F, which is not so hot that it destroys the vital nutrients, taste, and aroma of the oil. Compared to their refined, highly processed cousins (commonly found in the average supermarket), organic, unrefined oils appear slightly darker in color, are truer to taste (if eaten), have deeper aromas, and contain much higher amounts of essential fatty acids. They may also have a cloudy appearance at times.

It's important to note that most unrefined base oils — with the exception of avocado, coconut, extra-virgin olive, jojoba, and sesame — have a relatively short shelf life and tend to become rancid if stored at room temperature for more than 8 months, especially in warm weather. These oils should be refrigerated and used within 1 year.

If an oil you purchase has a strange or "off" smell (note that macadamia, calophyllum, sesame, coconut, and extra-virgin olive naturally have strong fragrances), then it's probably rancid and should be returned to where you bought it. Purchase base oils through reputable retailers with a high turnover of inventory, and always check the expiration date on the bottle.

Essential Oils

To me, essential oils are the soul or life force of the plant, embodying the plant's precious, aromatic hormones and many chemical compounds. They can aid in the regeneration and oxygenation of the skin, plus they provide blessed relief from common skin conditions, body ailments, and general discomforts.

Plants store essential oils in either tiny cellular reservoirs or intercellular spaces, depending on the plant. Pure essential oils are extracted primarily by steam distillation, with the exception of citrus oils, which are generally cold-pressed from the fruit's rind. A relative newcomer to extraction methodology is *carbon dioxide (CO_2) extraction*, a more expensive yet superior process conducted under relatively low heat without the use of steam or solvents. CO_2 extraction is most often used for the more expensive and oil-stingy plant materials, such as frankincense, myrrh, nutmeg, ginger, calendula blossom, and vanilla bean. As a general rule, for extraction purposes, lower pressure and lower temperature during processing, combined with high-quality organic herbs, ensure top-quality fragrance and therapeutic value.

Another extraction method is *solvent extraction*, in which a solvent such as petroleum ether, hexane, toluene, methane, or propane is used to extract the essential oil from the plant. Once the volatile oils, pigments, and waxes are extracted, the residual solvent is removed through evaporation under pressure. Now you have a soft, sticky wax called a *concrete*, which is processed with ethyl alcohol, chilled, and the solidified waxes filtered out, leaving the volatile compounds diluted in the alcohol. In the final processing step, the alcohol is removed by vacuum distillation.

A Note on Extraction Methods

Steam distillation and cold-pressing methods do not, in and of themselves, always yield a top-quality essential oil. Herbs can be steam-distilled at very high temperatures for a short duration, which can result in a poorer-quality essential oil than you'd get from using a lower temperature for a longer duration. And citrus rinds can be cold-pressed under very high pressure, which generates more heat than using a lower pressure. The only way you can be sure of top quality is to call the manufacturer — as I do — and find out how things are done.

The resulting oil is referred to as an *absolute*. Due to the synthetic residue remaining in the end product, this type of essential oil is not considered of therapeutic grade. Jasmine, rose, hyacinth, lavender, and mimosa are common absolutes and are recommended for fragrance use only. If an essential oil is an absolute, it will be indicated on the label.

Essential oils are usually liquid but can be quite viscous (as is the case for Australian sandalwood, ylang-ylang, oakmoss, vetiver, and patchouli), semi-solid (as for peppermint and rose, depending on the temperature), or even solid (such as orris root). To measure out one of these thicker essential oils from its bottle, you just have to set the bottle in a shallow bowl of warm water for a few minutes, so that it dissolves into a liquid you can measure out with a dropper.

When purchasing essential oils, never buy bottles that are sealed using a glass eyedropper with a rubber top. Essential oils are quite volatile and their vapors will rapidly degrade the rubber, allowing air to enter, diminishing the quality of your investment. Always purchase essential oil bottles with either a plastic-lined, hard screw-cap and extract what you need using a sterile glass eyedropper; or make sure the bottle is sealed with a hard plastic, drop-by-drop reducer cap, which is how most essential oil bottles under two ounces are sealed.

Sources of Essential Oils

The following are a few examples of the plant parts from which particular oils are derived:

ESSENTIAL OIL(S)	PLANT PART SOURCE
Lemongrass, palmarosa	Grass
Eucalyptus, peppermint, rosemary, spearmint	Leaves
Calendula, chamomile, lavender, neroli, rose, yarrow	Flowers
Cinnamon, sweet birch	Bark
Grapefruit, lemon, lime, orange	Rind
Fir, pine, spruce	Needles
Juniper	Berries
Cedar, rosewood	Wood
Ginger, orris, vetiver	Roots
Anise, cardamom, fennel	Seeds
Frankincense, myrrh	Resin

Chemically, essential oils have nothing in common with base or fixed oils. They do not contain fatty acids, are not prone to rancidity, and because of their minute molecular makeup evaporate easily (hence their other common name, *volatile oils*). They react with water much as fatty oils do — by floating to the top. They do, however, readily lend their scent to water and watery solutions such as aloe vera juice or gel and vinegar. Essential oils blend quite readily with base oils and other fats, and they dissolve in 100 percent pure ethyl alcohol, and to some degree in 80-proof ethyl alcohol, making them an ideal formulary ingredient.

How Do Essential Oils Affect the Body?

An essential oil can potentially contain hundreds of aromatic molecules (some of which are quite fragrant and others not so much). The ever-so-tiny molecules will rapidly penetrate the skin whether applied "neat" or diluted in a carrier oil, and the vapors easily penetrate the mucous membranes of the respiratory system when inhaled. Through both application and inhalation, the molecules travel quickly through the capillaries and into the circulatory system which transports them around the body.

Additionally, through our sense of smell, the aromatic vapors stimulate the olfactory nerve — the only nerve in the body that is in direct contact with the external environment — and transmit odor signals directly to the limbic system of the brain; the same area of the brain that houses and triggers memories, emotions, desires, and appetites. As the molecules travel through the body, the oils' complex array of components interact with the body's own chemistry, exerting therapeutic effects — sometimes profoundly so — initiating various physiological and psychological functions, such as relief from pain, healing of damaged skin tissue, stimulation or relaxation of the senses, release of hormones, or a positive boost in mood or cognitive ability.

Keep Away from Children and Pets

Store all your herbal supplies safely away from children and pets. All ingredients, and essential oils in particular, have the potential to be toxic if ingested and/or applied to the skin improperly. Essential oils are safe for use on children if used as directed in a particular child-safe recipe, but if swallowed, inhaled excessively, poured on the skin, or rubbed into the eyes or mucous membranes, they could be extremely irritating and debilitating, if not fatal. I'm not trained in veterinary aromatherapy, but I do know that the same toxicity rules should be observed with pets as well.

When in Doubt, Check It Out

Anytime you use essential oils and herbs, it's a good idea to follow general safety precautions. Many moons ago, when I was but a novice, I decided to make some bath oil using lemon essential oil. I mixed a tablespoon of almond oil and a few drops of oh-so-fragrant, refreshing lemon oil and poured it into my running bath water, anticipating an aromatic, skin-tingling bath. Ahhh, I could hardly wait!

I removed my robe and slipped right in. It felt and smelled so good . . . at first. Within minutes, my uplifting bath had me feeling like I'd just sat down on a hill of Texas fire ants! I immediately rinsed off and doused myself with cold aloe vera gel, which helped a little, but I continued to itch and burn for the rest of the evening. Apparently lemon oil and my skin don't play well together.

The moral of the story is that just because something is all natural doesn't mean it can't irritate your skin! Nearly everyone is allergic to something at some point in their lives, whether synthetic or natural. When making any healing recipe, never use a new ingredient without first doing a patch test, especially if the ingredient is an unfamiliar essential oil, herb, or herbal extract.

HOW TO DO AN ESSENTIAL OIL PATCH TEST

Combine 1 or 2 drops of the essential oil in question with ½ teaspoon base oil, such as almond, sesame, or soybean, in a small bowl. Apply a dab on your wrist, inside your upper arm, behind your ear, or behind your knee, and wait 12 to 24 hours. If no irritation develops, it is generally safe to use the essential oil.

Essential Oil Safety Tips

It takes approximately 40 rosebuds to produce just a single precious drop of rose otto essential oil. It takes nearly eight million jasmine blossoms, hand-picked before the heat of the day on the day the flowers open, to produce just over 2 pounds of superior essential oil. For tart, sweet lemon balm (also known as melissa), one of the rarest and most often adulterated essential oils, you'd need 2,000 pounds or more of fresh leaves to make 1 pound of essential oil. Not surprisingly, these are three of the most expensive essential oils on the market.

Thankfully, not all plant materials are that stingy with their essential oil. A pound of essential oil can be extracted from approximately 50 pounds of eucalyptus leaves or 150 pounds of lavender blossoms, and the prices are accordingly lower.

The point is that essential oils are highly concentrated forms of herbal chemical energy, and they must be used with caution. Few essential oils may be used *neat* (undiluted) on the skin, the exceptions being lavender, carrot seed, tea tree, German chamomile, rose, Australian sandalwood, and geranium (rose geranium). Always dilute an essential oil in a base oil unless you know it's safe to use neat. It's important to educate yourself about the properties of and contraindications for each essential oil before you use it.

If you rub or splash an essential oil into your nose or eyes — which can cause excruciating pain — immediately flush the affected area with an unscented, bland fatty oil such as olive, almond, corn, soybean, peanut, or generic vegetable. Full-fat cream, half-and-half, or whole milk makes an acceptable substitute for the fatty oil in an emergency. Using plain water does not help; essential oils are attracted to fats alone. Should the pain continue or should severe headache or respiratory irritation develop, seek prompt medical attention.

Storing Essential Oils

Essential oils retain their healing properties for 5 to 10 years if properly stored in a dark, dry, cool place, and some actually improve with age. The exception to this is citrus oils: They will remain potent for only 6 to 12 months unless refrigerated. When refrigerated, they may last for up to 2 years if not opened frequently.

To prolong the shelf life of an essential oil, do not store the oil in a bottle with a rubber dropper top. The strong vapors emitting from the oil will gradually weaken the rubber and allow air to enter the bottle, and the precious volatile healing properties will evaporate prematurely. If you intend to keep a particular bottle of oil longer than 6 months, seal it with a plastic screw-top cap and use a clean dropper to dispense the oil. Most oils, though, come with plastic caps and drop-by-drop "reducers" for easy application.

If you are serious about purchasing and using real, quality essential oils, I recommend that you educate yourself by reading a couple of good books on the topic and taking a local aromatherapy class, if one is available. I also recommend that you call the company whose oils you want to use and talk to someone in-the-know about the origins of their oils and production methods used. I purchase my essential oils from a handful of companies I've come to know and trust (see Resources).

Infused Oils

To *infuse* a plant means to steep or soak plant material (leaves, bark, flowers, roots, resins, fruits, and the like) in a menstruum such as water, alcohol, or oil in order to extract the soluble properties. An herbal infused oil is a base or fatty oil that has absorbed the fat-soluble properties of a chosen herb that was allowed to soak or macerate in the warmed oil for a period of time. When the maceration is complete, the herb matter is strained out and the infused oil is bottled for future use. The infused oil can be used by itself as a simple medicinal oil or added to oil blends, salves, or balms. Culinary infused oils that you may

be familiar with include oregano oil, basil oil, garlic oil, truffle oil, and rosemary oil.

Infused oils can be created by two different methods, depending on the particular herb you are using, the season of the year, and whether the herb is dried or freshly wilted. SOLAR OR SUN INFUSION METHOD. The herbs and base oil are combined in a sealed glass jar and placed outside, or in a sunny south-facing window, to infuse for several weeks in the warm sun and the moonlight, then strained, labeled, and bottled. STOVETOP METHOD. The herbs and oil are combined in a saucepan or double boiler, uncovered, and warmed on a stovetop burner set just shy of a simmer (125° to 135°F) for 4 to 6 hours, then strained, labeled, and bottled.

I prefer the solar infusion method. It may not be the quickest, but I feel that by allowing the universal energy systems to create the healing potion according to their timetable, not mine, I receive a super-charged medicine, a true gift from Mother Nature. She provides the medicinal plants and the solar and lunar energy. I simply join them together and reap the benefits. I call solar-infused oils "plant spirit vibrational earth medicine in a bottle."

I'm not trying to imply that the stovetop method is second-rate — it isn't, by any means. It's relatively quick, and I understand that not everyone will want to wait a month for

Buyer Beware

You will pay more for a company's commitment to quality, but it's worth every penny if the product is pure and natural and truly benefits your physical and mental health. Unfortunately, some essential oils on the market are poor quality, so be aware of the distinguishing features of a top-of-the-line product:

• The product label should note the common name followed by the botanical Latin name and variety or chemotype, if applicable. The words *organic* or *ethically wildcrafted* should definitely appear, as well as *therapeutic grade* or *pharmaceutical grade*. If neither of these last two descriptors is on the label, look for them in the company's literature.

• Top-shelf essential oils often vary slightly in their scent, viscosity, and color from batch to batch. This is a sign of true quality and should be considered completely normal and natural.

• Essential oils are highly volatile and evaporate quickly. To see this for yourself, place a drop on a sheet of plain paper, spread it around, and leave it for at least 5 hours and up to 24. A pure essential oil will evaporate, leaving either no stain or a very small one. If the oil is strongly colored, it may leave a residual pigment stain.

A base or fatty oil, such as almond, sunflower, or apricot kernel, will leave a greasy stain much like that made by potato chips kept in a paper bag. If your drop of essential oil leaves an obviously greasy stain, it has probably been diluted with a base oil, which should be noted on the label.

• Fatty oils have a greasy feel; essential oils do not. Rub a little olive, sesame, almond, or generic vegetable oil between your fingers and notice how slippery it is. An essential oil may initially seem a bit greasy, but it feels more like water and is absorbed quickly. If the essential oil feels like fatty oil, it has probably been diluted.

a solar-infused oil to be ready. The stovetop method produces a superior, high-quality infused oil, and it is especially useful if you are infusing fresh thick plant material that tends to be damp or moist, such as ginger or comfrey root, calendula blossoms or rosebuds, or the resinous leaves of rosemary or sage.

The constant heat helps evaporate the excess moisture. (Almost all fresh plant material should be wilted before being infused; see page 38.) And the stovetop method is the only method I use to make infused oil of Solomon's seal root — almost always using the dried root — as the steady electric heat seems to make a better extraction.

A Note on Yield

The amount of oil or liniment you will actually produce for any given recipe can vary quite a bit, depending for one thing on whether you use fresh, dried, or partially wilted herbs. The force with which you press out the herb matter also affects the yield — the harder you squeeze, the more precious drops you will gain.

Living in northern coastal Maine, I often use the stovetop method, as I can't depend on the sun as a reliable heat source. Trying to make solar oils in a cool, often cloudy locale, whether summer or winter, will generally produce moldy or fermented infused oils, especially if you're using fresh herbs, resulting in medicinally weak oils — a waste of both base oil and herb.

In part 2, you will find the recipes and best methodologies (from my experience) for creating my favorite infused oils. My top can't-live-without-them infused oils are made either singularly or in combination from the following 28 herbs and spices:

- Arnica
- Bhringaraj
- Calendula
- Cayenne pepper
- Chamomile
- Chickweed
- Cinnamon bark
- Cloves
- Comfrey
- Fir needles
- Ginger
- Lavender
- Lemon balm
- Lemon peel
- Meadowsweet
- Mugwort
- Mullein
- Myrrh resin
- Oregon grape root
- Plantain
- Rosemary
- Roses
- Sage
- Solomon's seal root
- St. John's wort
- Sweet violet
- Thyme
- Yarrow

I frequently find the following five infused oils available from better health food stores and herb suppliers: arnica, comfrey, calendula, rosemary, and St. John's wort. I always prefer to make my own infused oils, but when pressed for time or out of herb stock, or just plain feeling lazy, I do purchase them from reputable companies (see Resources).

Herbs

Learning the history, uses, and properties of herbs can be fascinating. As you try your hand at some of these recipes and come across herbs that intrigue you, I suggest you look them up in two or three herb books; study all their possible uses, both historical and current; and learn their growth habits, harvesting and storage requirements, and possible contraindications.

But don't stop there: Try to grow the plants or ethically wild-harvest them, if you can, and get to know them on their own turf, where they're energetic, green, and live. Observe the colors, textures, and aromas of the plants in all seasons. If growing or wild harvesting is not practical, at least become familiar with various herbs in their dried state.

Taste them (fresh and dried, if possible). Put a bit of plant material in your mouth and determine which of the six tastes (sweet, sour, salty, pungent, bitter, or astringent) the plant

. . . and the fruit thereof shall be for meat and the leaf thereof for medicine.

—Ezekiel 47:12

has to offer. Does it leave a warming or cooling sensation in your mouth? Knowing more about the plants you include in your preparations will augment the direct experience you gain when working with them.

All of the herbs — leaves, stems, flowers, buds, seeds, twigs, barks, berries, rinds, and roots — called for in the recipes in this book are relatively common, easy to find (of course, there are a few exceptions, such as the East Indian herb bhringaraj), and used in dried form unless otherwise specified. If you have access to freshly grown herbs, then you may want to dry and process them yourself, using the following instructions. Recently processed herbs smell wonderful, and their vital nutrients and medicinal components are at their peak — they'll make your products all the more delightful!

Ethical Wildcrafting

Ethical wildcrafting or wild harvesting is the act of harvesting your herbs directly from the wild, while taking care to leave behind enough healthy plants to continue to repopulate and spread into the surrounding environment. United Plant Savers (see Resources) is an organization dedicated to replanting endangered and threatened medicinal plants. Here are some of their wildcrafting tips:

• Think about the plant community and how many plants it can manage without — not how many plants you need in order to make products or profits.

• Treat native plant complexes like the fine perennial gardens that they are.

• Do not upset in any manner undisturbed native soil — it is rare and precious.

• Take only as many plants as you can reasonably use; strive for zero waste.

• Replant the areas you are harvesting from. Scatter seeds, replace crowns, and plant roots. Leave plenty of mature and seed-producing plants to reproduce.

• Start a replanting project in your area to help reestablish endangered and threatened species.

• Know the endangered plant species in your bio-region.

Tips for Harvesting and Drying Herbs

You may be surprised by how easy it is to dry and process many of the fresh herbs from your garden or farmers' market. No matter which technique you choose, it's best to dry the herbs as soon as they're picked (or purchased) to fully preserve their beneficial properties. Here are some key points:

• Always use a sharp knife or hand pruners when harvesting.

• Gather herbs in early to midmorning, just after any evening dew has had a chance to dry, but before the sun becomes too hot.

• Harvest flowers, such as yarrow, calendula, roses, or chamomile, as soon as the flowers have just opened. Harvest buds, such as lavender, as soon as the buds are mature and well formed, but have not yet opened. A bud or

How to Do a Patch Test with Herbs

In a small bowl, combine ½ teaspoon of the fresh or dried, finely chopped herb with 1 to 2 teaspoons or so of boiling water. Let the herb absorb and mingle with the water for a few minutes. Apply a dab of the "herb paste" to the inside of your upper arm or wrist; cover with an adhesive strip and leave in place 12 to 24 hours. If no irritation develops, the herb is generally safe to use.

bloom that is past its prime does not have the fragrance, color, or bounty of volatile oils of a fresher specimen.

• Harvest herbs that are free of insects and disease and have not been treated with pesticides.

• Herbs should be relatively dirt-free, but if they're dusty, you can rinse them quickly in cool water and immediately pat them dry with a paper towel or soft, lint-free cloth. Note: Many herbalists who grow organic herbs or harvest from wild clean places don't rinse their herbs prior to use, as the rain is a good natural cleanser, and if the surrounding area is well mulched, there probably won't be much dirt. I do recommend rinsing any herbs you purchase.

• Handle herbs carefully; the leaves and flowers can bruise easily. To remove dirt from harvested roots, gently scrub with a vegetable brush and then rinse them thoroughly.

Herbs can take anywhere from 4 days to several weeks to dry completely, depending on weather conditions and the thickness of the material. Roots, berries, bark, twigs, and seeds take the longest due to their density and/or high moisture content. The ideal temperature for drying is between 65°F and 85°F. When dried herbs are ready for storage, leaves and stems will be brittle, but not so dry as to shatter easily; flower petals and buds will feel semi-crisp; roots will be hard or ever-so-slightly pliable; and berries, barks, and seeds will be very hard and dry.

Avoid overdrying herbs; it can diminish their valuable properties. No matter what part of the plant you are drying, never dry it to the point that it crumbles into absolute dust when squeezed.

Store dried herbs in a cool, moisture-free place away from direct sunlight — preferably in a dark cabinet, for up to 1 year. Zip-lock freezer bags, glass jars, plastic tubs, and metal tins make great storage containers.

HANG-DRYING HERBS To dry your herbs by hanging, simply gather a small handful of stems of a single herb into a bundle and secure them with string, a rubber band, or a zip-tie. Hang the bundles upside down in a well-ventilated, dimly lit area where the humidity is low, if possible. Leave plenty of room between bundles to ensure good air circulation and to keep scents from mingling, especially if you are hanging different varieties of herbs together. Because many herbs look similar when dried, you may find it helpful to label your bundles.

SCREEN-DRYING HERBS Most herbs can be successfully dried on screens or tightly stretched netting. The open mesh allows air to flow freely around the plant and quickly evaporate its moisture content. Many commercial herb farms use the screen-drying method, as it is efficient and space-saving, especially if screens are stacked.

To prepare herbs for screen drying, separate all the parts of the plants you will be drying: flowers, buds, leaves, stems, roots, berries, barks, seeds, and twigs. Spread them on screens by type in a single layer, leaving enough space between the plant parts to allow for good air circulation. Place the screens in a well-ventilated, dimly lit area where the humidity is low, if possible. I like to set mine atop small blocks of wood in my garden shed. Stacking the screens to save space is fine, as long as you allow for adequate ventilation.

If you're setting up screens outside, put them in a mostly shady area and be sure to bring them in at night to avoid the evening dew. Cover the plant material with a single layer of cheesecloth, if you wish, to keep out airborne debris. Keep an eye on the weather, too — you don't want fog, drizzle, or rain to ruin your hard-earned harvest. Soggy, moldy herbs are fodder for the compost heap and a real "downer" for your mood. Of course,

---

What is a weed? A plant whose virtues have not been discovered.

— Ralph Waldo Emerson

---

drying herbs outdoors is a more feasible option if you live in an arid climate with minimal threat of frequent rainfall and high humidity.

Wilting (Partially Drying) Herbs

Wilting is the drooping and withering of the leaves or other parts of a plant that is the first stage of drying. When you make an infused oil from fresh herbs, you need to wilt the herbs first; the process removes sufficient moisture from the plant material to inhibit mold and bacterial growth without affecting the healing properties. The herbs that I most commonly wilt (but also occasionally use in dried form) are calendula, lavender, roses, chamomile, comfrey leaves, mullein flowers, mugwort, plantain, thyme, rosemary, sweet violet, sage, chickweed, fir needles, yarrow, and meadowsweet flowers. Additionally, St. John's wort flowers and lemon balm leaves must always be used freshly wilted as they lose most of their potency if used in dried form.

The process of wilting is simple. Let's take calendula blossoms as an example. To make 3 cups of freshly wilted flowers, pick approximately double that amount to allow for shrinkage. Flowers with petals, like roses, shrink considerably when wilted, while lavender buds and chamomile flowers don't as much. You'll learn through trial and error how much fresh material to pick — it's not an exact science.

To begin, simply snip the calendula blossoms from the plants after the morning dew has dried, but before the sun gets too warm. These are thick, resinous flowers, so gently tear or shred them a bit by hand to expose more surface area so that they dry more evenly. Spread the flowers and their bits of attached greenery on a clean screen, pillowcase, or length of lint-free cloth (a long strip of paper towels will do as well) in a warm, still location that is mostly shady and is protected from wafting animal dander, dust, and flies. I usually wilt my herbs on a table in my study or in the backseat of my car — away from my curious cats.

Allow the flowers to sit for 24 to 48 hours, depending on temperature and humidity. If humidity is very high, add another 24 hours. You should notice a distinct change in texture, from firm and fresh to limp and soft, or even a bit on the leathery side, especially if the temperature is over 90°F and humidity quite low. The size of the flower will diminish as the water evaporates out of the plant material. The amount of shrinkage depends on the temperature and level of humidity: the warmer and drier, the greater the reduction in herb size.

Use Promptly

Unliked dried herbs, which can be stored in airtight containers at room temperature for up to 1 year, wilted herbs are still relatively fresh and cannot be stored for any length of time. They must be prepared a couple of days prior to when you intend to make a given recipe.

CHAPTER 3

Tools of the Trade

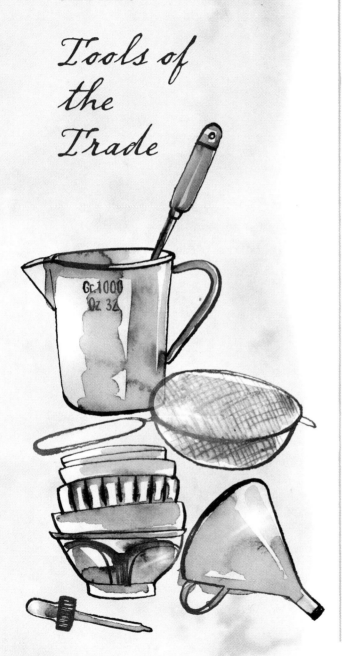

The idea of making your own topical medicines and formulas from natural ingredients may seem a bit daunting, but it really shouldn't be. It's easy and soul-satisfying and can be a lot of fun. Only basic kitchen equipment and cooking skills are necessary for producing wonderfully fresh, health- and wellness-nurturing creations. It's a simple and ancient art that anyone can do. If you can boil water, chop vegetables for a salad, make tea, or melt butter, then putting together these recipes will be as easy as, well, pie!

"Cleanliness is next to godliness" — there's a good reason I say this in nearly every natural body-care book I write. I cannot emphasize enough that the containers for your remedies need to be as sterile as possible, *dry*, and dust-free, and that your hands should be just-washed and dried as well. Ideally all implements should be boiled, but that's not always practical or even possible.

The next best alternative is to run everything through the dishwasher or to soak implements for 15 minutes in very hot, soapy water to which you've added 1 tablespoon of bleach for each gallon of water. Give them a good scrub, rinse them thoroughly, and dry them well. The goal is to minimize the potential for harmful bacterial growth in your preservative-free products.

Preparation Tools

Common, easy-to-find kitchen tools are all you need to make the herbal remedies in this book. Inexpensive tools are likely to wear out quickly and have to be replaced, but midrange quality is fine (unless you want to indulge yourself with a top-of-the-line blender, coffee grinder, or tincture press). Here's what you'll need.

BLENDER. This is great for blending freshly wilted plant matter with ethyl alcohol prior to preparing a liniment, or for mixing a small amount of fresh herb juice with a bit of ethyl alcohol as a preservative. I also use it to pulverize dried flowers, buds, and leaves to near powder consistency, though it's not suitable for really tough herbs such as dried roots, bark, or twigs. A food processor also works well for grinding dried flowers, buds, and leaves, as does a coffee grinder, though the coffee grinder will grind only in small amounts.

BOWLS. You'll need a variety of sizes in glass, enamel, plastic, stainless steel, or ceramic — no copper or aluminum, as they can react adversely with some of the chemical compounds in the herbs. I use small bowls or custard cups for mixing small clay packs for minor afflictions such as insect bites or splinters. I use medium to large bowls for mixing clay packs when I need sufficient product to cover a larger area. Large bowls are convenient for handling larger quantities of herbs or for mixing several varieties of herbs and also for making body and foot powders.

COFFEE FILTERS. A paper coffee filter is my filter of choice because it retains *all* herbal particulate matter when straining liniments and infused oils. I use the small or medium unbleached basket-style filters as liners for handheld mesh strainers and the bigger basket-style ones to line a pasta colander for straining larger quantities. Avoid the cone-style filters, as the glue sometimes dissolves, especially when it comes into contact with ethyl alcohol.

A doubled layer of cheesecloth, an old nylon stocking, a muslin bag or piece of muslin fabric, a linen seed-sprouting bag, or any finely woven mesh bag makes a good substitute, though some herbal particulate matter may filter through and then the product will require re-straining.

COFFEE GRINDER. This gadget gets more use than any other piece of equipment I own aside from my blender and 2-quart saucepan. A seed or nut grinder would work just as well. I use it primarily to grind small quantities of dried flowers, buds, and leaves to near powder consistency. Sometimes it can handle very small pieces of dried roots and bark if they're not too hard. Be sure to use separate grinders for your herbal remedies and your coffee!

CUTTING BOARD. My favorite cutting board is one of those flexible plastic mats, which I can place atop my wooden board and then use to carry the chopped ingredients directly to the bowl, blender, or saucepan. Don't process your herbs on a board that is used for dairy or meat products; I recommend having one just for herbal remedies. Remember to keep your boards or mats scrupulously clean at all times; they can harbor bacteria in grooves and scratches.

DOUBLE BOILER. A double boiler is a two-part pot designed to moderate the heat that comes off a stovetop burner. The bottom section holds simmering water, while the ingredients go in the top part. I have both a 1½- and 2-quart size double boiler. I occasionally use a double boiler to melt hard or thick ingredients, such as beeswax or coconut oil, or to warm liquid oils when making salves and balms. It is handy for making infused oils that require a low temperature.

Not Too Hot

When making products that contain fatty ingredients, such as oils, waxes, or butters, low heat is the key. If you simmer, overheat, boil, or scorch these ingredients, they'll be ruined. In this case, the saying "a watched pot never boils" is a good thing! In making herbal remedies, always keep a watchful eye on what you are doing.

The advantage of this tool is that it produces a gentle, even, relatively low heat, making it impossible to scorch or boil your ingredients if you happen to get called away from the kitchen or get distracted. Usually, though, I simply use a basic stainless steel pan over the absolute lowest setting on my stove. By the way, don't attempt to make your own double boiler or you could ruin two perfectly good saucepans because they might not come apart — I know that from personal experience!

DROPPER (GLASS). Use a dropper, sometimes also called an eyedropper, for measuring essential oils by the drop. Glass is preferable to plastic because it doesn't retain scent or color from the oils, and some essential oils, especially citrus oils, will degrade plastic and rubber. After each use, rinse the dropper with hot water, then pour isopropyl rubbing alcohol or 100 percent ethyl alcohol through it to sterilize it. Most essential oils come in small bottles with "drop-by-drop" reducers for easy application, eliminating the need for a dropper, but glass droppers are also handy for dispensing small amounts of liniments and medicinal oils onto cuts and scrapes, blisters, cold sores, and other minor ailments.

FOOD PROCESSOR (FULL-SIZE OR SMALL). This can be used for grinding dried flowers, buds, leaves, and very small pieces of dried roots and bark (as long as they aren't rock hard) to a near powder consistency. I have better success with this appliance than with a blender when it comes to finely processing dried herbs. This piece of equipment blends body powders quite nicely, too.

FUNNEL (PLASTIC OR STAINLESS STEEL). A small one comes in handy for pouring liquids into narrow-necked storage bottles. If you don't have one the right size, you can make a funnel from aluminum foil in a snap; with the minimal exposure involved, there is no real risk of aluminum leaching into your product as there is when using aluminum pots and pans.

MEASURING CUPS AND SPOONS. Preparing herbal remedies sometimes requires exact measurements, which is where these come in handy. Glass, plastic, or stainless steel is fine. Glass measuring cups with handles have easy-to-read markings and can be used in the microwave, which can be convenient for warming or melting ingredients (just don't overheat them!).

MORTAR AND PESTLE. The mortar and pestle is a classic symbol of medicine that connects the healing science with its herbal roots, though its use has gone out of fashion. If you become a serious herbalist, buy one or two and display them prominently on a shelf in your kitchen. I recommend a larger model with a mortar approximately 6 inches in diameter

for crushing freshly wilted material to a near pulp-like consistency when making infused oils. It is also handy for combining essential oils and powdered clay in preparation for making clay packs and body powders.

PANS. I use myriad sizes, from a tiny ¾-quart pan to 1-, 2-, and 3-quart pans made of enamel, glass, or stainless steel. Don't use aluminum or copper, which can react with the chemical compounds in the herbs, especially the acids and resins, and leach the metals into the products you're making. They can also affect the beneficial qualities of the herbs and discolor the end product.

PARING KNIVES. Always keep several very sharp blades at your disposal for cutting and peeling just about anything. I cut or shave beeswax and cocoa butter with a paring knife instead of using a cheese grater — it's easier on my knuckles. (But if I have big chunks of beeswax or cocoa butter, I'll simply place them in a plastic freezer bag and smash the chunks to bits with my handy hammer!)

SCALE. You don't need one for the recipes in this book, but it can be eye-opening to see how much space 4 ounces of fluffy, dried chamomile flowers take up compared to 4 ounces of dried Solomon's seal or comfrey root. When I first began making personal care products, I used my scale constantly. Now I can usually judge by sight the amount of an ingredient I'm

Math and Making Medicine

Don't wring your hands and get your nerves in a tizzy because the word *math* appears here! Whether you're a beginner or an experienced maker of herbal remedies, it's good to know a few simple measurement equivalents. Commit these to memory and they'll make preparation of your products a bit quicker, especially if you want to customize a recipe or make a larger or smaller batch than is indicated in a recipe's yield. The measurement equivalents are *very close* approximates.

BY THE MILLILITER

1 ml = 20–25 drops

5 ml = ⅙ fluid ounce = 100 drops

15 ml = ½ fluid ounce = 300 drops

30 ml = 1 fluid ounce = 600 drops

60 ml = 2 fluid ounces = 1,200 drops

BY THE TABLESPOON

⅓ tablespoon = 1 teaspoon

1 tablespoon = 3 teaspoons = ½ fluid ounce

2 tablespoons = 28 grams = 1 fluid ounce

4 tablespoons = ¼ cup = 2 fluid ounces

16 tablespoons = 1 cup = 8 ounces or ½ pint

BY THE OUNCE

1 ounce = 28 grams

8 ounces = 1 cup = ½ pint

16 ounces = 2 cups = 1 pint

32 ounces = 4 cups = 2 pints = 1 quart

128 ounces = 1 gallon = 16 cups = 4 quarts or 3.8 liters

measuring. For accuracy, buy a metric scale, a postal scale at an office supply store, or a quality kitchen scale at a kitchen-supply or department store. Make sure it has a substantial basket or flat surface on which you can place your ingredients.

SPATULAS (RUBBER). Collect a variety of sizes for scooping out balms, salves, shea butter, and wet clay from any type of container. Short, narrow spatulas are handy for filling small jars with thickened salves and balms or for transferring products from one container to another.

SPOONS (WOODEN). You really need only two, small and medium in size, but they're indispensable. A stainless steel iced tea spoon works well for blending liquids in tiny pans if you don't have a short, narrow wooden spoon handy.

STIRRING UTENSILS. Regular wooden chopsticks, ½-inch-diameter dowels, old flatware knives and forks, and the long ends of wooden spoons all come in handy for stirring, blending, and poking into tall containers, as well as for dredging sludgy, oil-sodden herbs from the bottom of saucepans or canning jars. I use a really neat maple branch that I found in my woods — it's ultra smooth, has a slight flare at one end, and fits my hand perfectly. This slick stick is my favorite medicine-making companion, aside from Lilly, my attentive Maine Coon

Cat, who occasionally requests a tiny custom jar of "catnip dream balm" when she smells fresh catnip wafting through the kitchen!

STRAINER (BAMBOO, WIRE, OR FABRIC MESH). Use this to strain herbs and flowers from liquids in various liniment and infused oil recipes or to support a finer filter, such as a layer of muslin or paper towel, or a paper coffee filter, when straining smaller particles.

THERMOMETER (YOGURT OR CANDY). It's important to monitor the temperature of your herb and oil mixtures during the infusion process. Whatever type of thermometer you choose, make sure it reads temperatures that begin at the lower end of the scale, say around 100°F.

TURKEY BASTER. Perfect for decanting: removing the watery layer that sometimes forms in the bottom of the canning jar when you're making a solar oil infusion. Don't use the same baster you use for your turkey; keep a separate baster for making herbal remedies.

WHISKS (VARIOUS SIZES). I use a tiny one for blending moist clay pack recipes in custard cups, and a large one for gently blending drops of essential oils into larger quantities of dry clay, prior to adding the liquid ingredient, or when making a batch of herbal body or foot powders.

Storage Containers

When you make herbal remedies, you must have something to store them in, plain and simple. The more attractive and user-friendly the containers for storing your handmade products, the better, though many high-end cosmetics and posh, spa-quality products are packaged in containers that cost more than the ingredients they contain! Aesthetic appeal is especially important if you intend to give your products as gifts. Personally, I am more apt to reach for one of my handmade remedies if I store it in a container that looks nice enough to sit on my bathroom countertop.

See Resources for mail-order and online companies that sell storage wares, or visit antiques stores and flea markets for ornamental bottles, jars, and tins (not rusty ones, of course!). An unattractive recycled jar — though utilitarian — simply will not do for your special herbal remedy products filled with healing love energy!

BOTTLES (½ OUNCE TO 16 OUNCES). I use dark glass and plastic bottles for storing infused oils and massage oil blends, fingernail conditioning oils, facial elixirs, and liniments. If you're using glass, choose amber, dark green, or cobalt blue, especially if the product will be exposed to bright light for an extended period of time. The tint in the glass helps preserve the natural properties of herbs, base oils, and essential oils. For traveling, or if your home is full of small children and pets, clear or opaque plastic bottles might be preferable to avoid breakage. Just be sure to store them away from light once they're filled.

CANNING JARS (½ PINT TO 1 GALLON). These clear glass jars are suitable for storing dried herbs, powdered clay, liniments, and infused herbal oils (when kept away from light) and for making solar-infused oils and liniments. The cute half-pint size is perfect for packaging a generous portion of salve or balm. Slap on a custom label, tie a bit of pretty raffia around the lid, and voilà!, you have a beautiful and useful present!

CREAM JARS (¼ OUNCE TO 8 OUNCES). Perfect for storing balms and salves, these are available in clear or opaque plastic, or clear, amber, green, or cobalt blue glass — the last two being my favorite due to their aesthetic appeal and classic apothecary look. Small condiment jars or the tiniest baby food jars have a cute, squat shape (just make sure the lids fit snugly).

LABELS. All containers should be labeled with the contents, instructions for use, the date the product was made or stored, and the expiration date. A plain white sticker will do, but by all means, if you are giving the product as a gift, attach a fancier label disclosing the pertinent information. If you find that you enjoy making plenty of herbal remedies for friends and family, then design a label that is uniquely yours by using a computer label program, or hand-print your labels and neatly tape them to the container, or perhaps find a local print shop that can help you with custom design. Just make sure your ink is water- and smear-proof!

PLASTIC TUBS. Plastic food storage containers with airtight lids are readily available in a variety of sizes and shapes. I use them to store dried herbs and varieties of dry clay powder.

SPRITZER BOTTLES (GLASS OR PLASTIC). These are good for packaging any recipe that requires a spray application, such as some liniments or deodorants. Spritzer bottles are also convenient for applying herbal liniments to cuts, scrapes, blisters, insect bites or stings, or hot feet.

SQUEEZE BOTTLES. Available in clear or opaque plastic, these are great storage containers for infused oils, oil blends, and liniments,

Warning

Do not use plastic containers for storing oil blends that contain substantial amounts of essential oils, as the oils can degrade the plastic and leach plastic chemicals into the product.

and they make perfect travel containers. As a personal preference, I don't like to store products that contain a substantial amount of essential oils (more than 12 drops per ounce of base oil or alcohol) in plastic, as they can degrade it over time, leaching the plastic's chemicals into the product. I like glass and love its heft, look, and feel.

TINS (¼ OUNCE AND LARGER). Metal containers have a lovely, old-fashioned appeal and are attractive when decorated with a custom-made label, making them great gift-giving containers, especially for luscious lip balms or travel-size portions of salves and balms. I like to use the larger tins to store dried herbs and powdered clay. They're relatively airtight and keep out light and bugs.

WOOZY BOTTLES. Designed mainly as wine and vinegar containers, these tall, narrow-necked, decorative glass bottles are super for storing liquid medicinal remedies. They can be beautiful, too, with a sprig of fresh herb in a liniment, or a showy color from ingredients such as the vibrant red of St. John's wort flowers, the sunshine orange of calendula flowers, or the deep blue-green of German chamomile essential oil.

ZIPLOCK FREEZER BAGS. These make good, inexpensive storage containers for dried herbs and varieties of powdered clay. If you use them to store dried herbs, keep them in a dry, cool, dark place and use the herbs within 6 months to a year. Note: The slide-lock freezer bags are *not* airtight, as indicated on the box. Air quickly leaks into the bag through a tiny gap between the slide mechanism and the edge of the bag, so I suggest using the double-zipper style instead.

Recycling Storage Containers

If you plan to recycle previously used glass, plastic, or ceramic containers for storage purposes, be sure to wash them thoroughly first. You can either run them through the dishwasher or soak them for 15 minutes in very hot, soapy water with a splash of added bleach. After they've soaked, scrub thoroughly, rinse, and allow them to dry completely. Do not store your cosmetics in containers that have previously held medicine, poisons, household cleansers (other than dishwashing liquid), any spoiled and moldy food, or fertilizers. Do not reuse rusty tins or lids. When using a recycled container, make sure it has a tight-fitting lid or that you can purchase a new replacement lid for it. Use your own good judgment about what containers *are* and *are not* safe to use.

PART 2 **A Collection of Herbal Recipes**

The creative art of making medicine was as natural to our ancestors as eating, breathing, and walking are for us. It was just second nature to them — a necessity for survival. Making herbal healing and comfort-enhancing remedies can help deepen our relationship with plants and the earth and keep us connected to our primal roots. From personal experience as an herbalist, I find there is nothing as satisfying as harvesting, drying, and blending herbs into truly useful remedies: an aromatic, analgesic balm for an elderly neighbor, for example, or a calming massage oil for an infant's colicky tummy. Crafting these remedies makes me reflect and remember that this type of healing practice is as old as the human race — a living lineage of wholeness, connectedness, and love.

A recipe of any kind — culinary, cosmetic, personal care, or medicinal — takes you on a guided journey toward a delightful result. In this chapter, I share tried and true recipes from my three decades of experience, listed by ailment or health concern. I've tried to keep the instructions straightforward and have included a bonus use or two where appropriate, so that you can customize the formulation for other health concerns.

Unlike formulations of centuries past, these recipes incorporate the use of new blending equipment, ingredient extraction technologies, and preservation methods, along with a wider array of ingredients, which enable homemade formulations to rival many commercially available products, sans synthetics.

Before we begin, it's important to note a few points about the recipes themselves:

- All herbs called for are in *dried* form unless otherwise specified.
- Each ingredient is included for a specific reason — it contributes to the integrity of the final product.
- Make it a priority to acquire ethically wildcrafted or organically grown herbs that trumpet vibrant color, deep aroma, and robust flavor (if you decide to taste them). Your herbal remedies will only be as good as the quality of herbs you use.
- Always label and date each preparation and make note of the storage requirements.

As your knowledge of topical herbal remedies grows and you gain valuable blending experience, I encourage you to customize these recipes to suit your personal specifications and desires. As your skills develop, experiment and add your own special touches.

Ready? Let's get started! Go slowly, read each recipe twice, absorb the instructions, and then proceed with joy and good intent — the result can only be fine, holistic herbal remedies made with love. Be creative and enjoy the process!

Important Caution

If a formula is not specifically designated as safe for infants or young children, then it is *not* recommended for their use.

ALOPECIA *(Balding)*

A lush, glorious head of hair is desired by both genders, so sudden hair loss or progressive thinning can be quite demoralizing. Alopecia or balding is much more common in men than in women, and it has a long list of potential causes: hormonal imbalances, genetic factors, localized skin conditions, pituitary or thyroid deficiencies, smoking, lack of exercise, poor scalp hygiene, vitamin and mineral deficiencies, insufficient protein, chronic stress, frequent swimming in chlorinated pools, harsh dyes or bleaches, sudden traumatic stress, excessive shampooing, and overuse of hot styling tools.

Hair loss can also be a side effect of certain prescription medications and of cancer treatments such as chemotherapy and radiation. And, of course, natural thinning often occurs as part of the aging process, as the hair follicles begin to shrink and produce thinner, finer hairs with a shorter life span.

When seeking to remedy hair loss, take into consideration lifestyle, nutritional, and personal care habits. I highly recommend the following:

- Eat a whole-food diet that includes plenty of easily digestible protein such as eggs, fish, sprouted grains and beans, raw nuts and nut butters, and sea vegetables.

- Eat lots of sulfur-containing onions, garlic, cabbage, kale, and eggs, as sulfur does amazing things for hair health.

- Get ample fresh air and sunshine daily.

- Observe a natural hair-care regimen by shampooing only once or twice a week, using a chemical-free shampoo followed by a nutrient-rich conditioner.

- Begin taking yoga classes and practice plenty of inverted postures (if you're physically able) to increase blood flow to your head.

- Walk daily to keep your circulation up.

- Manage the stress level in your life.

If you suspect a medical condition might be causing your hair loss, locate a holistic physician and perhaps a good dermatologist. They can be wonderful allies in your journey to regrow your crowning glory.

The following two recipes are actually scalp treatments, because the primary problem with balding lies with the hair follicles and microcirculatory system deep within the dermal layer of the scalp. If the hair follicles are still "alive" or active, then the possibility for hair regrowth remains.

Herbal Scalp Conditioner and Stimulator

This blend of rosemary, basil, and lemon helps stimulate circulation, cleanse and oxygenate the follicles, encourage hair growth, and nourish the roots. It also aids in balancing sebum production, so don't be afraid to use it if your scalp is oily. It has a sharp, fresh fragrance and may cause the scalp to slightly tingle. If you wish, you can actually sleep with this blend on your scalp and hair for ultimate conditioning. If your hair and scalp are very dry, like mine, you may not need to shampoo after treatment at all.

It usually takes a minimum of 3 months to see noticeable new growth. Many people, though, notice a dramatic improvement in the texture and appearance of existing hair much sooner, even after the first use, especially if the hair is quite dry, overprocessed, or straw-like.

Bonus This oil blend also makes a great pain-relieving massage oil for arthritic joints and can help ease the pain of tense, sore muscles. A few drops rubbed into the temples, followed by a brief period of quiet time with the eyes closed, will provide welcome relief from a muscle-tension headache.

30 drops rosemary (chemotype *verbenon*) essential oil

15 drops basil essential oil

15 drops lemon essential oil

10 drops geranium essential oil

5 drops clove essential oil

½ cup jojoba base oil

EQUIPMENT: *Dropper, dark glass bottle with dropper top or screw cap*
PREP TIME: *15 minutes, plus 24 hours to synergize*
YIELD: *½ cup*
STORAGE: *Store at room temperature, away from heat and light; use within 2 years*
APPLICATION: *3 times per week*

Add the rosemary, basil, lemon, geranium, and clove essential oils drop by drop directly into a storage bottle. Add the jojoba base oil. Cap the bottle and shake vigorously for 2 minutes to blend. Label the bottle and place in a dark location that's between 60° and 80°F for 24 hours so that the oils can synergize.

APPLICATION INSTRUCTIONS: Shake well before using. Place 1 to 2 teaspoons of the oil blend in a small bowl. Using your fingertips, gradually massage the entire amount into your dry scalp for several minutes, making sure to rub a little down the length of your hair and onto the ends. Wrap your hair completely with plastic wrap or a plastic shower cap, then cover it with a very warm, damp towel. Replace with another warm towel once the first has cooled.

Leave on for at least 30 to 45 minutes, or overnight (if you do this, remove the plastic and sleep with a dry towel on your pillow to absorb the oil). Then rinse and lightly shampoo your hair with a chemical-free, low-sudsing product, if needed. Follow with a conditioner, if desired.

BHRINGARAJ "RULER OF THE HAIR" SCALP NOURISHING OIL

Bhringaraj is famous in India for its use in natural hair tonics, being the primary ingredient in most Ayurvedic hair oils. With consistent use, it promotes strong, healthy hair growth and helps maintain the hair's natural color and luster. Quite beneficial for those who are turning prematurely gray! It is one of the best hair and scalp rejuvenators for people with a pitta personality — these "take charge" types tend to have a ruddy complexion and often exhibit impatience and a hot temper. According to the teachings of Ayurveda, bhringaraj cools the head and calms the mind and is balancing for all constitutions/personalities. The sesame oil in this formula is nourishing, grounding, and balancing and a great conditioner for all hair types.

Warning: Works on all hair types, but *not all colors*. This formula will temporarily stain blond, bleached, or white hair.

¾ cup bhringaraj leaf powder

2 cups unrefined sesame base oil

1,000 IU vitamin E oil

EQUIPMENT: *1½-quart saucepan or double boiler, stirring utensil, candy or yogurt thermometer, strainer, fine filter, funnel, glass or plastic storage container*
PREP TIME: *4 hours*
YIELD: *Approximately 1½ cups*
STORAGE: *Store at room temperature, away from heat and light; use within 1 year*
APPLICATION: *3 times per week*

Combine the bhringaraj powder and sesame base oil in a 1½-quart saucepan or double boiler. Stir thoroughly to blend. The mixture should look almost like soupy black mud. Bring the mixture to just shy of a simmer, between 125° and 135°F. Do not let the oil actually simmer — it will degrade the quality of your infused oil. (If you're using a saucepan, set the heat to the absolute lowest setting.) *Do not* put the lid on the pot.

Allow the herb to macerate in the oil over low heat for 4 hours. Check the temperature every 30 minutes or so with a thermometer and adjust the heat accordingly. If you're using a double boiler, add more water to the bottom pot as necessary, so it doesn't dry out. Stir the infusing mixture at least every 30 minutes or so, as the powder likes to settle into a thick paste.

After 4 hours, remove the pan from the heat and allow to cool for 15 minutes. While the oil is still warm, carefully strain it through a fine-mesh strainer lined with a fine filter such as muslin or, preferably, a paper coffee filter, then strain again if necessary to remove all herb debris. Squeeze the herb paste to extract as much of the precious oil as possible. Discard the marc.

Add the vitamin E oil and stir to blend. The resulting bhringaraj oil should be deep blackish-green in color. Pour the finished oil into a storage container, then cap, label, and store in a dark cabinet.

APPLICATION INSTRUCTIONS: Place 1 to 2 teaspoons of the oil in a small bowl. Using your fingertips, gradually massage the entire amount into your dry scalp for several minutes, making sure to rub a little down the length of your hair and onto the ends. Wrap your hair completely with plastic wrap or a plastic shower cap, then cover it with a very warm, damp towel. Replace with another warm towel once the first has cooled. Leave on for at least 30 to 45 minutes, or overnight (if you do this, remove the plastic and sleep with a dry towel on your pillow to absorb the oil). Then rinse and lightly shampoo your hair with a chemical-free, low-sudsing product, if needed. Follow with a conditioner, if desired.

Bonus This oil, with its cooling and calming properties, can be massaged into the feet just before bedtime to induce relaxation.

. . . and forget not that the earth delights to feel your bare feet and the winds long to play with your hair.

— KAHLIL GIBRAN

ANXIETY *(Nervous Tension)*

Many people feel anxious or apprehensive at times, with symptoms such as shallow breathing, heart palpitations, perspiration, nausea, and quivering, clammy hands. Situations beyond our control (the weather, the economy, world peace) can cause anxiety, as can those things that affect us more directly (working, paying bills, making presentations, dealing with difficult people).

Some anxiety is to be expected, but too much nervous tension can wreak havoc on the ability to live a balanced life, often resulting in negative thinking, procrastination, recurring and uncontrollable thoughts, irritability, poor dietary and lifestyle habits, antisocial behavior, and insomnia.

Making some dietary and lifestyle adjustments may help reduce the anxiety in your life. Eliminating caffeine, sugar, refined foods, and too much chocolate is recommended, as these foods can set your already jangled nerves further on edge. Try to enjoy nutrient-rich comfort food on a regular basis.

Taking a daily walk or slow jog in nature, letting loose on a punching bag, and practicing meditation and yoga all can do wonders to calm an overactive mind and relieve pent-up emotions, as can turning off the television news and radio talk shows. The remedies offered here should help relieve tension, but by all means, seek professional help if you are feeling overwhelmed.

Cool Your Jets: Pulse Point Inhalant Balm

This aromatic balm lends incredible soothing effects to help balance a central nervous system that is on edge. A tiny amount can be massaged on any spot where you feel tension, or you can inhale the calming aroma directly from the jar as needed to mentally relax. I recommend it for nervous tension, anxiety, headaches, and insomnia.

Note: This is an aromatherapeutically concentrated formula, so use only a pea-size portion as directed.

4 tablespoons refined shea butter (unrefined shea butter will work, but its stronger fragrance will often mask the aroma of the essential oils)

30 drops lavender essential oil

25 drops bergamot essential oil

10 drops geranium essential oil

EQUIPMENT: *Small saucepan or double boiler, stirring utensil, plastic or glass jar or tin*
PREP TIME: *15 minutes, plus up to 24 hours to thicken*
YIELD: *Approximately ¼ cup*
STORAGE: *Store at room temperature, away from heat and light; use within 1 year*
APPLICATION: *Up to 3 times per day*

Warm the shea butter in a small saucepan (a ¾-quart size works great) or double boiler over low heat, until it is just melted. Remove from the heat. Add the lavender, bergamot, and geranium essential oils directly to your storage container, then slowly pour in the liquefied shea butter. Gently stir the balm to blend. Cap and label the container and set it aside until the balm has thickened.

Unlike beeswax, shea butter takes a long time to completely thicken, and this formula may need up to 24 hours, depending on the temperature in your kitchen. When it's ready, it will be very thick, semi-hard, and white (or creamy yellow if you've used unrefined shea butter).

APPLICATION INSTRUCTIONS: "A little dab'll do ya," as the saying goes. Use this concentrated formula judiciously — a pea-size amount or less is truly all you need for the total application. Using more might cause lightheadedness or grogginess. Massage into your temples, under your nose, on your throat, on the nape of your neck, on your chest, or on your pulse points — wrists, inside of elbows, back of knees, and just under the earlobes. To use the balm as a relaxing inhalant, breathe deeply from the jar for 10 to 15 breaths.

"SWEET ANNIE" SERENITY BODY OIL

This lovely, ever-so-lightly fragranced herbal oil will help soothe your nerves and instill a sense of calm. It's perfect on a morning when you are facing an especially hectic, anxiety-ridden day, and it's wonderful massaged into your skin from head to toe just before going to sleep, to relax away the day's tensions and ease insomnia. I also recommend it for relaxing tight, stiff muscles or relieving a tension headache. And dry skin loves this oil! Note that there are two steps to making this oil: first you make a mugwort-infused oil, then you add essential oils for the final product.

1½ cups dried or 3 cups freshly wilted mugwort leaves (see page 38 for information on wilting)

3 cups extra-virgin olive or almond base oil (use almond if you want a lighter feel and fragrance)

2,000 IU vitamin E oil

10 drops clary sage essential oil

10 drops sweet marjoram essential oil

EQUIPMENT: *2-quart saucepan or double boiler and candy or yogurt thermometer (for stovetop method), 1-quart canning jar and plastic wrap (for solar infusion method), stirring utensil, strainer, fine filter, funnel, glass or plastic storage containers*

PREP TIME: *4 hours (stovetop method) or 1 month (solar infusion method) to make the infused oil; 10 minutes to make the body oil*

YIELD: *Approximately 2½ cups*

STORAGE: *Store at room temperature, away from heat and light; use within 1 year*

APPLICATION: *Daily or as desired*

STOVETOP METHOD: If you're using wilted mugwort leaves, cut or tear the leaves into smaller pieces to expose more surface area to the oil. Combine the herb and the base oil in a 2-quart saucepan or double boiler and stir thoroughly to blend. The mixture should look like a thick, leafy green soup. Bring the mixture to just shy of a simmer, between 125° and 135°F. Do not let the oil actually simmer — it will degrade the quality of your infused oil. *Do not* put the lid on the pot.

Allow the herb to macerate in the oil over low heat for 4 hours. Check the temperature every 30 minutes or so with a thermometer and adjust the heat accordingly. If you're using a double boiler, add more water as necessary, so the pan doesn't dry out. Stir the infusing mixture at least every 30 minutes or so, as the herb bits tend to settle to the bottom of the pot.

After 4 hours, remove the pan from the heat and allow to cool for 15 minutes. While the oil is still warm, carefully strain it through a fine-mesh strainer lined with a fine filter such as muslin or, preferably, a paper coffee filter, then strain again if necessary to remove all herb debris. Squeeze the herbs to extract as much of the precious oil as possible. Discard the marc.

Add the vitamin E oil and stir to blend. The resulting mugwort oil should be deep green in color, especially with olive oil as the base. Pour the finished oil into a storage container, then cap, label, and store in a dark cabinet.

SOLAR-INFUSION METHOD: If you're using wilted mugwort leaves, cut or tear the leaves into smaller pieces to expose more surface area to the oil. Place the herb in a widemouthed 1-quart canning jar. Drizzle the base oil over the plant matter until the oil comes to within 1 inch of the top of the jar. You may need more or less oil than the recipe calls for depending on whether you use dried or wilted mugwort. The dried herb may pack in the bottom and the wilted herb matter will settle with the weight of the oil, so don't worry if it looks as though you don't have enough plant matter in the jar. Gently stir to remove air bubbles and make sure that all the plant matter is submerged.

Place a piece of plastic wrap over the mouth of the jar (to prevent the metal lid from coming into contact with the herb) and tightly screw on the lid. Shake the jar several times to blend thoroughly. Put the jar in a warm, sunny location such as a south-facing windowsill, and allow the herb to infuse for 1 month. Shake the jar every day for 30 seconds or so.

After 1 month, carefully strain the oil through a fine-mesh strainer lined with a fine filter such as muslin or, preferably, a paper coffee filter, then strain again if necessary to remove all herb debris. Squeeze the herbs to extract as much of the precious oil as possible. Discard the marc. Add the vitamin E oil and stir to blend. The resulting mugwort oil should be deep green in color, especially with olive oil as the base.

Pour the finished oil into a storage container, then cap, label, and store in a dark cabinet.

PREPARING THE BODY OIL: Pour 1 cup of mugwort-infused oil into a storage bottle and add the clary sage and marjoram essential oils. Cap, label, and shake well to blend. Store in a dark cabinet.

APPLICATION INSTRUCTIONS: Shake well before using. Massage over the entire body, or whatever parts you desire, after your morning shower or prior to bedtime, on dry or damp skin. Allow the oil to soak in for 5 to 10 minutes before getting dressed.

Bonus This oil blend will calm an agitated, fidgety, irritable young child if massaged into the lower legs and feet just prior to bedtime, or whenever the little one needs to unwind a bit.

SIMPLE LAVENDER-INFUSED OIL

The subtle, light, balancing aroma of freshly made lavender-infused oil is simply exquisite. This basic three-ingredient oil is guaranteed to tame your tension when massaged over your entire body. As a lavender lover, I use this oil morning and night whenever my life seems like a roller-coaster ride of demands and stresses. Rubbed into your neck, chest, hands, and feet at bedtime, it will help still your mind, calm your nerves, and lull you into blissful sleep — not to mention superbly soften your skin! I also recommend it for soothing tension headaches and relaxing tight, stiff muscles. It's extremely gentle, healing, and slightly antibacterial.

1½ cups dried or 2½ cups freshly wilted lavender buds (see page 38 for information on wilting)

3 cups almond base oil

2,000 IU vitamin E oil

EQUIPMENT: *2-quart saucepan or double boiler and candy or yogurt thermometer (for stovetop method), 1-quart canning jar and plastic wrap (for solar infusion method), stirring utensil, strainer, fine filter, funnel, glass or plastic storage containers*
PREP TIME: *4 hours (for stovetop method) or 1 month (for solar infusion method)*
YIELD: *Approximately 2½ cups*
STORAGE: *Store at room temperature, away from heat and light; use within 1 year*
APPLICATION: *Daily, as desired*

STOVETOP METHOD: If you're using wilted lavender, strip the buds and bits of greenery from the stems; discard the stems. Doing this mashes the buds a bit to release more of their essential oil into the infusion. Feel free to add the greenery to the infusion. Combine the lavender and the almond base oil in a 2-quart saucepan or double boiler and stir thoroughly to blend. The mixture should look like a dark purple lavender-bud soup. Bring the mixture to just shy of a simmer, between 125° and 135°F. Do not let the oil actually simmer — it will degrade the quality of your infusion. *Do not* put the lid on the pot.

Allow the herb to macerate in the oil over low heat for 4 hours. Check the temperature every 30 minutes or so with a thermometer and adjust heat accordingly. If you're using a double boiler, add more water to the bottom pot as necessary, so it doesn't dry out. Stir the infusing mixture at least every 30 minutes or so, as the herb bits tend to settle to the bottom.

After 4 hours, remove the pan from the heat and allow to cool for 15 minutes. While the oil is still warm, carefully strain it through a fine-mesh strainer lined with a fine filter such as muslin or, preferably, a paper coffee filter, then strain again if necessary to remove all herb debris. Squeeze the herbs to extract as much of the precious oil as possible. Discard the marc.

Add the vitamin E oil and stir to blend. The resulting lavender oil will be golden or greenish-gold in color. Pour the finished oil into storage containers, then cap, label, and store in a dark cabinet.

SOLAR-INFUSED METHOD: If you're using wilted lavender, first strip the buds and bits of greenery from the stems; discard the stems. Doing this mashes the buds a bit to release more of their essential oil into the infusion. Feel free to add the greenery to the jar. Place the lavender in a widemouthed 1-quart canning jar. Drizzle the almond base oil over the lavender buds until the oil comes to within 1 inch of the top of the jar. You may need more or less oil than the recipe calls for depending on whether you use dried or wilted lavender. The dried herb may pack in the bottom and the wilted herb will settle with the weight of the oil, so don't worry if it looks as though you don't have enough plant matter in the jar. Gently stir to remove air bubbles and make sure that all the plant matter is submerged.

Place a piece of plastic wrap over the mouth of the jar (to prevent the metal jar lid from coming into contact with the herb) and tightly screw on the lid. Shake the jar several times to blend the herb and oil thoroughly. Place the jar in a warm, sunny location such as a south-facing windowsill, and allow the herb to infuse for 1 month. Shake the jar every day for 30 seconds or so.

After 1 month, carefully strain the oil through a fine-mesh strainer lined with a fine filter such as muslin or, preferably, a paper coffee filter, then strain again if necessary to remove all herb debris. Squeeze the herb to extract as much of the precious oil as possible. Discard the marc. Add the vitamin E oil and stir to blend. The resulting lavender oil will be golden or greenish-gold in color.

Pour the finished oil into containers, then cap, label, and store in a dark cabinet.

APPLICATION INSTRUCTIONS: Massage over the entire body, or wherever desired, after your morning shower or prior to bedtime, on dry or damp skin. Allow the oil to soak in for 5 to 10 minutes before getting dressed.

Bonus This oil is the perfect choice to use as a diaper-rash preventive or on any irritated, environmentally ravaged skin. The thin, ultra-sensitive skin of the elderly benefits as well.

ARTHRITIS *(Osteoarthritis)*

Osteoarthritis, also known as degenerative arthritis or degenerative joint disease, is a chronic disorder characterized by degeneration of joint cartilage and adjacent bone that can cause pain, stiffness, localized soft tissue swelling, redness, heat, inflammation, and decreased movement of the joint. It is the most common joint disorder and affects many people to some degree by the age of 70. It also affects almost all animals with a backbone, even fish, but two animals that don't develop it are sloths and bats — both of which hang upside down. Interesting. I'm going shopping for inversion boots!

Treatment can include appropriate, low-impact exercises that stretch and strengthen the muscles, tendons, and ligaments, such as yoga and Pilates, plus a daily gentle walk or swim, in order to help increase a joint's range of motion, maintain healthy cartilage, and strengthen surrounding muscles so that they better absorb shock. Application of heat to the joint, very warm baths, and dressing properly to avoid chill are also beneficial.

On a dietary note, many people find significant relief from the severity of arthritic flare-ups when they eliminate the eight foods most likely to cause food sensitivities: wheat, soy, dairy, chocolate, eggs, peanuts, refined sugar, and corn. These foods, which we modern folk eat far too often and in too great a quantity, often can result in bloating, inflammation, pain, fatigue, stiffness, and myriad other uncomfortable symptoms. A blood test can determine if you do indeed have food sensitivities or allergies. The addition of probiotics, gamma-linolenic acid from evening primrose oil or borage oil, and omega-3 fatty acids from flaxseeds, walnuts, fish, or chia seeds can help ease inflammation, as can eating a predominately vegetarian diet.

A holistic physician, naturopath, herbalist, massage therapist, or acupuncturist may be of therapeutic assistance, if need be. The following herbal remedies can also deliver comfort, easing the pain and other unwelcome symptoms that accompany this disease.

HEALING HOT PEPPER AND GINGER LINIMENT

This formula has the opposite energy of Arthritis Pain-Away Mentholated Oil (on the next page). Instead of being chilling, it is quite heating and is recommended for treating arthritic joints with poor circulation that are cool to the touch while being quite stiff and painful. Both cayenne pepper and ginger rank at the top of the herbal "heat list" and help break up stagnation in the joints and surrounding tissues, stimulating blood flow and circulation. This is a nongreasy formulation. The herbal properties will remain on the skin after application, but the alcohol will evaporate.

Note: Do *not* apply to abraded, cut, punctured, or recently shaved skin, as it will sting like crazy! A tingling, warming feeling is to be expected, but if an uncomfortable reaction such as a red, stinging rash or a burning sensation occurs, wash the area with soap and water immediately and discontinue use.

1 cup fresh ginger, finely chopped, sliced, or grated

1 teaspoon cayenne

1 teaspoon vegetable glycerin

2½ cups unflavored vodka

EQUIPMENT: *1-quart canning jar, plastic wrap, strainer, fine filter, funnel, glass or plastic storage containers*

PREP TIME: *10 minutes, plus 4 weeks for extraction*

YIELD: *Approximately 2½ cups*

STORAGE: *Store at room temperature, away from heat and light; use within 2 years*

APPLICATION: *1 or 2 times per day, or as tolerated*

Place the ginger, cayenne, and glycerin in a 1-quart canning jar and pour the vodka over them. Place a piece of plastic wrap over the mouth of the jar (to prevent the metal lid from coming into contact with the herbs), then screw on the lid. Shake the jar for about 30 seconds to blend the contents thoroughly.

Store the jar in a cool, dark place for 4 weeks so that the vodka can extract the valuable chemical components from the herbs. Shake the jar for 15 to 30 seconds each day.

At the end of the 4 weeks, strain the herbs through a fine-mesh strainer lined with a fine filter such as muslin or (preferably) a paper coffee filter, then strain again if necessary to remove all herb debris. You want to remove *all* the pepper particulate. Press or squeeze the herbs to release all the valuable herbal extract. Discard the marc. Pour the liquid into storage containers, then cap, label and store in a dark cabinet.

APPLICATION INSTRUCTIONS: Briskly massage a small amount of liniment into any area that is cool to the touch and affected by arthritic stiffness and pain. *Always wash your hands afterward.*

Bonus Massage this liniment into tight muscles and cold feet to increase warmth and blood flow.

ARTHRITIS PAIN-AWAY MENTHOLATED OIL

This is an extremely powerful, pungent mentholated formula with a cooling energy that will soothe hot, red, inflamed, stiff joints and surrounding tissue. It is effective for throbbing backache and sore muscles as well. Menthol crystals, generally available from larger herb suppliers (see Resources), are derived from the Mentha arvensis species of mint and provide a strong, almost biting minty vapor and analgesic properties. The oil is not recommended for use during cold weather, as it will cause the area of application to become quite chilled. Instead, apply it during the warmer months when a bit of cooling might be welcome.

Note: Keep the oil away from mucous membranes — nose, eyes, and mouth.

3 tablespoons plus
1 teaspoon almond,
apricot kernel, or soybean
base oil

2 teaspoons menthol
crystals

EQUIPMENT: *Small saucepan or double boiler, stirring utensil, funnel, dark glass bottle with dropper top or screw cap*
PREP TIME: *15 minutes*
YIELD: *Approximately ¼ cup*
STORAGE: *Store at room temperature, away from heat and light; use within 1 year*
APPLICATION: *3 times per day*

Combine the oil and menthol crystals in a small saucepan (a ¾-quart pan works great) over low heat or in a double boiler. Gently warm the mixture just until the menthol crystals dissolve. Remove from the heat. Stir a few times to blend the mixture thoroughly. Pour into a dark glass storage container, cap, and label.

APPLICATION INSTRUCTIONS: Shake well before using. Massage the oil into any spot where you experience arthritic pain with associated stiffness, heat, redness, and inflammation. Wash your hands after application, unless the treatment was applied to your hands, in which case, wearing cotton gloves is a good idea.

Bonus The aroma is guaranteed to decongest stuffed sinuses and help remedy a sinus headache. Inhale directly from the bottle or rub a few drops onto your chest and neck. Cover the area with warm clothing or a flannel cloth. The oil works wonderfully to ease spasms in back muscles as well.

Joint-Ease Balm

This aromatic balm sinks right in to soothe painful, red, stiff, swollen joints and surrounding tissue while moisturizing dry skin. It has potent vulnerary (tissue healing) and anti-inflammatory properties, which aid in the healing of damaged tissue. Massage into sore, overworked muscles or apply to bruises or sprains to relieve inflammation.

4 tablespoons refined shea butter (unrefined shea butter will work, but its stronger fragrance will often mask the aroma of the essential oils)

20 drops birch or wintergreen essential oil

10 drops German chamomile essential oil

15 drops lavender essential oil

5 drops helichrysum essential oil

EQUIPMENT: *Small saucepan or double boiler, stirring utensil, plastic or glass jar or tin*
PREP TIME: *15 minutes, plus up to 24 hours to thicken*
YIELD: *Approximately ¼ cup*
STORAGE: *Store at room temperature, away from heat and light; use within 1 year*
APPLICATION: *Up to 3 times per day*

Warm the shea butter in a small saucepan (a ¾-quart size works great) or double boiler over low heat, until it has just melted. Remove from the heat. Add the essential oils directly to your storage container, then slowly pour in the liquefied shea butter. Gently stir the balm to blend. Cap and label the container, and set it aside until the balm has thickened. Unlike beeswax, shea butter takes a long time to completely thicken, and this formula may need up to 24 hours, depending on the temperature in your kitchen. When it's ready, it will be very thick, semi-hard, and white (or creamy yellow if you've used unrefined shea butter).

APPLICATION INSTRUCTIONS: Use this concentrated formula judiciously — a pea-size amount is truly all you need to be effective. Massage into areas affected by arthritis pain, stiffness, and inflammation, as well as overworked muscles or apply ever-so-gently to bruises and sprains.

Bonus I keep a small jar of this balm in my backpack when hiking, as it also serves as a wonderful treatment for bug bites, cuts, scrapes, minor tissue swelling, blisters, and rashes.

St. John's wort—Infused Oil

This beautiful red oil offers an amazing array of benefits due to its antispasmodic, anti-inflammatory, analgesic, and nervine properties. It makes a fabulous, simple treatment for arthritis symptoms in the smaller joints such as fingers, hands, wrists, toes, and feet, but it can be massaged in anywhere you feel pain and stiffness with associated heat, redness, and inflammation.

Note: When making this oil, I use only the freshly wilted herb and solar infusion method of extraction, as I feel that this particular herb releases its best medicinal properties when processed in this gentle manner. Dried St. John's wort does not make good medicine when infused in oil — it is nearly inert.

3 cups freshly wilted St. John's wort flowering tops (see page 38 for information on wilting)

3–4 cups extra-virgin olive, almond, or soybean base oil (enough to completely cover the herb)

2,000 IU vitamin E oil

EQUIPMENT: *Rubber or latex gloves, widemouthed 1-quart canning jar, stirring utensil, plastic wrap, strainer, fine filter, funnel, glass or plastic storage containers*
PREP TIME: *1 month*
YIELD: *Approximately 2½ cups*
STORAGE: *Store at room temperature, away from heat and light; use within 1 year*
APPLICATION: *As desired*

If you don't want your hands stained a deep purplish-red, put on rubber or latex gloves, and then cut or tear the wilted herb into small pieces. Place the herb in a 1-quart canning jar. Drizzle the base oil over the plant matter until the oil comes to within 1 inch of the top of the jar. The herb matter will settle with the weight of the oil, so don't worry if it looks as though you don't have enough of it in the jar. Gently stir to remove air bubbles and make sure that all the plant matter is submerged.

Place a piece of plastic wrap over the mouth of the jar (to prevent the metal lid from coming into contact with the herb) and tightly screw on the lid. Shake the jar several times to blend the herb and oil thoroughly. Place the jar in a warm, sunny location such as a south-facing windowsill, and allow the herb to infuse for 1 month. Shake the jar every day for 30 seconds or so.

After 1 month, carefully strain the oil through a fine-mesh strainer lined with a fine filter such as muslin or, preferably, a paper coffee filter, then strain again if necessary to remove all herb debris. Squeeze the flowers to extract as much of the precious oil as possible. Discard the marc. Add the vitamin E oil and stir to blend. The resulting oil will be a deep blood-red or burgundy in color.

Pour the finished oil into storage containers, then cap, label, and store in a dark cabinet.

APPLICATION INSTRUCTIONS: Massage into fingers, wrists, hands, feet, back, or anywhere you have stiff, sore, achy, inflamed joints, pulled muscles or ligaments, or nerve trauma. Allow the oil to soak in for 5 to 10 minutes before getting dressed.

Bonus Massage this oil with its sweet-tart aroma over the entire body to bring comfort to pulled or tight muscles, strained ligaments, bruises, or nerve trauma. Spinal injuries and back pain respond positively to consistent treatment with this oil.

What's in a Name?

St. John's wort (*Hypericum perforatum*) is named after John the Baptist, as it traditionally blooms and is harvested on St. John's Day in late June. The botanical name comes from the Greek *hypericon*, meaning "over an apparition," which refers to the herb's supposed power to banish evil spirits.

Translucent dots on the leaves, which appear to be holes when held to the light, give the plant the second part of its botanical name. The petals have tiny black dots on their back edges where the medicinal hypericin constituents are stored. "Wort" is an old English term for a plant or herb.

ATHLETE'S FOOT

Athlete's foot is so named because this infection is most commonly seen on the feet of athletes who spend time around swimming pools, steam baths, locker rooms, and communal showers following exercise. These places are breeding grounds for fungus, and so are your shoes, with their dark, warm, moist environment.

Tinea pedis, the Latin name for fungal foot infection, is a skin disease caused by dermatophytes (tiny parasitic fungi) that thrive in warm, moist places. It usually occurs between the toes and on the soles of the feet. The symptoms can appear rather quickly and can include scaling, flaking, and peeling of the skin between the toes, intense itching, heat, redness, cracking, dryness, and finally the appearance of blisters and possible infection if the disease is allowed to progress without treatment. The blisters can break and allow the pesky fungi to penetrate the skin's surface, thus making the disease even more difficult to treat. Athlete's foot symptoms tend to recur quite easily once you've been infected. All treatments for athlete's foot should be applied continuously over a period of several weeks to several months until the condition is eradicated.

Remember to always wear shoes when at the gym or walking around the vicinity of a public pool. Keep feet dry, apply a bit of foot powder inside your socks, and wear breathable footwear.

Fungus Fighter: Usnea, Sage, and Lavender Liniment

*T*his potent antifungal liniment will help alleviate frequently unbearable oozing, itching, redness, and heat. It can also be applied to toenails and fingernails affected by fungus. And it freshens the feet and kills odor! Be forewarned: it will sting raw skin, but it works wonders.

1½ cups usnea lichen, dried or fresh (usnea is quite dry even when fresh, so there's no need to wilt it)

½ cup dried or 1 cup freshly wilted sage leaves (see page 38 for information on wilting)

½ cup dried or ¾ cup freshly wilted lavender buds

1 teaspoon vegetable glycerin

30 drops tea tree essential oil

20 drops thyme (chemotype *linalool*) essential oil

10 drops myrrh essential oil

3–4 cups unflavored vodka

EQUIPMENT: *1-quart canning jar, plastic wrap, strainer, fine filter, funnel, glass or plastic storage containers*
PREP TIME: *10 minutes, plus 4 weeks for extraction*
YIELD: *Approximately 2½ cups*
STORAGE: *Store at room temperature, away from heat and light; use within 2 years*
APPLICATION: *2 or 3 times per day*

If you're using fresh usnea or freshly wilted sage, cut or tear those herbs into smaller pieces to expose more surface area during maceration. If you're using freshly wilted lavender, strip the buds and any attached greenery from the stems; discard the stems. Feel free to add the bits of greenery into the jar.

Place all the herbs, the glycerin, and the tea tree, thyme, and myrrh essential oils in a 1-quart canning jar and pour the vodka over them, so that it comes to within ½ inch of the top of the jar. The herbs should be completely covered. Place a piece of plastic wrap over the mouth of the jar (to prevent the metal lid from coming into contact with the jar's contents), then screw on the lid. Shake the mixture for about 30 seconds to blend thoroughly. After 24 hours, top up with more vodka if necessary. The herbs will settle a bit in the jar, but that's okay. Store the jar in a cool, dark place for 4 weeks so that the vodka can extract the valuable chemical components from the herbs. Shake the jar for 15 to 30 seconds each day.

At the end of the 4 weeks, strain the herbs through a fine-mesh strainer lined with a fine filter such as muslin or, preferably, a paper coffee filter, then strain again if necessary to remove all herb debris. Press or squeeze the herbs to release all the valuable herbal extract. Discard the marc.

Pour the liquid into storage containers, then cap, label, and store in a dark cabinet.

(continued)

(continued)

APPLICATION INSTRUCTIONS: Shake well before each use. Apply enough liniment to completely soak your feet. Massage it in really well, including between the toes. Always treat both feet, even if only one may be affected. Let your feet dry before putting socks or shoes back on (you can speed up the process by using a blow dryer if you like). Follow up with foot powder, if desired.

> **Bonus** Apply by the drop to infected cuts, scrapes, bug bites, blisters, boils, bedsores or skin ulcers, poison plant rashes, and blemishes to help heal inflammation and kill bacteria.

FUNGUS-BE-GONE OIL DROPS

This aromatic herbal oil helps eliminate the scourge of athlete's foot and also fights nail fungus. It calms and soothes redness and itching, helps heal infection, and conditions the skin.

30 drops lavender essential oil

25 drops tea tree essential oil

20 drops thyme (chemotype *linalool*) essential oil

10 drops sage essential oil

5 drops cinnamon bark essential oil

5 drops clove essential oil

½ cup jojoba base oil

EQUIPMENT: *Dropper, dark glass bottle with dropper top or screw cap*
PREP TIME: *15 minutes, plus 24 hours to synergize*
YIELD: *Approximately ½ cup*
STORAGE: *Store at room temperature, away from heat and light; use within 2 years*
APPLICATION: *2 or 3 times per day*

Add the lavender, tea tree, thyme, sage, cinnamon, and clove essential oils drop by drop directly into a storage bottle. Add the jojoba base oil. Screw the top on the bottle and shake vigorously for 2 minutes to blend. Label the bottle and place in a dark location that's between 60° and 80°F for 24 hours so that the oils can synergize.

APPLICATION INSTRUCTIONS: Shake well before each use. Make sure your feet are dry. Apply a few drops to *both* feet, even if only one may be affected. Be sure to get some of the oil between the toes and on the toenails, and massage it in thoroughly. Allow the oil to sink in for a few minutes before putting on socks or hosiery.

You can also massage this oil into both feet just prior to going to the gym or public swimming pool and immediately after showering, before getting dressed. Follow up with foot powder, if desired.

> **Bonus** This formula is fabulous as an aid in healing infected wounds and blemishes.

BACKACHE

"Oh, my aching back" is the among the most frequent physical complaints heard by physicians, along with headache and fatigue. We've all had a backache at one time or another, brought on by sitting too long in front of a computer, taking a long drive without stopping to stretch, snow shoveling, spring yard cleanup, gardening, being a "weekend warrior," starting a new (too rigorous) exercise program — excessive physical strain of any variety on a body that is not conditioned to deal with the added muscular stress. Poor posture can also cause chronic back pain.

Muscle fatigue, swelling, soreness, stiffness, and aches are the result of muscles experiencing excessive tension. Muscle strain occurs when muscles are stretched beyond their normal limit. To minimize the potential for simple back pain (or any muscular pain, for that matter), always observe correct posture for whatever activity you are trying to accomplish and begin any new physical activity slowly, so that your muscles can become acclimated and strengthened.

Many people, myself included, find that after a long day of "being physical," taking a hot bath with 2 to 3 cups of Epsom salts added to the water dramatically decreases the pain and swelling of stressed muscles. Follow this with the application of a good herbal backache remedy (a friend comes in handy for this) and you're golden! See your physician or chiropractor if your pain worsens.

The following two remedies focus on muscular back pain brought on by excessive physical strain, whether in the lower back region or encompassing the entire back, shoulders, and neck.

Bobcat Balm #1

This balm contains an infusion of nature's finest plant healers, offering analgesic, anti-inflammatory, and vulnerary properties to help ease the pain of muscular tension and strain and repair damaged tissue. I recommend it for muscle pain, fatigue, swelling, soreness, stiffness, and tension anywhere in the body.

The balm doesn't require all the infused oil that this recipe makes; you can use the leftover infused oil to make Bobcat Balm #2 (page 234), which is useful for treating sore muscles of all types.

Note: To make the infused oil blend for this balm, I use only the stovetop method of extraction, as I feel that it enables these particular herbs to release their best medicinal properties.

½ cup dried or 1 cup freshly wilted meadowsweet flowers (see page 38 for information on wilting)

½ cup dried arnica flowers

½ cup dried Solomon's seal root

¼ cup fresh ginger, chopped or grated

3 cups almond, extra-virgin olive, or soybean base oil

3–4 tablespoons beeswax (depending on how firm you want the balm to be)

60 drops Scotch pine essential oil (optional, but it greatly intensifies the analgesic quality of the final product)

2,000 IU vitamin E oil

EQUIPMENT: *2-quart saucepan or double boiler, stirring utensil, candy or yogurt thermometer, strainer, fine filter, funnel, glass or plastic storage container (for the infused oil), glass or plastic jars or tins (for the balm)*
PREP TIME: *6 hours to infuse the oil, plus 20 minutes to make the balm and 30 minutes for it to thicken*
YIELD: *Approximately 2½ cups of infused oil and 1¼ cups of balm*
STORAGE: *Store at room temperature, away from heat and light; use within 1 year*
APPLICATION: *2 or 3 times daily, or as desired*

PREPARING THE HERBAL INFUSED OIL: If you're using freshly wilted meadowsweet flowers, strip the flowers and attached greenery from the larger stems. You may add any tiny stems and green leaves to the mix. Combine the meadowsweet, arnica, Solomon's seal, and ginger with the base oil in a 2-quart saucepan or double boiler and stir thoroughly to blend. The mixture should look like a thick, chunky herbal soup. Bring the mixture to just shy of a simmer, between 125° and 135°F. Do not let the oil actually simmer — it will degrade the quality of your infused oil. *Do not* put the lid on the pot.

Allow the herbs to macerate in the oil over low heat for 6 hours. Check the temperature every 30 minutes or so with a thermometer and adjust the heat accordingly. If you're using a double boiler, add more water to the bottom pot as necessary, so it doesn't dry out. Stir the infusing mixture at least every 30 minutes or so, as the herb bits tend to settle to the bottom.

After 6 hours, remove the pan from the heat and allow to cool for 15 minutes. While the oil is still warm, carefully strain it through a fine-mesh strainer lined with a fine filter such as muslin or, preferably, a paper coffee filter, then strain again if necessary to remove all herb debris. Squeeze the herbs to extract as much of the precious oil as possible. Discard the marc.

Add the vitamin E oil and stir to blend. The resulting infused oil will be golden or golden-green in color. Pour the finished oil into the storage container, then cap, label, and store in a dark cabinet.

PREPARING THE BALM: Combine 1 cup of the herbal infused oil with the beeswax in a small saucepan or double boiler, and warm over low heat until the beeswax is just melted. Remove from the heat and allow to cool for 5 minutes, stirring a few times. Add the essential oil, if desired. Stir again to blend. Pour into storage containers, cap, and label. Set aside for 30 minutes, until the balm has thickened.

APPLICATION INSTRUCTIONS: Have a friend or partner massage this remedy into your back, neck, arms, legs, or anywhere your muscles are sore and achy. Using it on skin that is prewarmed from a bath, shower, or heating pad encourages penetration.

Bonus Use this balm to soothe the discomfort of arthritic joints, gout, tendonitis, and sore feet.

FIRE AND ICE ANALGESIC MASSAGE OIL

*S*imultaneously warming and chilling, this is the ultimate soother for an inflamed, aching back. It can also be used for muscle pain, fatigue, swelling, soreness, stiffness, or tension in any part of the body. It smells gently refreshing, not overly medicinal.

20 drops eucalyptus (species *radiata*) essential oil

20 drops peppermint essential oil

15 drops cajeput essential oil

5 drops cinnamon bark essential oil

5 drops clove essential oil

½ cup jojoba base oil

EQUIPMENT: *Dropper, dark glass bottle with dropper top or screw cap*
PREP TIME: *15 minutes, plus 24 hours to synergize*
YIELD: *Approximately ½ cup*
STORAGE: *Store at room temperature, away from heat and light; use within 2 years*
APPLICATION: *1 or 2 times per day*

Add the eucalyptus, peppermint, cajeput, cinnamon, and clove essential oils drop by drop directly into a storage bottle. Add the jojoba base oil. Screw the top on the bottle and shake vigorously for 2 minutes to blend. Label the bottle and place in a dark location that's between 60° and 80°F for 24 hours so that the oils can synergize.

APPLICATION INSTRUCTIONS: Shake well before each use. Have a friend or partner massage this soothing remedy into your back, neck, arms, legs, or anywhere your muscles are sore and achy. Using it on skin that is prewarmed from a bath, shower, or heating pad encourages penetration.

Bonus Massage this oil into arthritic joints and inflamed tendons or use it to soothe and deodorize tired, aching feet.

BEDSORES AND PRESSURE SORES *(Skin Ulcers)*

Normal, healthy skin tissue has a rich blood supply that delivers oxygen to all its layers. If that blood supply is cut off for more than 2 to 3 hours, the skin begins to die from its outermost layer (the epidermis) inward. Constant pressure is the most common cause of reduced blood flow to the skin. Average movement in everyday life shifts pressure sources so that the blood supply isn't shut off for any prolonged period. The fat layer beneath the skin, especially over bony projections such as the heels and shoulders, pads the skin and keeps the blood vessels from being squeezed shut.

Bedsores or pressure sores, considered secondary skin lesions, are skin ulcers that result from a lack of blood flow and from irritation to the skin over a bony projection where the skin has been under pressure, such as from a wheelchair, splint, cast, bed, or other hard object, for a prolonged period. Individuals who are bedridden or confined to wheelchairs are most at risk.

Pressure sores also affect people suffering from nerve damage, such as diabetics and stroke victims. The sensation of pain motivates movement to a more comfortable position; people who cannot feel discomfort or pain are at risk of developing sores. Extremely thin or malnourished people who don't have sufficient protective fat layers generally heal more slowly and have a higher risk of developing skin ulcers.

When pressure from whatever source cuts off normal blood flow, the skin becomes starved for oxygen and becomes red, inflamed, sore, and possibly itchy. If the condition is allowed to progress, the area can become blistered, then raw and infected, with open, oozing sores exposing deeper layers of the skin. In the final stages, the ulcer will extend down through the skin and fat layers and into the muscle, eventually exposing the bone. At this point, the infection is a major problem and quite difficult to heal.

Prevention is of top priority. Careful daily inspection of those who are at risk by hospital attendants, a home care specialist, or family member is vital. Any sign of redness is a signal that immediate preventive action is needed. If you are caring for someone for whom bedsores or pressure sores are a potential concern, a health care specialist can advise as to the proper bedding, clothing, and skin care needed to prevent this malady. The following recipes aid the healing and offer comfort to mild- to-moderate level skin ulcers.

SAGE CHICK SALVE

This ever-so-gentle salve aids in healing tissue, relieving pain and associated itching, stimulating circulation, and reducing inflammation. It also helps eliminate potential odor emanating from infected bedsores or skin ulcers.

Note: I prefer to use the stovetop method of extraction for this formula, as I feel that these particular herbs release their best medicinal properties when processed in this manner.

½ cup dried or 1 cup freshly wilted chickweed leaves and stems (see page 38 for information on wilting)

½ cup dried or 1 cup freshly wilted meadowsweet flowers

½ cup dried or 1 cup freshly wilted sage leaves

3 cups extra-virgin olive base oil

3–4 tablespoons beeswax (depending on how firm you want the salve to be)

2,000 IU vitamin E oil

EQUIPMENT: *2-quart saucepan or double boiler, stirring utensil, candy or yogurt thermometer, strainer, fine filter, funnel, glass or plastic storage container (for the infused oil), glass or plastic jars or tins (for the salve)*

PREP TIME: *4 hours to infuse the oil, plus 20 minutes to make the salve and 30 minutes for it to thicken*

YIELD: *Approximately 2½ cups of infused oil and 1¼ cups of salve*

STORAGE: *Store at room temperature, away from heat and light; use within 1 year*

APPLICATION: *3 times daily, or as desired*

PREPARING THE INFUSED OIL: If you're using wilted herbs, first cut or tear the herbs into smaller pieces to expose more surface area to the oil. You may include the bits of greenery and tiny stems attached to the meadowsweet flowers. Combine the chickweed, meadowsweet, and sage with the olive base oil in a 2-quart saucepan or double boiler and stir thoroughly to blend. The mixture should look like a thick, pale green herbal soup. Bring the mixture to just shy of a simmer, between 125° and 135°F. Do not let the oil actually simmer — it will degrade the quality of your infused oil. *Do not* put the lid on the pot.

Allow the herbs to macerate in the oil over low heat for 4 hours. Check the temperature every 30 minutes or so with a thermometer and adjust the heat accordingly. If you're using a double boiler, add more water to the bottom pot as necessary, so it doesn't dry out. Stir the infusing mixture at least every 30 minutes or so, as the herb bits tend to settle to the bottom.

After 4 hours, remove the pan from the heat and allow to cool for 15 minutes. While the oil is still warm, carefully strain it through a fine-mesh strainer lined with a fine filter such as muslin or, preferably, a paper coffee filter, then strain again if necessary to remove all herb debris. Squeeze the herbs to extract as much of the precious oil as possible. Discard the marc.

Add the vitamin E oil and stir to blend. The resulting infused oil will be a rich green in color. Pour the finished oil into a glass or plastic storage container; cap, label, and store in a dark cabinet.

PREPARING THE SALVE: Combine 1 cup of the herbal infused oil and the beeswax in a small saucepan or double boiler, and warm over low heat until the beeswax is just melted. Remove from the heat and allow to cool for 5 minutes, stirring a few times. Pour into storage containers. Cap, label, and set aside for 30 minutes, until it has thickened.

APPLICATION INSTRUCTIONS: First, clean and disinfect the skin ulcer using a natural antibacterial solution or liquid soap. Pat dry. Apply a small dab of salve to each sore and gently massage into the affected and surrounding area. Place a sterile pad atop each sore; you can make one from cotton, several layers of flannel, or gauze — just make sure it won't stick to the sore. Fasten securely in place with medical tape.

Bonus Use this salve as an aid in healing cuts, scrapes, bug bites, blisters, rashes, and minor burns. It's gentle enough to use on infants. Good stuff!

What's the Difference between a Salve and a Balm?

Salves and balms (sometimes referred to as unguents or ointments) are basically the same delightful product: a fatty, semi-solid mixture of a base oil combined with beeswax, cocoa butter, or shea butter, or a blend of these three, and usually mixed with essential oils and/or infused with medicinal herbs. They can vary in consistency from soft and greasy to thick and relatively hard, depending on the ingredients used and the intended purpose.

Prepared as external healing agents, when applied to the skin they soften with body temperature and provide an emollient, vulnerary, nourishing, healing, protective effect. The oil, being compatible with the skin, delivers the medicinal herbal components down deep within the tissues where they are needed. The wax or butter solidifies and gives firmness to the finished product for ease of application plus offers additional skin-conditioning benefits.

The main difference between them is that salves are quite bland in the aroma department, containing minimal or no added essential oils, while balms contain a stronger, more potent fragrance due to a higher amount of volatile essential oils.

Skin Ulcer Comfort Drops

*E*asy-to-make and easy-to-apply medicinal herbal drops aid in healing tissue, relieving pain and associated itching, stimulating circulation, fighting infection, and reducing inflammation. They also help eliminate potential odor emanating from infected bedsores or skin ulcers.

Note: This is an aromatherapeutically concentrated formula, so use only by the drop as directed.

12 drops lavender essential oil

5 drops German chamomile essential oil

5 drops myrrh essential oil

5 drops tea tree essential oil

2 tablespoons jojoba base oil

EQUIPMENT: *Dropper, dark glass bottle with dropper top or screw cap*

PREP TIME: *15 minutes, plus 24 hours to synergize*

YIELD: *Approximately 2 table-spoons*

STORAGE: *Store at room temperature, away from heat and light; use within 2 years*

APPLICATION: *2 times per day*

Add the lavender, German chamomile, myrrh, and tea tree essential oils drop by drop directly into a storage bottle. Add the jojoba base oil. Screw the top on the bottle and shake vigorously for 2 minutes to blend. Label the bottle and place in a dark location that's between 60° and 80°F for 24 hours so that the oils can synergize.

APPLICATION INSTRUCTIONS: Shake well before each use. First, clean and disinfect the skin ulcer using a natural antibacterial solution or liquid soap. Pat dry. Apply 2 to 6 drops to each sore, depending on size, and gently massage into the affected and surrounding area. Place a sterile pad atop each sore; these can be made from cotton, several layers of flannel, or gauze — just make sure they won't stick to the sore. Fasten securely in place with medical tape.

Bonus Use these aromatic drops as an aid in healing cuts, scrapes, bug bites, blemishes, infected ingrown hairs, blisters, rashes, boils, minor burns, or any minor to moderate skin infection. A wonderful addition to your herbal first aid kit!

BLEMISHES

Blemishes, pimples, zits, pustules — whatever you want to call them, they are unsightly and always seem to rear their ugly heads at the most inopportune moment, don't they? Like right before you have to give a major presentation or have your picture taken! A blemish is considered a *primary skin lesion*, a structural change in the tissue, and it can develop on anyone's skin and on any part of the body. A single blemish, or a few, as happens with mild acne, is caused by a chronic inflammatory disorder of the skin, usually related to overactive sebaceous glands during adolescence, but blemishes can occur at any age due to hormonal fluctuations, dietary indiscretions, excessive exposure to sunshine, chronic stress, constipation, and poor hygiene and lifestyle habits.

Blemishes are not just reserved for teens, sad to say. "Adult acne" is common these days and tends to appear after 35 years of age, most often in women — just when you thought you'd outgrown it!

A blemish forms when the follicle, which contains the hair root and secretes sebum onto the surface of the skin, becomes clogged with oil, excess dead cells, and bacteria. Depending on the degree of infection that forms, it can swell and will occasionally rupture, allowing the debris to escape into the surrounding dermis — or midlayer of the skin — resulting in irritation and inflammation. The

body's "anti-infection soldiers," the white blood cells, rush in to fight against the bacteria, creating pus, a sticky, creamy-yellowish secretion. Thus you have the beginning of a pimple, which appears as an inflamed, red or blue-red lump.

When the pus-filled follicle ruptures near the surface of the skin, it is not so serious and will generally heal rapidly without leaving a permanent mark. However, remember what your mother said: "Don't pick your face!" When pimples are pinched or squeezed, the infectious material can spread deep into surrounding tissues, potentially resulting in painful cysts that take a long time to reach the surface and heal — damaging tissue and leaving scars and hyperpigmentation in their wake.

I can't stress this enough: It is of the utmost importance that your bowels move on a regular basis. Chronic constipation forces the body to reabsorb into the bloodstream toxins that would otherwise have been eliminated, thus leaving those toxins searching for another way to exit the body, frequently via your skin. A high-fiber diet that includes plenty of water or herb tea is recommended for bowel health.

To prevent blemishes from progressing to more than just an aesthetic annoyance, try the formulas below to help soothe, cool, and heal these minor skin lesions.

CHAMOMILE CLEAR SKIN ELIXIR

Don't be afraid of applying an oil to oily skin. It just has to be the right oil, and jojoba oil (a wax ester) is so chemically similar to sebum that it won't exacerbate an already oily condition but instead will aid in oxygenating, properly moisturizing, and clearing the skin. This elixir helps balance problem skin resulting from overactive sebaceous glands. The combination of essential oils produces an antiseptic formula specifically designed to calm the skin, counteracting redness and inflammation. It also aids in normalizing dry areas, improves sluggish circulation, and stimulates new cell formation. This formula can be used on oily, blemished, acneic, combination, or normal skin.

Note: This is an aromatherapeutically concentrated formula, so use only by the drop as directed.

6 drops German chamomile essential oil

5 drops spike lavender (*Lavandula latifolia*) or lavender (*L. angustifolia*) essential oil

5 drops tea tree essential oil

2 drops clove essential oil

2 drops lemon essential oil

2 drops myrrh essential oil

2 tablespoons jojoba base oil

EQUIPMENT: *Dropper, dark glass bottle with dropper top or screw cap*
PREP TIME: *15 minutes, plus 24 hours to synergize*
YIELD: *Approximately 2 tablespoons*
STORAGE: *Store at room temperature, away from heat and light; use within 2 years*
APPLICATION: *2 times per day*

Add the German chamomile, lavender, tea tree, clove, lemon, and myrrh essential oils drop by drop directly into a storage bottle. Add the jojoba base oil. Screw the top on the bottle and shake vigorously for 2 minutes to blend. Label the bottle and place in a dark location that's between 60° and 80°F for 24 hours so that the oils can synergize.

APPLICATION INSTRUCTIONS: Shake well before each use. In the morning and evening, after cleansing, apply the appropriate toner, astringent, or herbal hydrosol to your skin. While your skin is still damp, lightly massage 3 to 5 drops of the elixir into your skin, beginning with the chest, moving to the throat, and then the face, using upward, outward, circular strokes. Apply to shoulders and back as well, if needed. Wait 5 minutes before applying sunscreen, additional moisturizer, or makeup.

The elixir can also be applied by the drop to individual blemishes after swabbing them with astringent or toner to remove excess oil. Witch Hazel and Yarrow Astringent (next page) is perfect for this purpose.

Bonus Apply this elixir by the drop to help heal cuts, scrapes, bruises, boils, rashes, insect stings and bites, infected ingrown hairs, minor burns, or any minor to moderate infection of the skin.

WITCH HAZEL AND YARROW ASTRINGENT

*T*his is an herbal facial liniment, so I call it an astringent, as it is used to remove excess oil from areas affected by blemishes, as well as to fight inflammation, reduce redness, kill offending bacteria, and heal damaged tissue. It can be used on blemished, acneic, oily, normal-to-oily, or combination skin. Be forewarned that it will sting raw skin, but it works wonders.

⅓ cup dried or ½ cup fresh witch hazel bark (there's no need to wilt the fresh bark, as it is already relatively dry)

⅓ cup dried or ⅔ cup freshly wilted yarrow flowers and leaves (see page 38 for information on wilting)

1½–2 cups unflavored vodka

EQUIPMENT: *1-pint canning jar, plastic wrap, fine-mesh strainer, fine filter, funnel, glass or plastic storage container*
PREP TIME: *10 minutes, plus 8 weeks for extraction*
YIELD: *Approximately 1½ cups*
STORAGE: *Store at room temperature, away from heat and light; use within 2 years*
APPLICATION: *2 or 3 times per day*

Bonus Apply to infected cuts, scrapes, bug bites, blisters, boils, poison plant rashes, contact dermatitis, or minor to moderate infection.

If you're using fresh bark, crumble it into small pieces. If you're using freshly wilted yarrow, tear or cut the herb into smaller pieces to expose more surface area to the alcohol. Place the witch hazel and yarrow in a pint-size canning jar and pour the vodka over them, so that it comes to within ½ inch of the top of the jar. The herbs should be completely covered. Place a piece of plastic wrap over the mouth of the jar (to keep the metal lid from coming into contact with the contents), then screw on the lid. Shake the mixture for about 30 seconds. After 24 hours, top up with more vodka if necessary. The herbs will settle a bit in the jar, but that's okay.

Store the jar in a cool, dark place for 8 weeks so that the vodka can extract the valuable chemical components from the herbs. Shake the jar for 15 to 30 seconds every day.

At the end of the 8 weeks, strain the herbs through a fine-mesh strainer lined with a fine filter such as muslin or, preferably, a paper coffee filter, then strain again if necessary to remove all herb debris. Press or squeeze the herbs to release all the valuable herbal extract. Discard the marc. Pour the liquid into a storage container, then cap, label, and store in a dark cabinet.

APPLICATION INSTRUCTIONS: Using a cotton ball or pad, apply to blemished areas on the face, throat, chest, shoulders, or back. Avoid the eye area.

THYME AND PEPPERMINT CLAY PACK

This clay pack or blemish mask stimulates circulation and blood flow to the energetically stagnant blemish, purges excess oil and bacteria from the clogged follicle, and helps shrink and tighten the follicle, thus drying and healing the offending pimple. Specifically designed as a spot treatment for individual inflamed, infected, or oozing blemishes and clusters of blemishes, it is very drying if applied to large areas of unaffected or normal skin. So unless your skin is extremely oily, do not use it as you would a regular facial mask that is intended to cover the entire face and part of the neck.

1 tablespoon green clay, finely ground

1 tablespoon or so aloe vera juice or purified water

1 drop peppermint essential oil

1 drop thyme (chemotype *linalool*) essential oil

EQUIPMENT: *Small bowl, spoon or tiny whisk*
PREP TIME: *5 minutes*
YIELD: *1 or more treatments (depending on the number of blemishes)*
STORAGE: *Refrigerate any leftovers; use within 1 week*
APPLICATION: *Once daily*

In a small bowl or custard cup, use a spoon or tiny whisk to combine the clay with enough of the aloe vera juice or water to form a smooth, rather thick, spreadable paste. It should not be soupy in consistency; if it is, add more clay to thicken it. Stir in the peppermint and thyme essential oils. Use immediately.

APPLICATION INSTRUCTIONS: Cleanse each blemish using your favorite astringent or toner to remove excess oil; pat dry. Using a cotton swab or your clean finger, apply a thick dab of clay pack onto each pimple and allow to dry for at least 30 minutes. The clay will harden and may tingle and crack as it dries. Rinse with cool water.

If you have any leftover moist clay pack mixture, tightly cover the little bowl with plastic wrap and store in the refrigerator, where it will keep for up to 1 week. If the mixture starts to dry out, add a tad more aloe vera juice or water and stir well before using.

French Lavender Drops: Serious Blemish Treatment

I occasionally use lavender essential oil "neat" or undiluted to ward off infection, ease a tension headache, or dry up blemishes, cystic acne, or cold sores. I can almost guarantee that applying this essential oil blend directly to a blemish will reduce the blemish in size by at least 50 percent within 24 hours! The blend fights bacterial proliferation, eases inflammation and redness, and aids in skin cell regeneration.

I recommend using these herbal drops to treat hormonal or adult acne that tends to develop after age 35, especially along the jawline. Adult acne is notorious for leaving red "stains" or hyperpigmentation marks on the skin that can take up to 6 months to fade. With the application of these concentrated herbal drops at the first sign of a blemish breakout, the resultant stains are a thing of the past, or at least greatly minimized. Remember — don't pick your blemishes!

Note: This is an aromatherapeutically concentrated formula, so use only by the drop as directed.

2 drops rosemary (chemotype *verbenon*) essential oil

2 drops tea tree or niaouli essential oil

2 drops thyme (chemotype *linalool*) essential oil

1 drop German chamomile essential oil

1 tablespoon lavender essential oil

EQUIPMENT: *Dropper, dark glass bottle with dropper top or screw cap*
PREP TIME: *15 minutes, plus 24 hours to synergize*
YIELD: *Approximately 1 tablespoon*
STORAGE: *Store at room temperature, away from heat and light; use within 2 years*
APPLICATION: *2 times per day*

Add the rosemary, tea tree, thyme, and German chamomile essential oils drop by drop directly into a storage bottle. Add the lavender essential oil. Screw the top on the bottle and shake vigorously for 2 minutes to blend. Label the bottle and place in a dark location that's between 60° and 80°F for 24 hours so that the oils can synergize.

APPLICATION INSTRUCTIONS: Shake well before each use. In the morning and evening, after cleansing the affected blemish or blemished area, apply the appropriate toner, astringent, or herbal hydrosol to your skin. Pat dry.

Apply 1 drop to each blemish, and gently tap it into the skin and surrounding area.

Bonus This is highly potent herbal medicine with a gentle touch! Apply it by the drop to cuts, scrapes, punctures, burns, bug bites and stings, boils, bedsores and skin ulcers, blisters, ingrown toenails, and ingrown hairs.

BLISTERS *(Friction)*

Everyone has had a friction blister on a foot or hand at one time or another. These blisters are formed on the feet by friction against the skin from an ill-fitting shoe or abrasive hosiery, and on the hands by unaccustomed, repetitive activity such as raking, laying bricks, or swinging with your kids on the jungle gym. The whitish pockets of skin that form in response to the friction fill with clear fluid between the skin's inner and outer layers. You can actually feel when a blister is beginning to form. The spot feels warm, irritated, inflamed, and then downright painful if you don't remove the friction and pressure.

In addition to the remedies that follow, Sage Chick Salve (page 74) is quite soothing for blistered skin. Keep some handy in your medicine chest, backpack, and gym bag. For blisters caused by burns, see Burns (Minor) on page 96.

To Pop or Not to Pop?

Schools of thought differ on whether or not to pop a blister. Some say to leave it alone, whether large or small. Wash the area and swab it with a disinfectant, pat dry, apply a bit of medicinal salve or treatment oil, cover it with an adhesive bandage or moleskin, and let nature take her course. Others suggest that if you pop the blister, especially if it's a large one, healing will take place faster. If a blister breaks on its own, treat it the same as if you'd just popped it.

To open a blister, first wash and dry the area thoroughly. Swab the blister with a disinfectant and carefully puncture the edge with a flame-sterilized needle or razor blade. Drain the fluid, but don't peel off any skin. Allow the layers of skin to adhere. Cleanse with disinfectant again and pat dry. Apply medicinal salve or treatment oil, then cover the area with a bandage.

Regardless of your approach, always remove the bandage at night to allow the blister to breathe and dry out. Reapply the disinfectant, salve, and bandage in the morning after your shower.

Note: Do not attempt self-treatment of blisters if you have circulatory problems or are diabetic.

SIMPLE BLISTER BARRIER AND TREATMENT OIL

*T*his easy-to-make formula serves as an effective blister preventive barrier for the feet and a remedial treatment for both feet and hands once blisters have formed. Extra thick, with staying power, it conditions skin, helps heal damaged tissue, acts as a mild astringent, reduces inflammation, and prevents infection.

15 drops lavender essential oil

3 drops lemon essential oil

1 tablespoon castor base oil

1 tablespoon vitamin E oil

EQUIPMENT: *Dropper, dark glass bottle with dropper top or screw cap*
PREP TIME: *15 minutes, plus 24 hours to synergize*
YIELD: *Approximately 2 tablespoons*
STORAGE: *Store at room temperature, away from heat and light; use within 1 year*
APPLICATION: *2 times daily, or as desired*

Add the lavender and lemon essential oils drop by drop directly to a storage bottle. Add the castor and vitamin E oils. Screw the top on the bottle and shake vigorously for 2 minutes to blend. Label the bottle and place in a dark location that's between 60° and 80°F for 24 hours so that the oils can synergize.

APPLICATION INSTRUCTIONS: Shake well before each use. To prevent blisters from forming on your feet, apply a thin coating to dry feet prior to doing any physical activity (and make sure your footwear fits properly). To treat new blisters, see To Pop or Not to Pop (opposite page), and apply 1 or 2 drops of this oil to each blister.

Bonus Apply 1 drop per nail and massage thoroughly to condition dry fingernails and cuticles and encourage growth. Omit the essential oils and it can be used as a thick lip gloss!

TENDER TISSUE DISINFECTANT AND REPAIR LINIMENT SPRAY

This lightly fragranced spray cleanses and gently dries oozing blisters, inhibits the growth of bacteria, and reduces inflammation. I recommend it for friction blisters on the hands or feet; be aware that it will sting raw skin or open wounds.

1 cup unflavored vodka
25 drops myrrh essential oil
25 drops palmarosa essential oil

EQUIPMENT: *Plastic or glass spritzer bottle*
PREP TIME: *5 minutes*
YIELD: *Approximately 1 cup*
STORAGE: *Store at room temperature, away from heat and light; use within 2 years*
APPLICATION: *3 times daily, or as needed*

Combine the vodka with the myrrh and palmarosa essential oils in a spritzer bottle. Screw the cap on the bottle and shake vigorously to blend. Label, date, and store in a dark cabinet.

APPLICATION INSTRUCTIONS: Shake well before using. To treat new blisters, see To Pop or Not to Pop on page 82, and use this spray formula as the disinfectant. If you walk around barefoot a lot, spray it onto your blistered areas several times per day to speed healing and prevent infection.

Bonus This is an effective healing agent for blemishes, boils, cuts, scrapes, oozing rashes, and any minor infection of the skin.

BODY ODOR

Sweat is colorless, basically odorless, watery, salty, and ever-so-slightly oily when produced by a healthy body. Only when it's combined with naturally occurring sebum, bacteria, yeasts, and hormones, plus any chemical residue on your skin, does it become odoriferous.

Standard commercial deodorants are among the most irritating personal care products we regularly apply to our bodies today. The majority of deodorants and antiperspirants on the market are filled with deleterious ingredients such as pore-clogging aluminum, petroleum byproducts, and preservatives. Some deliver such a heavy dose of synthetic fragrance that it may provoke nausea, sneezing, sinus and respiratory inflammation, and rashy skin.

Fortunately, chemical-free deodorants are simple to make and work remarkably well, though they do not perform like an antiperspirant and keep your underarms or feet dry. A puff of a natural deodorizing powder, such as simple baking soda, helps if excess moisture is a problem.

Herbs and essentials oils, when blended with vodka, deliver natural antiseptic and cleansing properties that effectively neutralize or minimize body odor. I think you'll find that the herbal fragrances offered by the following recipes are gender-neutral and will appeal to all.

HERBAL FRESH DEODORANT SPRAY

*T*his is one of my favorite homemade deodorants, with a delightful "green" aroma that leaves you feeling fresh and clean. It fights odor-causing bacteria and tones and tightens sweat glands and pores. Keep a small bottle with a few cotton pads on hand for when you need to freshen up a bit.

1½ cups usnea lichen, dried or fresh (usnea is quite dry even when fresh, so there's no need to wilt it)

½ cup dried or 1 cup freshly wilted sage leaves (see page 38 for information on wilting)

½ cup dried or ¾ cup freshly wilted lavender buds

1 teaspoon vegetable glycerin

30 drops lavender essential oil

30 drops rosemary (chemotype *verbenon*) essential oil

30 drops thyme (chemotype *linalool*) essential oil

3–4 cups unflavored vodka

EQUIPMENT: *1-quart canning jar, plastic wrap, strainer, fine filter, funnel, glass or plastic storage containers or spritzer bottles*
PREP TIME: *10 minutes, plus 4 weeks for extraction*
YIELD: *Approximately 2½ cups*
STORAGE: *Store at room temperature, away from heat and light; use within 2 years*
APPLICATION: *Up to 4 times per day*

If you're using freshly wilted sage, cut or tear it into smaller pieces to expose more surface area during maceration. If you're using freshly wilted lavender, strip the buds and any attached greenery from the stems; discard the stems. Place the usnea, sage, and lavender, along with the glycerin and the lavender, rosemary, and thyme essential oils, in a 1-quart canning jar and pour the vodka over them, so that it comes to within ½ inch of the top of the jar. Place a piece of plastic wrap over the mouth of the jar (to prevent the metal lid from coming into contact with the jar's contents), then screw on the lid. Shake the mixture for about 30 seconds. After 24 hours, top up with more vodka if necessary. The herbs will settle a bit in the jar, but that's okay.

Store the jar in a cool, dark place for 4 weeks so that the vodka can extract the valuable chemical components from the herbs. Shake the jar for 15 to 30 seconds each day.

At the end of the 4 weeks, strain the herbs through a fine-mesh strainer lined with a fine filter such as muslin or, preferably, a paper coffee filter, then strain again if necessary to remove all herb debris. Press or squeeze the herbs to release all the valuable herbal extract. Discard the marc.

Pour the liquid into storage containers, then cap, label, and store in a dark cabinet.

APPLICATION INSTRUCTIONS: Shake well before each use. Spray onto clean, dry underarms and feet or apply with a cotton pad or cloth and rub in. Allow to dry before getting dressed. Follow with a deodorizing body powder, if desired.

LEMON AND SAGE DEODORANT SPRAY

*M*en, women, and teens enjoy this deodorant with its light, citrusy-woodsy aroma. It fights odor-causing bacteria, tones and tightens sweat glands and pores, and leaves you feeling ultra-cool and confident. Keep a small bottle with a few cotton pads handy for when you need to freshen up a bit.

1 cup unflavored vodka

15 drops Atlas cedar essential oil

15 drops lemon essential oil

15 drops sage essential oil

½ teaspoon vegetable glycerin

Rind of 1 lemon, cut into long, thin strips

EQUIPMENT: *Glass or plastic storage container or spritzer bottle*

PREP TIME: *10 minutes*

YIELD: *1 cup*

STORAGE: *Store at room temperature, away from heat and light; use within 2 years*

APPLICATION: *Up to 4 times per day*

Pour the vodka into the storage container or spritzer bottle. Add the Atlas cedar, lemon, and sage essential oils, along with the glycerin and lemon rind. Shake vigorously to blend. You may leave the citrus rind in the bottle for up to 1 month, then remove. Label and store the container in a dark cabinet.

APPLICATION INSTRUCTIONS: Shake well before each use. Spray onto clean, dry underarms and feet or apply with a cotton pad or cloth and rub in. Allow to dry before getting dressed. Follow with a deodorizing body powder, if desired.

Bonus This formula doubles as an astringent and antiseptic liquid cleanser for your hands, face, or entire body, for that matter (avoid the eyes and mucous membranes). Use for impromptu cleansing when a bath or shower is not convenient.

BOILS *(Furuncles)*

This is not a skin affliction that you hear about very often, thank goodness, as boils are not only painful and unpleasant, but they can cause a generalized infection if not treated properly. A boil is an acute, circumscribed, deep inflammation of the subcutaneous layers of the skin, hair follicle, or gland that has a dead, suppurating (pus-filled) inner core, generally resulting from staphylococcus bacteria that enter the skin through the hair follicle. The core is ultimately expelled or reabsorbed into the skin, depending on the severity of inflammation and health of the individual.

Boils most frequently form on the buttocks, breasts, face, and neck, and they are particularly painful on the nose, fingers, or ears. For some individuals, boils are a recurrent malady, and occasionally "boil epidemics" have occurred among teens and young adults who live in crowded quarters and have poor hygiene.

Treatment of Boils

Never squeeze a boil in an attempt to purge the infection — you will only encourage the spread of bacteria into surrounding areas, and very possibly you will injure skin tissue. Instead, keep the area scrupulously clean to prevent new lesions from forming nearby and follow these steps:

- Gently wash the boil with soap and water, pat dry, then swab with a strong, skin-safe disinfectant such as Oregon Grape Root and Echinacea Root Liniment (opposite page).
- Apply 2 drops of Anti-Infection Compound Oil (page 90) to the lesion(s) followed by a hot, moist compress made with very salty water and applied for 10 to 15 minutes. Be careful not to use overly hot water, as you can burn your skin.
- Pat the area dry and apply 2 more drops of Anti-Infection Compound Oil.

- Repeat the entire procedure two or three times a day to help bring the infection to a head and draw out the pus. Take care to avoid injury or trauma to the affected areas.
- Once the pus has been expelled, apply 1 or more drops (depending on the size of the boil) of Anti-Infection Compound Oil to each boil twice daily. Cover with a bandage, if desired.

If there is no improvement in 4 or 5 days or if the lesion persists, spreads, or becomes larger, contact your health care provider. An antibiotic or even surgical excision may be necessary. Boils, particularly in the nose, can lead to a staph infection in the brain if not treated. Most doctors will prescribe an oral antibiotic to prevent this from happening.

Oregon Grape Root and Echinacea Root Liniment

This makes a very strong antibacterial herbal medicine — your ally in the war on painful, infected boils. It deeply cleanses and dries oozing pus and blood, tightens tissue, promotes skin cell regeneration, cools heat and inflammation, and helps destroy infectious bacteria. Be aware that it will sting raw skin.

½ cup dried or 1 cup freshly wilted echinacea root (see page 38 for information on wilting)

½ cup dried or 1 cup freshly wilted Oregon grape root

1–2 cups unflavored vodka

EQUIPMENT: *1-pint canning jar, plastic wrap, fine-mesh strainer, fine filter, funnel, glass or plastic bottle*

PREP TIME: *10 minutes, plus 8 weeks for extraction*

YIELD: *1 to 1¼ cups*

STORAGE: *Store at room temperature, away from heat and light; use within 2 years*

APPLICATION: *3 times per day*

Bonus Use this powerful yet safe liniment to cleanse and promote healing on *any* skin infection, from minor to major.

If you're using freshly wilted roots, coarsely chop or grate them to expose more surface area during extraction. Place the echinacea and Oregon grape roots in a 1-pint canning jar and pour the vodka over them, so that it comes to within ½ inch of the top of the jar. The herbs should be completely covered. Place a piece of plastic wrap over the mouth of the jar (to prevent the metal lid from coming into contact with the jar's contents), then screw on the lid. Shake the mixture for about 30 seconds. After 24 hours, top up with more vodka if necessary.

Store the jar in a cool, dark place for 8 weeks so that the vodka can extract the valuable chemical components from the herbs. Shake the jar for 15 to 30 seconds each day.

At the end of the 8 weeks, strain the herbs through a fine-mesh strainer lined with a fine filter such as muslin or, preferably, a paper coffee filter, then strain again if necessary to remove all herb debris. Press or squeeze the herbs to release all the valuable herbal extract. Discard the marc.

Pour the liquid into a storage container, then cap, label, and store in a dark cabinet.

APPLICATION INSTRUCTIONS: Follow the directions in Treatment of Boils (opposite page), using this formula as a disinfectant. Follow with Anti-Infection Compound Oil (next page).

ANTI-INFECTION COMPOUND OIL

Potent yet gentle, this easy-to-make oil aids in the fight against infectious staphylococcus bacteria, reduces painful inflammation, helps heal tissue, and conditions skin to keep scarring at bay. It also helps eliminate potential odor emanating from infected boils.

Note: This is an aromatherapeutically concentrated formula, so use only by the drop as directed.

10 drops tea tree essential oil

6 drops thyme (chemotype *linalool*) essential oil

5 drops German chamomile essential oil

2 drops myrrh essential oil

2 tablespoons calophyllum base oil

EQUIPMENT: *Dropper, dark glass bottle with dropper top or screw cap*
PREP TIME: *15 minutes, plus 24 hours to synergize*
YIELD: *Approximately 2 tablespoons*
STORAGE: *Store at room temperature, away from heat and light; use within 1 year*
APPLICATION: *3 times per day*

Add the tea tree, thyme, German chamomile, and myrrh essential oils drop by drop directly into a storage bottle. Add the calophyllum base oil. Screw the top on the bottle and shake vigorously for 2 minutes to blend. Label the bottle and place in a dark location that's between 60° and 80°F for 24 hours so that the oils can synergize.

APPLICATION INSTRUCTIONS: Shake well before each use. Use by the drop, following the directions in Treatment of Boils (page 88).

Bonus Use these aromatic drops on cuts, scrapes, bug bites, infected ingrown hairs, blisters, bedsores or skin ulcers, rashes, minor burns, or any other minor to moderate skin infection.

BRUISES *(Contusions)*

Bruises are an unavoidable part of life. When you bump into a hard object, whether it's banging your shin on a table or hitting the dashboard in a car accident, lymph and blood seep into the subcutaneous tissue, causing that lovely multicolored discoloration we all know. Depending upon the initial trauma, bruises may result in some degree of pain, swelling, heat, and damaged tissue. A minor bruise really doesn't require any type of treatment, but if you turn blue from the slightest bump (like I do!) or have fair or thin skin, then a bit of immediate remedial care is recommended to speed healing and minimize discoloration and capillary damage.

The following remedies will help lessen the severity of the painful symptoms of a minor to moderate bruise and the degree of discoloration. The sooner you begin treatment after the initial injury, the quicker you will heal and the less visible the bruise will be.

Bruise-Be-Gone Balm

This is a fresh summer-flower medicine, full of healing solar energy! Upon quick application — immediately after you experience skin trauma — it ever-so-gently cools the heat of a newly bruised area, thereby reducing swelling and pain, plus it aids in mending damaged tissue, minimizing the potential ugliness of the bruise.

St. John's wort–infused oil is a specific treatment for deep, painful muscle tissue and nerve damage. It has analgesic as well as vulnerary properties.

Note: When making this oil, I use only the freshly wilted herbs and solar infusion method of extraction, as I feel that these particular herbs release their best medicinal properties when processed in this manner. Calendula flowers are very thick and sticky, so let them wilt for at least 72 hours before using them.

1½ cups freshly wilted calendula flowers (see page 38 for information on wilting)

1½ cups freshly wilted St. John's wort flowering tops

3–4 cups extra-virgin olive, almond, or soybean base oil (enough to completely cover flowers)

2,000 IU vitamin E oil

3–4 tablespoons beeswax (depending on how firm you want the balm to be)

10 drops helichrysum essential oil (optional, but it does increase the anti-inflammatory properties of the formula)

EQUIPMENT: *Rubber or latex gloves, 1-quart canning jar, stirring utensil, strainer, fine filter, funnel, glass or plastic storage container (for the infused oil), glass or plastic jars or tins (for the balm)*
PREP TIME: *1 month to infuse the oil, plus 20 minutes to make the balm and 30 minutes for it to thicken*
YIELD: *Approximately 2½ cups of infused oil and 1¼ cups of balm*
STORAGE: *Store at room temperature, away from heat and light; use within 1 year*
APPLICATION: *3 or 4 times per day*

PREPARING THE INFUSED OIL: If you don't want your hands stained a deep purplish-red from the St. John's wort, wear rubber or latex gloves. Cut or tear the wilted calendula and St. John's wort into very small pieces to expose more surface area to the oil. Place the herbs in a wide-mouthed 1-quart canning jar. Drizzle the base oil over the plant matter until the oil comes to within 1 inch of the top of the jar. The wilted herb matter will settle with the weight of the oil, so don't worry if it looks as though you don't have enough plant matter in the jar. Stir gently to remove air bubbles and make sure that all plant matter is submerged.

Place a piece of plastic wrap over the mouth of the jar (to prevent the metal lid from coming into contact with the herbs) and tightly screw on the lid. Shake the jar several times to blend the herbs and oil thoroughly. Place the jar in a warm, sunny location such as a south-facing windowsill and allow the herb to infuse for 1 month. Shake the jar every day for 30 seconds or so.

After 1 month, carefully strain the oil through a fine-mesh strainer lined with a fine filter such as muslin or, preferably, a paper coffee filter, then strain again if necessary to remove all herb debris. Squeeze the herbs to extract as much of the precious oil as possible. Discard the marc. Add the vitamin E oil and stir to blend. If you used almond or soybean base oil, your infused oil will be deep golden or rusty red in color — gorgeous! If you used the olive oil, then it may have a greenish hue as well.

Pour the finished oil into a glass or plastic storage container, then cap, label, and store in a dark cabinet.

PREPARING THE BALM: Combine 1 cup of the herbal infused oil with the beeswax in a small saucepan or double boiler, and warm over low heat until the beeswax has just melted. Remove from the heat and allow to cool for 5 minutes, stirring a few times. Add the essential oil, if using. Stir again to blend. Pour into storage containers, cap, and label. Set aside for 30 minutes until the balm has thickened.

APPLICATION INSTRUCTIONS: Gently massage a fingerful of balm into any newly bruised area that is exhibiting pain, heat, discoloration, and inflammation. Follow with an ice-cold compress or ice pack for 10 to 15 minutes. Repeat this procedure three or four times per day, depending upon the severity of bruise, for the first 2 days, until the swelling subsides. You can continue to apply this balm two or three times per day until the bruise heals. Continued application is especially recommended if the trauma was severe, with possible injury to underlying muscle tissue.

Bonus Use this aromatic balm as an aid in healing cuts, scrapes, bug bites, blemishes, infected ingrown hairs, blisters, rashes, boils, minor burns, or any minor to moderate skin infection. A wonderful addition to your herbal first aid kit!

LAVENDER ICE: MENTHOLATED HEALING OIL

Lavender Ice — doesn't that sound like a delicious, sweet, purple sorbet? Instead, this highly aromatic recipe is intended to minimize the potential ugliness that your skin could suffer from bangs and bumps. Upon quick application — immediately after the trauma — it cools the heat of a newly bruised area, reducing swelling and pain, plus it aids in mending damaged tissue. This is strong medicine, containing potent peppermint-derived menthol concentrate, so be aware that your skin will feel quite chilled upon application, which is a good thing!

Note: Avoid contact with the mucous membranes — the nose, eyes, and mouth.

3 tablespoons plus
1 teaspoon almond, apricot kernel, or soybean oil

2 teaspoons menthol crystals

30 drops lavender essential oil

EQUIPMENT: *Small saucepan or double boiler, stirring utensil, dark glass bottle with dropper top or screw cap*
PREP TIME: *15 minutes*
YIELD: *Approximately ¼ cup*
STORAGE: *Store at room temperature, away from heat and light; use within 1 year*
APPLICATION: *3 or 4 times per day during the first 2 days after injury*

Combine the oil and menthol crystals in a small saucepan (a ¾-quart size works great) over low heat or in a double boiler. Gently warm the mixture just until the crystals dissolve. Remove from the heat. Stir a few times to blend the mixture thoroughly. Pour into a storage bottle and add the lavender essential oil. Screw the top on the bottle, then shake vigorously for 2 minutes to blend. Label and store in a dark cabinet.

APPLICATION INSTRUCTIONS: Shake well before using. Gently massage a few drops into any newly bruised area that is exhibiting pain, heat, discoloration, and inflammation. Follow with an ice-cold compress or ice pack for 10 to 15 minutes. Repeat this procedure three or four times per day for the first 2 days, until the swelling subsides. Wash your hands after application, unless treatment is intended for your fingers or hands, in which case I recommend wearing cotton gloves while the oil soaks in.

Bonus The aroma is guaranteed to decongest stuffed sinuses and help remedy a sinus or tension headache. Inhale directly from the bottle or rub a few drops onto your chest and neck. Cover area with warm clothing or flannel sheet.

RED AND BLUE OIL

I didn't intend to create this particular hue when formulating this remedy, but the mix of red, golden brown, and deep blue in this oil blend actually looks like that of a bad bruise. Go figure. An extremely powerful anti-inflammatory and skin cell regenerator with a unique earthy-creamy-tart aroma, this oil gets right to the business of remedying your ugly bruise — pain, inflammation, tissue damage, and all. It's recommended for new bruises that are just beginning to become discolored, swollen, and hot, and for continued use on skin and muscles suffering from severe trauma.

8 drops German chamomile essential oil

5 drops birch or wintergreen essential oil

3 drops helichrysum essential oil

2 drops lemon essential oil

1 tablespoon calophyllum base oil

1 tablespoon rosehip seed base oil

EQUIPMENT: *Dropper, dark glass bottle with dropper top or screw cap*
PREP TIME: *15 minutes, plus 24 hours to synergize*
YIELD: *Approximately 2 tablespoons*
STORAGE: *Store at room temperature, away from heat and light; use within 1 year*
APPLICATION: *3 or 4 times per day*

Add the German chamomile, birch, helichrysum, and lemon essential oils drop by drop directly into a storage bottle. Add the calophyllum and rosehip seed base oils. Screw the top on the bottle and shake vigorously for 2 minutes to blend. Label the bottle and place in a dark location that's between 60° and 80°F for 24 hours so that the oils can synergize.

APPLICATION INSTRUCTIONS: Shake well before each use. Gently massage a few drops into any newly bruised area that is exhibiting pain, heat, discoloration, and inflammation. Follow with an ice-cold compress or ice pack for 10 to 15 minutes. Do this three or four times per day for the first 2 days, until the swelling subsides. You can continue to apply this oil two or three times per day until the bruise heals. Continued application is especially recommended if the trauma was severe, with possible injury to underlying muscle tissue.

Bonus Use this blend to heal and comfort all types of inflammations — skin, muscular, and joint.

BURNS *(Minor)*

This section deals with common, everyday, nonchemical, nonelectrical burns such as those resulting from boiling water splatters or hot steam from the teapot, spattering cooking oil, or accidently touching a hot surface. These first-degree or superficial second-degree burns damage only the epidermis (they outermost layer of the skin); they don't penetrate into the dermis (the second layer of the skin that houses nerves and blood vessels). Yes, they are painful and may eventually blister and peel, but they will most likely heal without becoming infected or resulting in a scar if proper care is observed.

Approximately 80 percent of burns can be dealt with successfully at home and don't warrant a trip to the emergency room or professional intervention — you just need to be prepared, because accidents do happen to everyone.

Treating Burns

The first step to treating a minor burn at home is to immediately cool the burned area in *one* of the following ways:

- Use Quench-the-Heat Aloe Liniment (opposite page).
- Immerse the burned area in cold water.
- Gently run cold tap water over the area.
- Apply a generous amount of aloe vera juice or gel to the burn.
- Apply a cold, wet compress to the burn.
- Apply an ice pack (or a bag of frozen vegetables) wrapped in a dishtowel to the burn.

Important note: Do not apply ice directly to the skin, and do not apply a salve, balm, or oil to a fresh burn, as the fat can insulate the skin and slow the cooling process, creating further tissue damage.

It's important to immediately cool the heat to diminish the potential for scarring and further tissue damage. I highly recommend the use of aloe vera juice; it works miracles with regard to the healing of burns and skin preservation. Do whatever works for the situation at hand, and keep it up until all burning sensations have subsided. Depending on the size and severity of the burn, this may take 15 to 30 minutes or more.

After the burned area has *completely* cooled, rinse the wound with soap and water, remove any debris, gently pat dry, and apply an anti-inflammatory, antiseptic, and skin-cell-regenerating product, such as Burn Recovery Oil (page 98). You may bandage the area with gauze or leave it exposed, as you prefer, though it is vital that you protect the burn from dirt and further injury.

If the burn is of an electrical or chemical nature or you suspect severe second- or third-degree damage, call 911 immediately.

QUENCH-THE-HEAT ALOE LINIMENT

This recipe for a nonalcoholic liniment uses cooling aloe vera juice with lavender essential oil to speed the recovery of damaged tissue. These two ingredients have vulnerary properties and work to reduce inflammation and pain. This is my go-to "burn juice." I always keep a bottle of it in the door of my refrigerator for those unavoidable kitchen burns. Use it as initial treatment of minor skin burns or sunburn, and continue use until skin is completely healed.

Note: If you wish to use aloe gel from a fresh plant leaf, split open the leaf, scrape or squeeze out the gel, and apply the gel directly to the burn. Discard the leaf.

1 cup commercially prepared aloe vera juice

80 drops lavender essential oil

EQUIPMENT: *Plastic or glass spritzer bottle*
PREP TIME: *5 minutes*
YIELD: *Approximately 1 cup*
STORAGE: *Refrigerate; use within 6 months*
APPLICATION: *As necessary or desired*

Combine the aloe vera juice and lavender essential oil in a spritzer bottle and shake vigorously to blend. Label, and store in the refrigerator.

APPLICATION INSTRUCTIONS: Shake well before each use. Follow the advice given in Treating Burns (opposite page). This aloe liniment should be applied as soon as possible after the skin is burned, either by spraying it directly on the area or using it to soak a compress. Repeat several times per day, if desired, for up to several weeks, until the skin is completely healed.

Bonus You can use this formula to relieve the sting of sunburn and the itch of dermatitis, and as a gentle toner for oily and normal skin.

Burn Recovery Oil

This lovely oil is just what burned, damaged flesh needs — it contains antiseptic and anti-inflammatory properties, promotes the growth of healthy new skin tissue, and aids in conditioning the epidermis, increasing flexibility and suppleness and thus preventing potential scars. Use it on burned skin and surrounding area after the initial heat and inflammation have subsided to prevent potential infection and scarring.

Note: This is an aromatherapeutically concentrated formula, so use only by the drop as directed.

7 drops rosemary (chemotype *verbenon*) essential oil

5 drops German chamomile essential oil

5 drops lavender essential oil

3 drops carrot seed essential oil

2 drops sage essential oil

1 tablespoon jojoba base oil

1 tablespoon rosehip seed base oil

EQUIPMENT: *Dropper, dark glass bottle with dropper top or screw cap*
PREP TIME: *15 minutes, plus 24 hours to synergize*
YIELD: *Approximately 2 tablespoons*
STORAGE: *Store at room temperature, away from heat and light; use within 1 year*
APPLICATION: *3 times per day*

Add the rosemary, German chamomile, lavender, carrot seed, and sage essential oils drop by drop directly into a storage bottle. Add the jojoba and rosehip seed base oils. Screw the top on the bottle and shake vigorously for 2 minutes to blend. Label the bottle and place in a dark location that's between 60° and 80°F for 24 hours so that the oils can synergize.

APPLICATION INSTRUCTIONS: Shake well before each use. Follow the advice given in Treating Burns (page 96). Apply by the drop to affected skin and surrounding area after the initial heat and inflammation have subsided, then use once or twice per day until the burn has healed.

Bonus These aromatic drops aid in healing cuts, scrapes, bug bites, infected ingrown hairs and ingrown toenails, blisters, rashes, or any minor skin infection.

After-the-Burn Skin Conditioning Salve

Except for a hint of honey aroma, this is a relatively fragrance-free, velvety-textured conditioning salve for even the most sensitive skin. It moisturizes and aids in renewing elasticity and flexibility of the skin, thereby reducing the potential for scarring.

5 tablespoons soybean base oil

1 tablespoon beeswax

1 tablespoon cocoa butter

1 tablespoon refined shea butter (unrefined shea butter will work, but its stronger fragrance will often dominate the formula)

EQUIPMENT: *Small saucepan or double boiler, stirring utensil, plastic or glass jar or tin*
PREP TIME: *30 minutes, plus 12 hours to thicken*
YIELD: *½ cup*
STORAGE: *Store at room temperature, away from heat and light; use within 1 year*
APPLICATION: *As desired*

Combine the soybean oil, beeswax, cocoa butter, and shea butter in a small saucepan or double boiler, and warm over low heat until all the solids are just melted. Remove from the heat and allow to cool for 5 to 10 minutes. Stir a few times to blend the mixture thoroughly. Pour into a storage container, then cap and label. Allow the salve to harden overnight at room temperature. Because both cocoa butter and shea butter are included, the salve may continue to change texture slightly for another 24 hours.

APPLICATION INSTRUCTIONS: Apply a small dab of salve to the affected skin and surrounding area, and massage it in gently. Use as often as desired; in fact, use it anywhere your skin is dry, damaged, chafed, and in need of TLC.

Bonus This salve conditions dry lips, cuticles, nails, and cracked feet and can be used on a baby's bottom to prevent diaper rash. It's wonderful for preventing stretch marks on expanding belly and breasts before, during, and after pregnancy, and it also works as an after-sun "skin rescue."

CHILDREN'S ILLNESSES AND DISCOMFORTS

Infants and young children (under the age of 8) have delicate, sensitive systems, especially their digestive, integumentary (skin), respiratory, and nervous ones. They need extra-gentle care when they're experiencing distress. Luckily, quite a few of their everyday, minor medical needs can be met quite nicely with the topical application of herbal remedies.

"Ever-so-gentle," "nonirritating," and "nontoxic" are the key words to look for on a commercial personal-care product for young children.

And, of course, these terms apply to the herbal remedies I'll discuss here, variations of which have been used successfully for hundreds of years to treat children's ailments and discomforts. This is a tried-and-true collection of extremely pleasant, soothing, and mild formulations to care for your precious little ones. These formulas are also recommended for those with ultra-sensitive skin, such as the elderly, or those who simply prefer super-mild formulas for personal-care needs.

TUMMY TROUBLES BELLY OIL

This warming oil, with its luscious combination of sweet, spicy, woodsy, and apple-like aromas, leaves baby smelling cared for and cozy. When massaged into a distressed, achy belly, it delivers relaxing energy plus antispasmodic, anti-inflammatory, and carminative properties — exactly what's needed to soothe and calm the painful spasms of colic and excess gas.

Note: You may substitute Chamomile Baby Massage Oil (page 106) for the almond or soybean oil.

2 drops cardamom essential oil

2 drops Roman chamomile essential oil

2 drops sweet marjoram essential oil

¼ cup almond or soybean base oil

EQUIPMENT: *Dropper, dark glass bottle with dropper top or screw cap*
PREP TIME: *15 minutes, plus 24 hours to synergize*
YIELD: *¼ cup*
STORAGE: *Store at room temperature, away from heat and light; use within 1 year*
APPLICATION: *Up to 2 times per day*

Put the cardamom, Roman chamomile, and sweet marjoram essential oils directly into the storage bottle, drop by drop. Add the base oil. Screw the top on the bottle and shake vigorously for 2 minutes to blend all the ingredients. Label the bottle and place in a dark location that's between 60° and 80°F for 24 hours so that the oils can synergize.

APPLICATION INSTRUCTIONS: Shake well before each use. Lay the infant on his or her back, then pour a small amount of oil into your hands and rub them together to warm it. Gently massage the oil into the baby's belly in a clockwise direction, beginning at the navel, spiraling outward and then down the child's left thigh. This stimulates the colon to release gas and helps quiet spasms. Repeat several times.

Bonus This oil makes for a nice foot or full body massage to calm and soothe cranky toddlers, often lulling them into blissful sleep! I love this blend so much that I frequently use it as a "winter warming oil" for the bath or as a massage oil applied to damp *or* dry skin right before bed to help me unwind.

MULLEIN EARACHE RELIEF OIL

*T*he tall, stately mullein plant, with its giant, fuzzy "donkey ear" leaves, is my go-to herb for earaches. The golden flowers have a gentle, neutral to slightly cooling energy, with anti-inflammatory, vulnerary, astringent, analgesic, and sedative properties — just what's needed to ease the pain and inflammation of a minor to moderate earache.

If your young one is prone to earaches, take a look at his or her diet and avoid any mucous-forming foods, such as cow's milk, butter, yogurt, cheese, nuts and nut butters, white rice, white flour, white sugar, and cold citrus juices, especially in the winter.

Note: See your health care practitioner if an earache gets worse or lasts for more than a few days.

3 cups freshly wilted mullein flowers (see page 38 for information on wilting)

3 cups extra-virgin olive base oil

2,000 IU vitamin E oil

EQUIPMENT: *2-quart saucepan or double boiler and candy or yogurt thermometer (for stovetop method), quart-size canning jar and plastic wrap (for solar infusion method), stirring utensil, strainer, fine filter, funnel, glass or plastic storage containers*
PREP TIME: *4 hours (stovetop method) or 1 month (solar infusion method)*
YIELD: *Approximately 2½ cups*
STORAGE: *Store at room temperature, away from heat and light; use within 1 year*
APPLICATION: *3 times per day until the earache is better*

STOVETOP METHOD: Combine the freshly wilted mullein flowers and olive base oil in a 2-quart saucepan or double boiler and stir thoroughly to blend. The mixture should look like a thick, yellow, flower-petal slurry. Bring the mixture to just shy of a simmer, between 125° and 135°F. Do not let the oil actually simmer — it will degrade the quality of your infused oil. *Do not* put the lid on the pot.

Allow the flowers to macerate in the oil over low heat for 4 hours. Check the temperature every 30 minutes or so with a thermometer and adjust the heat accordingly. If you're using a double boiler, add more water to the bottom pot as necessary, so it doesn't dry out. Stir the mixture at least every 30 minutes or so, as the flowers tend to settle to the bottom.

After 4 hours, remove the pan from the heat and allow to cool for 15 minutes. While the oil is still warm, carefully strain it through a fine-mesh strainer lined with a fine filter such as muslin or, preferably, a paper coffee filter, then strain again if necessary to remove all flower debris. Squeeze the flowers to extract as much of the precious oil as possible. Discard the marc.

Add the vitamin E oil and stir to blend. The resulting mullein flower oil should be a golden green color. Pour the finished oil into storage containers, then cap, label, and store in a dark cabinet.

SOLAR-INFUSED METHOD: Place the freshly wilted mullein flowers in a wide-mouthed 1-quart canning jar. Drizzle the olive base oil over the plant matter until the oil comes to within 1 inch of the top of the jar. You may need more or less oil than the recipe calls for depending on the size of the wilted mullein flowers. The flowers will settle with the weight of the oil, so don't worry if it looks as though you don't have enough plant matter in the jar. Gently stir to remove air bubbles and make sure that all the plant matter is submerged.

Place a piece of plastic wrap over the mouth of the jar (to prevent the metal lid from coming into contact with the herb) and tightly screw on the lid. Shake the jar several times to blend the herb and oil thoroughly. Place the jar in a warm, sunny location such as a south-facing windowsill, and allow the flowers to infuse for 1 month. Shake the jar every day for 30 seconds.

After 1 month, carefully strain the oil through a fine-mesh strainer lined with a fine filter such as muslin or, preferably, a paper coffee filter, then strain again if necessary to remove all flower debris. Squeeze the herb to extract as much of the precious oil as possible.

Discard the marc. Add the vitamin E oil and stir to blend. The resulting mullein flower oil should be golden-green in color.

Pour the finished oil into storage containers, then cap, label, and store in a dark cabinet.

APPLICATION INSTRUCTIONS: Gently warm 1 teaspoon (½ teaspoon for each ear) of oil to the temperature of comfortable bath water; it should feel just warm on the inside of your wrist, and definitely not hot. Lay the child on his or her side, with the offending ear facing up, and apply a very warm, slightly moist, thick washcloth over the entire ear. Leave it in place until it cools to just barely warm, then repeat. The warmth and moisture help increase circulation in and around the inflamed ear.

Using a dropper, place ½ teaspoon (approximately 50 drops) of the warm mullein oil into the ear canal and insert a wad of cotton to hold the oil inside. Gently massage some of the warm oil all around the outside of the ear to help ease inflammation and move stagnant lymph fluid.

Repeat the process with the child's other ear, even if it is not infected, as the ear canals are connected and infection can easily spread from one to the other.

Repeat 3 times per day until the ear feels better.

LAVENDER AND ROSEMARY CRADLE CAP OIL

*C*radle cap is a type of infantile *seborrheic dermatitis — an inflammation of the upper layers of the skin with overactive sebaceous (oil) glands, causing greasy, thick, crusty, yellowish scales, with occasional tiny red pimples, on the scalp, face, ears, and sometimes the groin and underarms. It often runs in families, and cold weather can make the symptoms worse. Though unsightly, it isn't contagious or painful, though it sometimes itches a bit, and infants and toddlers soon outgrow it as their sebaceous glands and digestive system mature. Stubborn cases of diaper rash often accompany the scalp rash.*

With any skin disease involving the sebaceous glands, especially on the scalp, I prefer to use jojoba oil as the primary ingredient in the treatment formula because of its chemical similarity to human sebum and the fact that it oxygenates the follicles. It has natural anti-inflammatory properties, penetrates extremely well with minimal oily residue, and balances oil production while conditioning the hair and skin quite nicely. Both lavender and rosemary essential oils help fight infection and odor, stimulate cell renewal, and heal tissue. The evening primrose oil nourishes the skin and is anti-inflammatory.

Note: If you already have some on hand, you can use Mullein Earache Relief Oil (see previous recipe) as a substitute for the jojoba oil used here.

Cradle Cap and Diet

If you're breastfeeding and your infant has cradle cap, avoid excessive consumption of citrus juices, dairy products, grains, meat or fish, and refined foods, and absolutely avoid artificial preservatives, flavorings, sweeteners, and colorings, as these can irritate the still-developing digestive system of your infant. Adding probiotics plus omega-3 fatty acids, evening primrose oil, or borage oil to your own diet often improves the symptoms of cradle cap.

5 drops lavender essential oil

5 drops rosemary (chemotype *verbenon*) essential oil

7 tablespoons jojoba base oil

1 tablespoon evening primrose base oil

EQUIPMENT: *Dropper, dark glass bottle with dropper top or screw cap*
PREP TIME: *15 minutes, plus 24 hours to synergize*
YIELD: *½ cup*
STORAGE: *Store at room temperature, away from heat and light; use within 6 months*
APPLICATION: *2 times per day*

Add the lavender and rosemary essential oil drops directly into a storage bottle. Add the jojoba and evening primrose base oils. Screw the top on the bottle and shake vigorously for 2 minutes to blend. Label the bottle and place in a dark location that's between 60° and 80°F for 24 hours so that the oils can synergize.

APPLICATION INSTRUCTIONS: Shake well before each use. Gently massage ½ to 1 teaspoon of the oil into the dry scalp two times per day — morning and evening. Don't apply so much that it makes a runny, oily mess. Allow the oil to remain on the scalp after application, blotting with a soft cotton towel to absorb any excess. When it's time for the next treatment (after 12 hours), many of the crusts can be removed with another gentle massage and wiped away with a soft cloth. The oil softens the scales and the massage helps loosen them. *Gentle* is the key word here. Do not rub roughly or pick off the crusts or scabs. They will slough off with time and repeated applications of oil. Shampoo no more than twice a week, using a chemical-free, low-sudsing baby shampoo, so as not to further irritate the scalp.

Bonus This super-mild formula helps heal everyday boo-boos, plus it makes a soothing foot massage oil for little ones — especially when applied just before bedtime or nap time.

CHAMOMILE BABY MASSAGE OIL

*D*elicate, fragile, tender skin needs ultra-mild, conditioning care to keep it soft, supple, hydrated, nourished, and healthy as an effective barrier to the outside world. This fresh and oh-so-useful recipe is straight from the garden. The simple luxury of almond oil infused with chamomile flowers, with their anti-inflammatory and vulnerary properties and apple-like, relaxing aroma, is all that's needed to care for your young one's skin.

If you grow only one herb in your garden, you must grow a patch of German chamomile flowers. In addition to using them for bath, facial, and massage oils, you can brew them for tea, make sleep pillows, and use the infused oil for sleep and dream balms.

Note: For this recipe, I prefer to use the solar infusion method with freshly wilted flowers, as this process yields a sweeter and fresher scent, but the dried flowers work nicely, too.

2 cups dried or 3 cups freshly wilted chamomile flowers (see page 38 for information on wilting)

3–4 cups almond base oil (enough to completely cover flowers)

2,000 IU vitamin E oil

EQUIPMENT: *Widemouthed 1-quart canning jar, stirring utensil, plastic wrap, strainer, fine filter, funnel, glass or plastic storage containers*
PREP TIME: *1 month*
YIELD: *Approximately 2½ cups*
STORAGE: *Store at room temperature, away from heat and light; use within 1 year*
APPLICATION: *2 times per day, or as desired*

Place the chamomile flowers in a 1-quart canning jar. Drizzle the base oil over the plant matter until the oil comes to within 1 inch of the top of the jar. The dried herb may pack in the bottom and the wilted herb matter will settle with the weight of the oil, so don't worry if it looks as though you don't have enough plant matter in the jar. Gently stir to remove air bubbles and make sure that all the plant matter is submerged.

Place a piece of plastic wrap over the mouth of the jar (to prevent the metal lid from coming into contact with the herbs) and tightly screw on the lid. Shake the jar several times to blend the herbs and oil thoroughly. Place the jar in a warm, sunny location such as a south-facing windowsill, and allow the herb to infuse for 1 month. Shake the jar every day for 30 seconds or so.

After 1 month, carefully strain the oil through a fine-mesh strainer lined with a fine filter such as muslin or, preferably, a paper coffee filter, then strain again if necessary to remove all herb debris. Squeeze the flowers to extract as much of the precious oil as possible. Discard the marc. Add the vitamin E oil and stir to blend. The resulting chamomile oil will be golden in color.

Pour the finished oil into storage containers, then cap, label, and store in a dark cabinet.

APPLICATION INSTRUCTIONS: After a warm bath, pat the skin almost dry. Apply a small amount of infused oil onto the slightly moist skin, massaging it in with gentle, circular motions (always toward the heart) until it is completely absorbed. This oil can easily be massaged into dry skin anytime you desire — it sinks in so nicely. Allow oil to soak into skin for at least 5 minutes before dressing.

Bonus Use every day as an all-over oil; it's especially beneficial for thin, fragile, and sensitive skin. It sinks right in with nary an oily residue.

His mother put him to bed, and made some chamomile tea; and she gave a dose of it to Peter! "One table-spoonful to be taken at bed-time."

— BEATRIX POTTER,
The Tale of Peter Rabbit

SLEEPY SALVE

*A*n ever-so-soothing salve with the essence of my favorite garden flowers, designed especially to escort your young one to a calmer, more peaceful place, whether that be a relaxed, less stressed state or sound sleep.

Note: I prefer to use the stovetop method to brew this infused oil blend, as I like the more potent, relaxing aroma that results.

½ cup dried or ¾ cup freshly wilted chamomile flowers (see page 38 for information on wilting)

½ cup dried or ¾ cup freshly wilted lavender buds

½ cup dried or 1 cup freshly wilted rose (*Rosa damascena* or *Rosa rugosa*) petals

3 cups almond or soybean base oil

3–4 tablespoons beeswax (depending on how firm you want the salve to be)

2 drops lavender essential oil (optional)

2 drops Roman chamomile essential oil (optional)

2,000 IU vitamin E oil

EQUIPMENT: *2-quart saucepan or double boiler, stirring utensil, candy or yogurt thermometer, strainer, fine filter, funnel, glass or plastic storage container (for the infused oil), glass or plastic jars or tins (for the salve)*

PREP TIME: *4 hours to infuse the oil, plus 20 minutes to make the salve and 30 minutes for it to thicken*

YIELD: *Approximately 2½ cups of infused oil and 1¼ cups of salve*

STORAGE: *Store at room temperature, away from heat and light; use within 1 year*

APPLICATION: *As desired*

PREPARING THE INFUSED OIL:

Combine the chamomile, lavender, and rose flowers with the base oil in a 2-quart saucepan or double boiler and stir thoroughly to blend. The mixture should look like a thick floral slurry. Bring the mixture to just shy of a simmer, between 125° and 135°F. Do not let the oil actually simmer — it will degrade the quality of your infused oil. *Do not* put the lid on the pot.

Allow the herbs to macerate in the oil over low heat for 4 hours. Check the temperature every 30 minutes or so using a thermometer and adjust the heat accordingly. If you're using a double boiler, add more water to the bottom pot as necessary, so it doesn't dry out. Stir the infusing mixture at least every 30 minutes or so, as the herb bits tend to settle to the bottom.

After 4 hours, remove the pan from the heat and allow to cool for 15 minutes. While the oil is still warm, carefully strain it through a fine-mesh strainer lined with a fine filter such as muslin or, preferably, a paper coffee filter, then strain again if necessary to remove all debris. Squeeze the flowers to extract as much of the precious oil as possible. Discard the marc.

Add the vitamin E oil and stir to blend. This infused oil blend will be golden-green in color.

Pour the finished oil into a storage container, then cap, label, and store in a dark cabinet.

PREPARING THE SALVE: Combine 1 cup of the herbal infused oil with the beeswax in a small saucepan or a double boiler, and warm over low heat until the beeswax is just melted. Remove from the heat and allow to cool for 5 minutes, stirring a few times. Add the lavender and Roman chamomile essential oils, if using, and stir thoroughly again. Pour into storage containers, cap, and label. Allow 30 minutes to set up and harden.

APPLICATION INSTRUCTIONS: Gently massage a dab of salve into the chest and back, around the ears, under the nose, and on the throat. Can be applied at any time of day to induce a sense of serenity.

Bonus Older children, teens, and adults benefit from this formula's mentally and physically soothing properties as well. It can be safely rubbed into bellies and breasts during and after pregnancy to help prevent stretch marks, or used to soften elbows, knees, and rough feet. It makes a nice lip salve, too.

HERBAL HEAD LICE TREATMENT

Head lice (Pediculosis capitis) are tiny, brownish-gray insects that thrive on the human scalp. They're about the size of a pinhead, visible to the naked eye though hard to see in darker hair. The females lay their cream-colored eggs or nits — *which look like dandruff — close to the scalp, firmly attached to hair strands (the eggs are harder to see in blond hair). An infestation of head lice does not denote poor hygiene; these insects jump from one clean or dirty head to another, especially in crowded places such as schools and dormitories, and they are easily transmitted by shared brushes, hats, and other personal items.*

If your child's head is itchy, suspect lice — most children don't develop dandruff. This formula will help eliminate lice and their hatching nits and is a natural alternative to the standard commercially available, chemical-based lice treatments, which can be quite irritating to the skin.

Note: This formula is intended for children over 6 years of age. Some children may be sensitive to an essential oil blend as concentrated as this one, so follow the application instructions to the letter.

10 drops eucalyptus (species *radiata*) essential oil

10 drops juniper or cedarwood essential oil

5 drops geranium essential oil

5 drops rosemary (chemotype *verbenon*) essential oil

2 drops lemon essential oil

¼ cup soybean or extra-virgin, unrefined coconut base oil

EQUIPMENT: *2-ounce glass bottle, small saucepan (if using coconut oil)*
PREP TIME: *15 minutes, plus 12 hours for patch test*
YIELD: *1 treatment*
STORAGE: *Do not store; mix as needed*
APPLICATION: *Every other day for 1 week*

Put the eucalyptus, juniper, geranium, rosemary, and lemon essential oils drop by drop directly into a 2-ounce glass bottle. Add the base oil. (If you choose coconut oil and it is solid, warm it over very low heat in a tiny saucepan until it is liquefied.) Screw the top on the bottle and shake vigorously for 2 minutes to blend.

Since this is a rather potent essential oil blend, *always do a patch test* before using this formulation on your child or yourself. Place 20 drops of the formula directly on the back of the neck at the base of the scalp, and rub it into the skin. Leave for 12 hours. If no stinging, itching, or redness results, proceed with treatment. A little tingling is to be expected when the oil is first applied; this is normal.

APPLICATION INSTRUCTIONS: Shake well before using. Drape a towel over the child's shoulders to catch any oil that might run down the neck. With the child's eyes closed, gently massage the entire amount of oil into the scalp and down the length of the hair, taking care to avoid the face and eyes. Be thorough and saturate the entire head. To keep the vapors from irritating the child's eyes, immediately cover the head with a shower cap or plastic bag, then wrap with a towel. *If at any time the child complains of his or her scalp stinging or itching unbearably, immediately shampoo to remove the formula.*

Allow the formula to remain on the head for 1 to 2 hours, with the cap and towel in place. Then, using a fine-toothed comb, starting with and moving up from the bottom inch of hair, comb the hair for 10 minutes. Wipe the comb frequently with a clean paper towel to remove nits and lice. Dispose of the paper towel in the trash.

Following the treatment, apply a natural, chemical-free shampoo directly to the oily hair and scalp, without wetting them first. Then wet the head and work up a lather. This seems to be the best way to break up the oil on the scalp.

Rinse with water to which you've added a few drops of lavender, rosemary (chemotype *verbenon*), or tea tree essential oil to maintain the insect repellent properties of the treatment. Shampoo again, if necessary. Follow with a conditioner, if desired. Repeat the treatment every other day for 1 week (three treatments total), making a fresh batch each time.

Lice-Deterrent Shampoo and Conditioner

Rosemary leaves and lavender buds have been used globally for thousands of years in hair-care preparations to discourage lice and other crawlies from taking up residence in the hair and scalp. Both of these herbs are well-established insect repellents, and they have cleansing, antiseptic, vulnerary, and skin regenerative properties as well.

Today, an easy way to take advantage of the lice-repelling benefits of these common herbs is to add 4 drops of lavender essential oil and 4 drops of rosemary (chemotype *verbenon*) essential oil to 8 ounces of a chemical-free shampoo, and to add the same amount to 8 ounces of a natural conditioner. This results in mild formulas that can be safely used daily by children of all ages with nary a worry of irritation. These essential oils add a pleasant, uplifting, refreshing fragrance to hair-care products that most children will enjoy.

BREATHE EASY BALM

If your child is suffering from a cold, the flu, or allergies, this is a most comforting, super-mild remedy that helps open blocked respiratory channels and ease breathing. The vapors are not so strong as to assault the nose as a mentholated rub or balm might, so no worries if you want to use this balm on your infant. If you decide to add the eucalyptus essential oil to the formula (and I hope you do), be sure to get the exact type specified, *as it is completely child-safe and significantly potentiates the antiviral and antibacterial capacity of the formula — plus the aroma really promotes clearing of mucous-clogged sinuses.*

½ cup dried or 1 cup freshly wilted peppermint leaves (see page 38 for information on wilting)

½ cup dried or 1 cup freshly wilted rosemary leaves

½ cup dried or 1 cup freshly wilted thyme leaves

3 cups extra-virgin olive base oil

3–4 tablespoons beeswax (depending on how firm you want the balm to be)

8 drops eucalyptus (species *radiata*) essential oil (optional)

2,000 IU vitamin E oil

EQUIPMENT: *2-quart saucepan or double boiler and candy or yogurt thermometer (for stovetop method), 1-quart canning jar (for solar infusion method), stirring utensil, fine strainer, fine filter, funnel, glass or plastic storage container and plastic wrap (for the infused oil), glass or plastic jars or tins (for the balm)*

PREP TIME: *4 hours (stovetop method) or 1 month (solar infusion method) to make the infused oil; 20 minutes to make the balm, plus 30 minutes for it to thicken*

YIELD: *Approximately 2½ cups of infused oil and 1¼ cups of balm*

STORAGE: *Store at room temperature, away from heat and light; use within 1 year*

APPLICATION: *As desired*

STOVETOP METHOD: If using wilted herbs, strip the leaves from the stems, discarding the stems, and then cut or tear the leaves into pieces to expose more surface area to the oil. Combine the peppermint, rosemary, and thyme with the olive base oil in a 2-quart saucepan or double boiler and stir thoroughly to blend. The mixture should look like a minced, leafy green soup. Bring the mixture to just shy of a simmer, between 125° and 135°F. Do not let the oil actually simmer — it will degrade the quality of your infused oil. *Do not* put the lid on the pot.

Allow the herbs to macerate in the oil over low heat for 4 hours. Check the temperature every 30 minutes or so and adjust the heat accordingly. If you're using a double boiler, add more water to the bottom pot as necessary. Stir the infusing mixture at least every

30 minutes or so, as the herb bits tend to settle to the bottom.

After 4 hours, remove the pan from the heat and cool for 15 minutes. While the oil is still warm, carefully strain it through a fine-mesh strainer lined with a fine filter such as muslin or, preferably, a paper coffee filter, then strain again if necessary to remove all debris. Squeeze the herbs to extract as much oil as possible. Discard the marc.

Add the vitamin E oil and stir to blend. This infused oil blend will be medium to dark green in color. Pour the finished oil into the storage container, cap, label, and store in a dark cabinet.

SOLAR-INFUSION METHOD: If you're using the wilted herbs, strip the leaves from the stems, discarding the stems, and then cut or tear the herbs into pieces to expose more surface area to the oil. Place the peppermint, rosemary, and thyme in the canning jar. Drizzle the base oil over the plant matter to within 1 inch of the top of the jar. You may need more or less oil depending on whether you used dried or wilted herbs. The dried herbs may pack in the bottom and the wilted herb matter will settle with the weight of the oil, so don't worry if it looks as though you don't have enough. Gently stir to remove air bubbles and make sure that all the plant matter is submerged.

Place a piece of plastic wrap over the mouth of the jar (to prevent the metal lid from coming into contact with the herbs) and tightly screw on the lid. Shake the jar several times to blend thoroughly. Place the jar in a warm, sunny location such as a south-facing windowsill, and allow the herb to infuse for 1 month. Shake the jar every day for 30 seconds or so.

After 1 month, carefully strain the oil through a fine-mesh strainer lined with a fine filter such as muslin or, preferably, a paper coffee filter, then strain again if necessary to remove all herb debris. Squeeze the herbs to extract as much of the precious oil as possible. Discard the marc. Add the vitamin E oil, stir to blend. The infused oil blend will be medium to dark green in color.

Pour the finished oil into a storage container, cap, label, and store in a dark cabinet.

PREPARING THE BALM: Combine 1 cup of the herbal infused oil with the beeswax in a small saucepan or double boiler, and warm over low heat until the beeswax is just melted. Remove from the heat and allow to cool for 5 minutes, stirring a few times. Add the essential oil, if desired. Stir again to blend. Pour into storage containers, cap, label, and set aside for 30 minutes to thicken.

APPLICATION INSTRUCTIONS: Apply a dab of the balm to the chest, back, and neck and under the nose as needed to encourage easier breathing. Cover the area (except the nose!) with a warm blanket or soft clothing.

MYRRH AND LAVENDER BOO-BOO CLEANSING WASH

This formula is a pleasantly aromatic, amber-colored liniment that I use in diluted form as an antiseptic, anti-inflammatory, and vulnerary wound wash to aid in the removal of debris and dirt from fresh wounds. It also helps dry the oozing of blisters and weeping rashes and aids in healing bug bites and stings.

Note: This formula will sting raw flesh and open wounds when used full-strength; it might sting a child's tender skin even when diluted.

2 cups dried or 2½ cups freshly wilted lavender buds (see page 38 for information on wilting)

½ cup myrrh gum powder

1 teaspoon vegetable glycerin

3–4 cups unflavored vodka

EQUIPMENT: *1-quart canning jar, plastic wrap, fine-mesh strainer, fine filter, funnel, glass or plastic storage containers*
PREP TIME: *10 minutes, plus 4 weeks for extraction*
YIELD: *Approximately 2½ cups*
STORAGE: *Store at room temperature, away from heat and light; use within 2 years*
APPLICATION: *As needed*

If you're using freshly wilted lavender, first strip the buds and bits of greenery from the stems; discard the stems. (Feel free to add the bits of greenery to the jar.) Place the lavender and myrrh with the glycerin in a 1-quart canning jar and pour the vodka over them, so that it comes to within ½ inch of the top of the jar. The herbs should be completely covered. Place a piece of plastic wrap over the mouth of the jar (to prevent the metal lid from coming into contact with the jar's contents), then screw on the lid. Shake the mixture vigorously for about 30 seconds. After 24 hours, top up with more vodka if necessary. The herbs will settle a bit in the jar, but that's okay.

Store the jar in a cool, dark place for 4 weeks so that the vodka can extract the valuable chemical components from the herbs. Because this liniment contains powdered myrrh, it must be shaken vigorously at least twice a day during the 4-week period in order to loosen and integrate the paste that tends to form at the bottom of the jar.

At the end of the 4 weeks, strain the herbs through a fine-mesh strainer lined with a fine filter such as muslin or, preferably, a paper coffee filter, then strain again if necessary to remove all herb debris. Press or squeeze the herbs to release all the valuable herbal extract. Discard the marc.

Pour the liquid into storage containers, then cap, label, and store in a dark cabinet. APPLICATION INSTRUCTIONS: Shake well before each use. Prepare a dilution of the liniment, using 4 teaspoons for every ½ cup purified water, then pour over the wound to remove dirt and debris. Repeat as necessary until the wound is clean. Pat dry or allow to air-dry, then apply an antiseptic salve or balm, such as Wound Magic Salve (page 202) or use Boo-Boo Rescue Drops (page 117).

Bonus Used full-strength, this is a highly effective facial astringent for very oily skin and a blemish spot treatment.

They presented unto Him gifts; gold, and frankincense, and myrrh.

— MATTHEW 2:11

SMOOTH-AS-A-BABY'S-BOTTOM "QUICKIE SALVE"

Diaper rash is irritating, itchy, and red, resulting in an uncomfortable, whining baby. This ever-so-quick-and-simple recipe can be made in a snap and travels well in the diaper bag. Used at every diaper change, it acts as a moisture barrier on the skin and serves as an excellent preventive, plus it helps heal and relieve the irritation of existing diaper rash. It smells pleasant, has a pale orange sherbet color, and is naturally calming.

If your child is prone to diaper rash, make sure your diet (if you're breastfeeding) and the baby's diet is not overly acidic or full of grain. In some children, the consumption of excessive citrus juices, dairy, and meats can cause their delicate skin to become red and rashy. And children under 2 years of age often have difficulty digesting grain and cow's milk, which can result in gas, diarrhea, and an irritating mucous discharge.

Note: This recipe can easily be doubled or tripled for a larger batch.

½ cup organic, all-vegetable shortening, at room temperature

3 drops calendula essential oil

3 drops lavender essential oil

3 drops sweet orange essential oil

EQUIPMENT: *Medium bowl, spoon or spatula, plastic or glass jar or tin*
PREP TIME: *15 minutes*
YIELD: *½ cup*
STORAGE: *Use within 6 months if stored at room temperature; within 1 year if refrigerated*
APPLICATION: *At each diaper change*

Combine the shortening with the calendula, lavender, and sweet orange essential oils in a medium bowl. Whip ingredients for 2 minutes, until thoroughly combined. Spoon into a storage container, then cap, label, and store.

APPLICATION INSTRUCTIONS: At every diaper change, thoroughly clean baby's bum, pat dry, then massage ½ teaspoon or so of the salve over the entire bottom area. Follow with a sprinkling of powder, if desired — but not so much as to make a sticky paste on the skin.

Bonus This soothing salve can be applied to the usual assortment of minor childhood scrapes and abrasions, plus it's fabulous for dry, cracked hands and feet.

BOO-BOO RESCUE DROPS

This is a gentle-on-the-skin, tough-on-germs remedy for those everyday minor cuts, scrapes, and bruises. The essential oils deliver effective anti-inflammatory, antiseptic, and vulnerary properties in an easy-to-make formulation that speeds healing to damaged tissue. It's completely child-safe, even for infants.

4 drops lavender or tea tree essential oil

2 drops myrrh essential oil

2 drops palmarosa essential oil

4 tablespoons extra-virgin olive base oil

EQUIPMENT: *Dropper, dark glass bottle with dropper top or screw cap*

PREP TIME: *15 minutes, plus 24 hours to synergize*

YIELD: *¼ cup*

STORAGE: *Store at room temperature, away from heat and light; use within 1 year*

APPLICATION: *2 or 3 times per day*

Add the lavender, myrrh, and palmarosa essential oils drop by drop directly into a storage bottle. Add the olive base oil. Screw the top on the bottle and shake vigorously for 2 minutes to blend. Label the bottle and place in a dark location that's between 60° and 80°F for 24 hours so that the oils can synergize.

APPLICATION INSTRUCTIONS: Shake well before each use. For cuts and scrapes, clean the affected area of all dirt and debris using a gentle soap, your favorite natural liquid disinfectant, or Myrrh and Lavender Boo-Boo Cleansing Wash (page 114). Pat dry or allow to air-dry, then apply a few drops, enough to cover the wound, and gently massage or tap with your finger into the skin. Cover with a sterile bandage, if desired.

For skin that has just been banged up and will probably form a bruise, apply a cold compress for 5 minutes, remove it for 5 minutes, then repeat the process twice more. Next, gently massage a few drops into the damaged area to calm inflammation and help prevent discoloration. Apply the oil up to three times per day for several days, until the bruise shows significant improvement.

COLD AND FLU SYMPTOMS

You know when a dreaded cold is coming on . . . your throat and voice feel a bit scratchy, your nose begins to run, your eyes resemble those of a frog, your energy dips, you get the chills, and in general you feel like a blob. Compound these symptoms with muscle aches, joint stiffness, occasional nausea, and fever, and you've got the flu. According to my wise grandmother, influenza used to be called "bone fever" because you ache right down to your marrow and it hurts for someone just to touch you.

When you want relief from your misery, instead of reaching for some chemical-filled pill or ill-tasting syrupy medicine that will just leave your brain feeling clogged, why not rely on the following four remedies, with their analgesic, antibacterial, antiviral, and respiratory-soothing properties? They're guaranteed to help ease symptoms and bring comfort so you feel better soon. Combine these treatments with more-than-ample bed rest, hot organic chicken or vegetable-garlic-onion soup, lots of herb tea, and hot baths with purifying herbal oils, and you've got the recipe for healing!

It's important that you be proactive, and I strongly suggest that you make all four of these remedies before cold and flu season arrives so you'll be armed and ready for defensive health maneuvers and a speedy recovery if the season's nasties do take hold.

RAVEN'S WINGS FOOT BALM

A foot balm to help relieve cold and flu symptoms? Yes, indeed! The soles of the feet are full of sweat glands and have an amazing ability to absorb the healing properties of herbs. This is one of my ultra-favorite remedies when I'm suffering from a bad cold or feel like the flu is trying to take hold. It's chock-full of antiviral, antiseptic, and respiratory-channel-clearing properties — in short, it will help your symptoms fly away on raven's wings. This formula can also be used as a cold and flu preventative, as it fortifies resistance and general immunity and keeps microbes at bay, so you might want to use it daily prior to cold and flu season.

Note: This is an aromatherapeutically concentrated formula, so use only in the pea-size portion as directed below. *Do not* slather it all over your body.

4 tablespoons refined shea butter (unrefined shea butter will work, but its stronger fragrance will often mask the aroma of the essential oils)

15 drops eucalyptus (species *radiata*) essential oil

10 drops cajeput essential oil

10 drops ravensara essential oil

10 drops rosemary (chemotype *verbenon*) essential oil

5 drops peppermint essential oil

2 drops cinnamon essential oil

2 drops clove essential oil

EQUIPMENT: *Stirring utensil, plastic or glass jar or tin*
PREP TIME: *15 minutes, plus up to 24 hours to completely thicken*
YIELD: *Approximately ¼ cup*
STORAGE: *Store at room temperature, away from heat and light; use within 1 year*
APPLICATION: *2 times per day*

Warm the shea butter in a small saucepan (a ¾-quart size works great) or double boiler over low heat, until it has just melted. Remove from the heat. Add the eucalyptus, cajeput, ravensara, rosemary, peppermint, cinnamon, and clove essential oils directly to your storage container, then slowly pour in the liquefied shea butter. Gently stir the balm to blend. Cap and label the container, and set it aside until the balm has thickened. Unlike beeswax, shea butter takes a long time to completely thicken, and this formula may need up to 24 hours, depending on the temperature in your kitchen. When it's ready, it will be very thick, semi-hard, and white (or creamy yellow if you've used unrefined shea butter).

APPLICATION INSTRUCTIONS: Massage a small dab into the sole of each foot and between the toes, twice per day. Put on socks immediately after. I also sometimes massage a bit of balm into my chest, as I find that the scent and healing properties really relieve sinus and lung congestion.

Bonus Helps heal cuts, scrapes, boils, insect bites, bedsores and skin ulcers, blisters, and any minor to moderate infection. Plus it smells wonderful!

WINTER DEFENSE BODY OIL

Traditional healers around the globe have used sage for centuries. With sage growing in your garden, you have an elixir of good health right outside your door. Their soft, gray-green leaves will be at the ready for making this potent, aromatically earthy, warming infused oil.

When massaged into the skin from head to toe on a daily basis, sage-infused oil aids in strengthening the body's immune system, supporting its defenses against outside invasion of the three main sources of disease: bacteria, viruses, and fungi. The oil conditions the skin, too, keeping it soft, elastic, and healthy.

I can hear you thinking, "If I put sage oil on my skin, won't I smell like Thanksgiving stuffing?" No worries. The fragrance may be rather potent in the bottle, but it becomes quite subtle upon application.

Note: I prefer to use the stovetop method of extraction for this formula, as I feel that the resinous sage leaves release their best medicinal properties and strongest aroma when processed in this manner.

1½ cup dried or 3 cups freshly wilted sage leaves (see page 38 for information on wilting)

3 cups extra-virgin olive, soybean, or almond base oil (use almond or soybean oil if you want a lighter fragrance and texture)

2,000 IU vitamin E oil

EQUIPMENT: *2-quart saucepan or double boiler, stirring utensil, candy or yogurt thermometer, strainer, fine filter, funnel, plastic or glass storage containers*
PREP TIME: *4 hours*
YIELD: *Approximately 2½ cups*
STORAGE: *Store at room temperature, away from heat and light; use within 1 year*
APPLICATION: *Once daily*

If you're using freshly wilted sage leaves, first cut or tear the slightly leathery leaves into small pieces to expose more surface area to the oil. Combine the leaves and base oil in a 2-quart saucepan or double boiler and stir thoroughly to blend. The mixture should look like a thick, pale green herbal soup. Bring the mixture to just shy of a simmer, between 125° and 135°F. Do not let the oil actually simmer — it will degrade the quality of your infused oil. *Do not* put the lid on the pot.

Allow the herb to macerate in the oil over low heat for 4 hours. Check the temperature every 30 minutes or so with a thermometer and adjust the heat accordingly. If you're using a double boiler, add more water to the bottom pot as necessary, so it doesn't dry out. Stir the infusing mixture at least every 30 minutes or so, as the herb bits tend to settle to the bottom.

After 4 hours, remove the pan from the heat and allow to cool for 15 minutes. While the oil is still warm, carefully strain it through a fine-mesh strainer lined with a fine filter such as muslin or, preferably, a paper coffee filter, then strain again if necessary to remove all debris. Squeeze the herbs to extract as much of the precious oil as possible. Discard the marc.

Add the vitamin E oil and stir to blend. The resulting infused oil blend will be a rich medium to dark green in color, depending on which base oil you chose. Pour the finished oil into storage containers, then cap, label, and store in a dark cabinet.

APPLICATION INSTRUCTIONS: For maximum benefit, massage this infused oil into slightly damp, warm skin — fresh from the shower or bath. Apply daily for at least a month prior to cold and flu season, and continue to use it throughout the winter.

Bonus Sage oil makes a terrific diaper rash preventive and is wonderful added to salves and balms to help heal minor skin afflictions, respiratory infections, and dry, rough skin on the feet, elbows, and knees.

Why should a man die when sage grows in his garden?

— POPULAR MEDIEVAL SAYING

THE ANCIENT SECRET

A potent antiviral, antibacterial cold and flu preventive called the "Thieves Formula" has been bandied about by herbalists for centuries. Its herbal ingredients change a bit, as does the menstruum, depending on who is concocting it and whether it's intended for topical application or oral intake. Some herbalists like to brew it in vinegar, some in ethyl alcohol, and some in oil. This particular formula uses vodka. The original Thieves Formula, as written in older herb texts, included highly protective essential oils and herbs said to have been used by thieves (orally, topically, and as inhalants) during the bubonic plague or "Black Death" of the Middle Ages to avoid contracting infection. Supposedly, even though nearly the entire population was dying of the plague, the thieves who stole valuables from the dead and dying never got sick.

Use this strongly aromatic remedy before, during, and after cold and flu season as a protective agent and a topical healing liniment spray if you do succumb. The benefit is derived via inhalation of the herbal properties as well as absorption into your bloodstream through your pores.

Note: This formula will sting raw skin or open wounds.

- ¼ cup dried or ½ cup freshly wilted lemon balm leaves (see page 38 for information on wilting)
- ¼ cup dried or ½ cup freshly wilted lavender buds
- ¼ cup dried or ½ cup freshly wilted peppermint leaves
- ¼ cup dried or ½ cup freshly wilted rosemary leaves
- ¼ cup dried or ½ cup freshly wilted sage leaves
- ¼ cup dried or ½ cup freshly wilted thyme leaves
- ¼ cup dried or ½ cup freshly wilted yarrow flowers and leaves
- 2 cinnamon sticks, crumbled, or 1 teaspoon ground cinnamon
- 2 tablespoons minced fresh lemon peel
- 1 tablespoon cloves, crushed, or 1 teaspoon ground cloves
- 15 drops eucalyptus (species *radiata*) essential oil
- 5 drops clove essential oil
- 1 teaspoon vegetable glycerin
- 3–4 cups unflavored vodka

EQUIPMENT: *1-quart canning jar, plastic wrap, fine-mesh strainer, fine filter, funnel, glass or plastic spritzer bottles*
PREP TIME: *10 minutes, plus 4 weeks for extraction*
YIELD: *Approximately 2½ cups*
STORAGE: *Store at room temperature, away from heat and light; use within 2 years*
APPLICATION: *2 or 3 times per day*

If you are using any freshly wilted herbs, strip the leaves, buds, and flowers off and discard the stems. Cut, tear, or gently mash the herbs using a mortar and pestle to expose more surface area. Place the lemon balm, lavender, peppermint, rosemary, sage, thyme, yarrow, cinnamon, lemon peel, and cloves in a 1-quart canning jar. Add the eucalyptus and clove essential oils, along with the glycerin. Pour the vodka to within ½ inch of the top of the jar. The herbs should be completely covered.

Place a piece of plastic wrap over the mouth of the jar (to prevent the metal lid from coming into contact with the jar's contents), then screw on the lid. Shake the mixture for about 30 seconds. After 24 hours, top up with more vodka if necessary. The herbs will settle a bit in the jar, but that's okay.

Store the jar in a cool, dark place for 4 weeks so that the vodka can extract the valuable chemical components from the herbs. Shake the jar at least once a day for 30 seconds, and two or three times per day if you've included cinnamon and clove powders, as they will settle into a paste.

At the end of the 4 weeks, strain the herbs through a fine-mesh strainer lined with a fine filter such as muslin or, preferably, a paper coffee filter, then strain again if necessary to remove all herb debris. Press or squeeze the herbs to release all the valuable herbal extract. Discard the marc. Pour the liquid into spritzer bottles, then cap, label, and store in a dark cabinet.

APPLICATION INSTRUCTIONS: Shake well before each use. Spray the formula onto your hands, then rub the liquid onto your throat, the back of your neck, your chest, your ears, and your temples. Do this two or three times daily. Massage the formula into your feet prior to bed and again before getting dressed in the morning. The aromatic medicinal properties extracted from the herbs will penetrate your nasal passages as well as the thousands of pores in your skin and feet and be absorbed into your bloodstream.

I recommend keeping a small spritzer bottle of this formula handy during the height of cold and flu season, so you can sanitize your hands frequently throughout the day.

Bonus Keep a bottle by the sink to spray on hands to eliminate the lingering odor of garlic, onions, or fish; it also acts as a hand sanitizer. Applied by the drop to fingernails and toenails, it will help get rid of fungus, and it can be used as a spot treatment for acne blemishes and other minor skin ailments.

SURROUND ME IN COMFORT: WARMING BATH OIL

Feeling all stuffed up? Got the chills, aches, pains, and general misery of a cold or flu? Then a detoxifying sweat session with this bath oil is just the thing you need to ease your symptoms, open your sinuses, warm your core, and relax your entire body so that you can sleep soundly and get the healing rest you so desperately need. Ginger, thyme, lavender, palmarosa, and pine essential oils deliver antiseptic and antiviral properties, stimulate sluggish circulation, induce perspiration, relieve muscle tension and aching joints, and even relieve headaches due to congestion.

Note: *Do not* partake of this heating therapy if you are running a fever, sweating, or are extremely weak and debilitated, as it will exacerbate your symptoms.

20 drops ginger essential oil

15 drops palmarosa essential oil

15 drops thyme (chemotype *linalool*) essential oil

15 drops Scotch pine essential oil

10 drops lavender essential oil

1 cup jojoba base oil

EQUIPMENT: *Dropper, dark glass bottle with dropper top or screw cap*
PREP TIME: *15 minutes, plus 24 hours to synergize*
YIELD: *Approximately 1 cup*
STORAGE: *Store at room temperature, away from heat and light; use within 2 years*
APPLICATION: *1 or 2 times per day*

Add the ginger, palmarosa, thyme, Scotch pine, and lavender essential oils drop by drop directly into a storage bottle. Add the jojoba base oil. Cap the bottle and shake vigorously for 2 minutes. Label the bottle and place in a dark location that's between 60° and 80°F for 24 hours so that the oils can synergize.

APPLICATION INSTRUCTIONS: This healing, detoxification process can be performed in the morning, if you are staying home for the day, and also at night before retiring. Turn up the heat or stoke the woodstove and make a mug of fresh ginger, cinnamon spice, or decaf chai tea, or just plain hot water with lemon juice. Run a hot bath, with the door closed.

When the tub is nearly full, add 1 to 2 tablespoons of bath oil under running water and swish to blend. Ease into the soothing bath and lie back for about 20 minutes while you sip your tea. Sweating helps release toxins from your pores.

Following your soak, gently pat yourself dry, and apply Winter Defense Body Oil (page 120) to your entire body and Raven's Wings Foot Balm (page 119) to the soles of your feet. Put on pajamas and socks, and climb under the covers. Do this once or twice daily for a few days, until you are well.

COLD HANDS AND FEET

My husband, Bill, informs me that when we exchanged our wedding vows, the "worse" part of "for better or for worse" did not include the nightly placement of my insanely cold hands and feet on his toasty belly and back! What can I say . . . we live in northern New England, and my extremities frequently get chilled. Bill is a big Marine of Greek extraction, thus extra burly and hot-natured, so why not take advantage of a nearby heat source? Right, ladies?

Are you in good or at least reasonably good health, but you still have chronically cold hands and feet, despite wearing shoes and socks all the time, plus gloves in the wintertime? Women, more often than men, complain of this annoying, sometimes painful problem, primarily due to their thinner skin, lower percentage of muscle mass, and slower metabolism. The extremities are the last place to receive blood flow, so anything you can do to improve the situation, the better. Here are some tips for encouraging better circulation:

- Make sure you get regular cardiovascular and muscle-toning exercise.
- Sunshine warms your very core, so try to absorb a little every day.
- Add to your diet heating herbs and spices that stimulate digestion and circulation, such as black pepper, cayenne, cinnamon, cloves, cumin, curry, ginger, horseradish, jalapenos, oregano, rosemary, savory, thyme, and turmeric.
- Discontinue iced drinks and avoid too many cold foods.
- Add warm, spiced soups and hot teas to your regular dietary intake.
- Forgo tight shoes, as they constrict blood flow to your feet. Go barefoot, wear loose sandals, or simply wear socks as often as possible.

All of these simple steps will help deliver warmth and welcome comfort to your icy toes and fingertips, as will the following warming remedies. I love these two formulas — they feel so good and condition your skin as well.

Herbal Spice Warming Hand and Foot Massage Oil

This remedy contains three of the most warming spices in the herb world: ginger, cayenne, and cloves. They definitely deliver heat and circulatory-stimulating benefits to cold hands and feet.

Note: I prefer to use the stovetop method of extraction for this formula, as I feel that these particular herbs release their best medicinal properties when processed in this manner.

1½ cups fresh ginger, finely chopped, sliced, or grated

1 tablespoon crushed cloves

1 teaspoon ground cayenne

2 cups sesame base oil

2,000 IU vitamin E oil

EQUIPMENT: *2-quart saucepan or double boiler, stirring utensil, candy or yogurt thermometer, strainer or, fine filter, funnel, glass or plastic storage container*
PREP TIME: *6 hours*
YIELD: *Approximately 1¾ cups*
STORAGE: *Store at room temperature, away from heat and light; use within 1 year*
APPLICATION: *As desired; may stain light-colored clothing*

Combine the ginger, cloves, and cayenne with the sesame base oil in a 2-quart saucepan or double boiler and stir thoroughly to blend. The mixture should look like a thick, cloudy, reddish orange slurry. Bring the mixture to just shy of a simmer, between 125° and 135°F. Do not let the oil actually simmer — it will degrade the quality of your infused oil. *Do not* put the lid on the pot.

Allow the herbs to macerate in the oil over low heat for 6 hours. Check the temperature every 30 minutes or so with a thermometer and adjust the heat accordingly. If you're using a double boiler, add more water to the bottom pot as necessary, so it doesn't dry out. Stir the infusing mixture at least every 30 minutes or so, as the herbs tend to settle to the bottom.

After 6 hours, remove the pan from the heat and allow to cool for 15 minutes. While the oil is still warm, carefully strain it through a fine-mesh strainer lined with a fine filter such as muslin or, preferably, a paper coffee filter, then strain again if necessary to remove all debris. Be sure that you have strained out all the cayenne pepper and clove particulate. Squeeze the herbs to extract as much of the precious oil as possible. Discard the marc.

Add the vitamin E oil and stir to blend. The resulting infused oil blend will be a striking reddish-orange color. Pour the finished oil into a storage container, then cap, label, and store in a dark cabinet.

APPLICATION INSTRUCTIONS: Briskly massage a small amount of this warming oil into cold feet and hands several times per day, or as desired. Wash hands after application; if treatment was for hands, I suggest donning gloves. If that's not practical, be careful not to rub your eyes or nose for approximately 30 minutes after application as the cayenne pepper residue may be irritating.

Bonus This formula makes an effective pain-easing, warming rub for stiff, cold, arthritic joints and tight muscles.

THYME TRAVEL HEATING BALM

This recipe is a solid version of the previous recipe, with the essential oils of thyme and cinnamon added. It travels well, and I frequently tuck a small jar of it into my suitcase when I will be sleeping in chilly air-conditioned hotel rooms or walking in cold temperatures for extended periods. It makes a great cold-weather hiking and camping balm.

7 tablespoons Herbal Spice Warming Hand and Foot Massage Oil (previous recipe)

1–2 tablespoons beeswax (depending on how firm you want the balm to be)

20 drops thyme (chemotype *linalool*) essential oil

5 drops cinnamon bark essential oil

EQUIPMENT: *Small saucepan, stirring utensil, glass or plastic jar or tin*

PREP TIME: *20 minutes to make the balm, plus 30 minutes for it to thicken*

YIELD: *Approximately ½ cup*

STORAGE: *Store at room temperature, away from heat and light; use within 1 year*

APPLICATION: *As desired; may stain light-colored clothing*

Warm the oil and beeswax in a small saucepan or double boiler over low heat, until the wax is just melted. Remove from the heat and allow to cool for 5 minutes, stirring a few times. Add the essential oils and stir again. Pour the mixture into a storage container, cap, and label. Allow 30 minutes to harden.

APPLICATION INSTRUCTIONS: Briskly massage a small amount of this warming balm into cold feet and hands several times per day, or as desired. Be careful not to touch your face, especially your eyes, for approximately 30 minutes after application; this formula contains potentially irritating residue from the cayenne pepper and the cinnamon and thyme essential oils.

COLD SORES AND GENITAL SORES
(Herpes Simplex)

Herpes simplex is a contagious virus affecting both men and women; it produces painful, fluid-filled blisters that manifest in and around the mouth and on the genitals. The virus can remain in a latent or inactive state for quite some time within the ganglia (masses of nerve tissues) in the infected area and periodically become reactivated and begin replicating, causing eruptions of blisters, usually in the same location as a previous infection.

A few days after a new breakout, the blisters will begin to dry, forming a thin, yellowish crust. Complete healing of the blisters takes up to 3 weeks. Eruptions may be triggered by physical or emotional stress, overexposure to sunlight, a fever, certain drugs or foods, or suppression of the immune system. Often the inciting factors are unknown.

Treating Herpes Outbreaks

As soon as you feel the familiar tingling, slightly burning sensation that signals an imminent outbreak, begin applying 1 or 2 drops of any the following remedies directly to the area two or three times per day. There is no guarantee that blisters will not form, but defensive measures are worth trying and the remedies are quite effective for many people.

To treat an existing sore, keep the infected area very clean by gently washing with mild soap and water, then thoroughly pat dry with a soft cloth or use a blow dryer turned on very low. Allowing the blisters to remain moist may worsen the inflammation and delay healing. After cleansing, apply 1 drop of any of the following remedies directly to the lesion(s). Repeat two or three times per day until the blisters are healed.

ANTIVIRAL ST. JOHN'S WORT HERPES DROPS

Used singularly, St. John's wort has effective antiviral, astringent, analgesic, nervine, anti-inflammatory, and vulnerary properties, but when combined with geranium, eucalyptus, tea tree, and spike lavender essential oils, it forms a synergized blend that offers dramatic results, bringing speedy comfort and healing to painful herpes blisters.

This recipe calls for only a small amount of St. John's wort–infused oil. If you have some already made (see the recipe on page 64), great. If not, then purchase a small bottle from your local health food store or herbal supplier. But I do recommend that you always have at least a cup of this multipurpose infused oil on hand — fresh and homemade is best, and much less expensive!

- 5 drops eucalyptus (species *radiata*) essential oil
- 5 drops tea tree essential oil
- 4 drops geranium essential oil
- 2 drops lemon balm essential oil (optional)
- 2 drops spike lavender (*Lavandula latifolia*) or lavender (*L. angustifolia*) essential oil
- 2 tablespoons St. John's wort–infused oil

EQUIPMENT: *Dropper, dark glass bottle with dropper top or screw cap*
PREP TIME: *15 minutes, plus 24 hours to synergize*
YIELD: *2 tablespoons*
STORAGE: *Store at room temperature, away from heat and light; use within 1 year*
APPLICATION: *2 or 3 times per day*

Add the eucalyptus, tea tree, geranium, lemon balm (if using), and spike lavender essential oils drop by drop directly into a storage bottle. Add the St. John's wort–infused oil. Screw the top on the bottle and shake vigorously for 2 minutes to blend. Label the bottle and place in a dark location that's between 60° and 80°F for 24 hours so that the oils can synergize.

APPLICATION INSTRUCTIONS: Shake well before using. Apply following the instructions in Treating Herpes Outbreaks (page 129).

Bonus A twice-daily application of this oil (with or without the lemon balm essential oil), helps mend damaged skin tissue and prevent potential infection resulting from minor-to-moderate cuts and scrapes, plus it delivers speedy healing and comfort to bruised skin.

LEMON-AID HERPES DROPS

I offer this high-strength formula for those of you who want to try lemon balm essential oil as your main antiviral agent. It's a soothing, skin-conditioning, ultra-healing blend with a quite pleasant earthy, lemony aroma.

15 drops lemon balm
    essential oil

5 drops myrrh essential oil

2 tablespoons calophyllum
   base oil

EQUIPMENT: *Dropper, dark glass bottle with dropper top or screw cap*
PREP TIME: *15 minutes, plus 24 hours to synergize*
YIELD: *2 tablespoons*
STORAGE: *Store at room temperature, away from heat and light; use within 1 year*
APPLICATION: *2 or 3 times per day*

Add the lemon balm and myrrh essential oils drop by drop directly into a storage bottle. Add the calophyllum base oil. Screw the top on the bottle and shake vigorously for 2 minutes to blend. Label the bottle and place in a dark location that's between 60° and 80°F for 24 hours so that the oils can synergize.

APPLICATION INSTRUCTIONS: Shake well before using. Apply following the instructions in Treating Herpes Outbreaks (page 129).

Lemon Balm Essential Oil — Worth Its Weight in Gold

Powerful yet very gentle, lemon balm or melissa essential oil is one of the most potent antiviral agents available in aromatherapy, with its specialty being that it aids in the rapid drying and healing of herpes blisters (including shingles or herpes zoster). It is extremely expensive, but if you tend to have recurrent breakouts and want to avoid pharmaceutical drugs, you might find it highly effective. It has the added aromatherapeutic benefit of deeply soothing your nerves and uplifting your psyche.

COOLING COMFORT HERPES DROPS

*T**his herbal formula offers effective antiseptic, antiviral, circulatory stimulant, and skin-conditioning properties with a balanced energy that will feel nice and cool when applied to burning, itching herpes lesions. The aroma could be described as creamy, soft eucalyptus — it's quite pleasant, actually.*

12 drops ravensara essential oil

6 drops eucalyptus (species *radiata*) essential oil

2 tablespoons calophyllum base oil

EQUIPMENT: *Dropper, dark glass bottle with dropper top or screw cap*
PREP TIME: *15 minutes, plus 24 hours to synergize*
YIELD: *2 tablespoons*
STORAGE: *Store at room temperature, away from heat and light; use within 1 year*
APPLICATION: *2 or 3 times per day*

Add the ravensara and eucalyptus essential oils drop by drop directly into a storage bottle. Add the calophyllum base oil. Screw the top on the bottle and shake vigorously for 2 minutes to blend. Label the bottle and place in a dark location that's between 60° and 80°F for 24 hours so that the oils can synergize.

APPLICATION INSTRUCTIONS: Shake well before using. Apply following the instructions in Treating Herpes Outbreaks (page 129).

Bonus Massage a drop or two of this formula under your nose and on your temples, throat, and chest to help relieve nasal stuffiness when suffering from a cold or the flu.

CRACKED SKIN *(Severely Dry Hands and Feet)*

The skin on the palms of your hands and soles of your feet doesn't contain any sebaceous (oil) glands to aid in natural lubrication, so it is prone to dryness, especially if neglected. Plus, your hands and feet are located at the extreme ends of the body, where blood flow may not always be at its strongest. Sometimes, even in spite of relatively decent care, they become uncomfortably dry and cracked. If you suffer from diabetes, heart disease, or other circulatory disorders, live in a dry climate or an area where winters are long and indoor heat dehydrating, or suffer from chronically cold hands and feet, then you are a prime candidate for severely dry, cracked skin.

Left untreated, extremely dry skin can develop deep cracks or fissures (known as secondary skin lesions) that actually penetrate into the dermis, or second layer of skin. These cracks, which most often appear on the heels, not only are unsightly but can allow infectious bacteria to enter the skin tissue and bloodstream, making them painful and potentially injurious to your health and well-being.

For preventive measures, make sure your diet includes plenty of omega-3 fatty acids from salmon, fish oils, walnuts, flax seeds, or chia seeds, as well as ample amounts of vitamins A, B complex, C, D, and E from whole foods and lots of hydrating fluids. Many people, myself included, find that the inclusion of evening primrose oil or borage oil capsules in their daily diets greatly improves moisture retention in the skin. Regular exercise is vital to enhance circulation, so be sure to take that walk or yoga class or visit the gym several times a week.

Always wear gloves when washing the dishes, working in the garden, or exposing your hands to cold weather or chemicals such as synthetic fertilizers, disinfectants, soaps, hair dye — all of these can be very damaging to skin tissue. Applying your favorite conditioning salve or cream before donning gloves will give your hands a "spa treatment" while you work! Feet benefit from a regular slathering as well, followed by socks or hosiery.

HERBAL CRACK SALVE

This cracked-skin remedy is my go-to, velvety "skin butter" that I use for nearly everything — lips, cuticles, brittle nails, shins, rough knees and elbows, dry nose when suffering from a cold, and even the ends of my curly, dry, color-treated hair! The herbs in this formula are strong skin conditioners and vulneraries with a gentle astringency; they work like magic to help heal and prevent uncomfortable fissured skin on hands and feet. Every medicine chest should have a jar.

Note: I prefer to use the stovetop method of extraction for this formula, as I feel that these particular herbs release their best medicinal properties when processed in this manner.

½ cup dried or 1 cup freshly wilted comfrey leaves (see page 38 for information on wilting)

½ cup dried or 1 cup freshly wilted plantain leaves

½ cup dried Solomon's seal root

3 cups extra-virgin olive base oil

2,000 IU vitamin E oil

3 tablespoons beeswax

1 tablespoon cocoa butter

EQUIPMENT: *2-quart saucepan or double boiler, candy or yogurt thermometer, stirring utensil, strainer, fine filter, funnel, glass or plastic storage container (for the infused oil), glass or plastic jars or tins (for the salve)*

PREP TIME: *5 hours to make the infused oil; 20 minutes to make the salve, plus 1 hour for it to thicken*

YIELD: *Approximately 2½ cups of infused oil and 1¼ cups of salve*

STORAGE: *Store at room temperature, away from heat and light; use within 1 year*

APPLICATION: *2 times per day or as desired*

PREPARING THE HERBAL INFUSED OIL: If you're using freshly wilted herbs, gently cut or tear the leaves into small pieces to expose more surface area to the oil. Combine the comfrey, plantain, and Solomon's seal with the olive base oil in a 2-quart saucepan or double boiler and stir thoroughly. The mixture should look like a thick, chunky, green herbal soup. Bring the mixture to just shy of a simmer, between 125° and 135°F. Do not let the oil actually simmer — it will degrade the quality of your infused oil. *Do not* put the lid on the pot.

Allow the herbs to macerate in the oil over low heat for 5 hours. Check the temperature every 30 minutes or so with a thermometer and adjust the heat accordingly. If you're using a double boiler, add more water to the bottom pot as necessary, so it doesn't dry out. Stir the infusing mixture at least every 30 minutes or so, as the herb bits tend to settle to the bottom.

After 5 hours, remove the pan from the heat and allow to cool for 15 minutes. While the oil is still warm, carefully strain it through a fine-mesh strainer lined with a fine filter such as muslin or, preferably, a paper coffee filter, then strain again if necessary to remove all debris. Squeeze the herbs to extract as much of the precious oil as possible. Discard the marc.

Add the vitamin E oil and stir to blend. The resulting infused oil blend will be a lovely golden-green color. Pour the finished oil into a plastic or glass storage container, then cap, label, and store in a dark cabinet.

PREPARING THE SALVE: Combine 1 cup of the herbal infused oil with the beeswax and cocoa butter in a small saucepan or double boiler over low heat, and warm until the solids are just melted. Remove from the heat and allow to cool for 5 minutes, stirring a few times. Pour into storage containers, cap, label, and set aside for 1 hour to harden.

APPLICATION INSTRUCTIONS: Massage a dab of salve into feet or hands at least twice daily to seal in moisture.

VEGAN LANOLIN

Want a cracked-skin remedy with an incredibly creamy texture that melts at body temperature and penetrates amazingly well? Then this is the one for you. It has all the moisturizing and conditioning benefits of lanolin, without the odd smell, stickiness, and potential irritation, plus it's vegan! It acts as a mild antiseptic, anti-inflammatory, and vulnerary.

4 tablespoons castor base oil

2 tablespoons cocoa butter

2 tablespoons shea butter, refined or unrefined

10 drops calendula, myrrh, or lavender essential oil

EQUIPMENT: *Small saucepan or double boiler, stirring utensil, plastic or glass jar or tin*
PREP TIME: *30 minutes, plus 24 hours to thicken*
YIELD: *Approximately ½ cup*
STORAGE: *Store at room temperature, away from heat and light; use within 1 year*
APPLICATION: *2 times per day, or as desired*

Combine the castor oil, cocoa butter, and shea butter in a small saucepan (a ¾-quart size works great) or double boiler over low heat, and warm until the solids are just melted. Remove from the heat and allow to cool for 5 to 10 minutes. Stir a few times to blend the mixture thoroughly.

Add the essential oil directly to the storage container, then slowly pour in the oil mixture. Gently stir to blend. Cap and label the container and set it aside until the balm has thickened. Unlike beeswax, cocoa and shea butters take a long time to completely thicken, and this formula may need up to 24 hours, depending on the temperature of your kitchen. The salve may continue to change texture slightly for another 24 hours.

APPLICATION INSTRUCTIONS: Massage a dab of the balm into feet or hands at least twice daily to seal in moisture.

Bonus This formula makes a wonderful conditioner for dry, brittle nails and ragged cuticles. Simply massage a tiny bit into each nail nightly. It also can be used as a lip balm or winter-weather facial shield during extreme outdoor exposure to protect your face.

CUTS AND SCRAPES

Cuts and scrapes are a part of everyday life. These minor-to-moderate, but still uncomfortable, skin injuries primarily involve the top two layers of skin, the epidermis and the dermis, though sometimes a hint of subcutaneous tissue is damaged, especially if you suffer a sharp knife cut or puncture wound. At-home treatment is usually sufficient to treat these wounds, provided any bleeding is quickly staunched and infection is kept in check. If the skin is torn or cut to the point that it might need stitching, use common sense as to whether professional medical attention is necessary.

You may have noticed that quite a few of the herbal remedies in this book can double as treatments for cuts and scrapes. This is because many plants in the herb kingdom have antiseptic properties that are useful for keeping bacterial infections at bay. The following formulas contain potent antiseptic, anti-inflammatory, and vulnerary properties yet are gentle on the skin. They can all be used to help heal rashes and inflamed skin, insect bites and stings, bedsores and skin ulcers, boils, blisters, ingrown hairs, and general skin infections.

ALOE DISINFECTING WOUND WASH

This super-easy wound wash should be in everyone's medicine cabinet. It rinses away dirt and debris while keeping microbes at bay, speeding the healing process. This remedy can also be used as a daily disinfecting treatment while the wound is healing. Take a small bottle with you when hiking or camping for on-the-spot treatment.

Note: This formula will sting slightly when applied to raw skin.

50 drops lavender essential oil

50 drops tea tree essential oil

1 cup commercially prepared aloe vera juice

1 cup unflavored vodka

EQUIPMENT: *Dropper, plastic or glass bottle*
PREP TIME: *10 minutes, plus 24 hours to synergize*
YIELD: *Approximately 2 cups*
STORAGE: *Store at room temperature, away from heat and light; use within 6 months*
APPLICATION: *2 times per day*

Add the lavender and tea tree essential oils drop by drop directly to the storage bottle. Add the aloe vera juice and vodka. Screw the top on the bottle and shake vigorously for 2 minutes to blend. Label the bottle and place in a dark location that's between 60° and 80°F for 24 hours so that the blend can synergize.

APPLICATION INSTRUCTIONS: Shake well before each use. If possible, cleanse the cut or scrape using mild soap and water. After the debris is rinsed away, pour this cleansing liniment directly over affected area, thoroughly rinsing and soaking the injury. Pat dry, then apply Herbal Heal-All Oil (opposite page) or your favorite chemical-free, wound-healing ointment or salve. Place a sterile pad atop the injury; you can make one from cotton, several layers of flannel, or gauze — just make sure it won't stick to the wound. Fasten securely in place with medical tape. If the cut or scrape is small, you may opt not to cover it with a bandage and allow it to be exposed to the air instead, provided you keep it clean. Apply formula twice daily if desired, until the wound heals.

Bonus Use this wash as a spot treatment for acne blemishes and bug bites and stings.

HERBAL HEAL-ALL OIL

This essential oil blend, with its fresh, herbaceous, medicinal aroma, will aid in healing just about any minor to moderate skin injury. You can also rub it onto cheekbones, temples, throat, and chest to help open respiratory channels and relieve sinus pain when suffering from a cold or the flu. It's great for easing headaches and stiff joints and muscles, too. This is a good multipurpose formula!

8 drops rosemary (chemotype *verbenon*) essential oil

8 drops tea tree or niaouli essential oil

4 drops eucalyptus (species *radiata*) essential oil

4 drops peppermint essential oil

2 drops birch or wintergreen essential oil

2 drops clove essential oil

¼ cup jojoba base oil

EQUIPMENT: *Dropper, dark glass bottle with dropper top or screw cap*
PREP TIME: *15 minutes, plus 24 hours to synergize*
YIELD: *Approximately ¼ cup*
STORAGE: *Store at room temperature, away from heat and light; use within 2 years*
APPLICATION: *2 times per day*

Add the rosemary, tea tree, eucalyptus, peppermint, birch, and clove essential oils drop by drop directly into a storage bottle. Add the jojoba base oil. Screw the top on the bottle and shake vigorously for 2 minutes to blend. Label the bottle and place in a dark location that's between 60° and 80°F for 24 hours so that the oils can synergize.

APPLICATION INSTRUCTIONS: Shake well before using. Twice per day, apply a few drops of this formula to clean cuts and scrapes to discourage infection and aid in healing. Place a sterile pad atop the injury, if desired; you can make one from cotton, several layers of flannel, or gauze — just make sure it won't stick to the wound. Fasten securely in place with medical tape.

Bonus This herbal blend repels biting bugs, especially black flies and mosquitoes, and I sometimes massage a few drops into my hair line and on my neck and chest to keep them from biting my face and ears while I'm gardening. They still hover, but they don't bite as frequently.

MEND SKIN: COMFREY-INFUSED OIL

T*hough it's an invasive, 3-foot-tall, bushy plant, comfrey, with its deep green, large fuzzy leaves, should be grown in every medicinal herb garden. The incredibly soothing infused oil made from the leaves and roots can be used for a great many topical healing purposes. It contains skin-mending constituents such as allantoin, zinc, and protein, as well as tissue-tightening tannic acid, which dramatically speed the healing of damaged skin and aid in the prevention of scarring.*

Note: Comfrey leaves and roots are rather mucilaginous or gooey (especially when used freshly wilted), so I prefer to use the stovetop method as it results in a very potent, effective medicinal formula without risk of residual moisture that would encourage the growth of mold.

1	cup dried or 2 cups freshly wilted comfrey root (see page 38 for information on wilting)
1	cup dried or 1½ cups freshly wilted comfrey leaves
3	cups extra-virgin olive base oil
2,000	IU vitamin E oil
20	drops spike lavender essential oil (optional, but will enhance the antiseptic properties)

EQUIPMENT: *2-quart saucepan or double boiler, stirring utensil, candy or yogurt thermometer, strainer, fine filter, funnel, plastic or glass storage containers*
PREP TIME: *5 hours to infuse*
YIELD: *Approximately 2½ cups*
STORAGE: *Store at room temperature, away from heat and light; use within 1 year*
APPLICATION: *2 times per day*

If you're using freshly wilted comfrey leaves, cut or tear the leaves into smaller pieces to expose more surface area to the oil. If you're using freshly wilted comfrey root, grate or finely chop the root. Combine the leaves and roots with the olive base oil in a 2-quart saucepan or double boiler and stir thoroughly to blend. The mixture should look like a thick, chunky, leafy green soup. Bring the mixture to just shy of a simmer, between 125° and 135°F. Do not let the oil actually simmer — it will degrade the quality of your infused oil. *Do not* put the lid on the pot.

Allow the herbs to macerate in the oil over low heat for 5 hours. Check the temperature every 30 minutes or so with a thermometer and adjust the heat accordingly. If you're using a double boiler, add more water to the bottom pot as necessary, so it doesn't dry out. Stir the infusing mixture at least every 30 minutes or so, as the herb bits tend to settle to the bottom.

After 5 hours, remove the pan from the heat and allow to cool for 15 minutes. While the oil is still warm, carefully strain it through a fine-mesh strainer lined with a fine filter such as muslin or, preferably, a paper coffee filter, then strain again if necessary to remove all debris. Squeeze the herbs to extract as much of the precious oil as possible. Discard the marc.

Add the vitamin E oil and spike lavender essential oil, if using, and stir to blend. The resulting comfrey oil will be deep green in color. Pour the finished oil into storage containers, then cap, label, and store in a dark cabinet.

APPLICATION INSTRUCTIONS: Twice per day, apply a few drops of this infused oil to clean cuts and scrapes *that are at least a few days old* and are completely free of infection. Place a sterile pad atop each injury, if desired; you can make one from cotton, several layers of flannel, or gauze — just make sure it won't stick to the wound. Fasten securely in place with medical tape.

Warning

Use comfrey-infused oil only on wounds that have already begun to heal. Do not use on *new* wounds, as the allantoin — a potent skin cell regenerator — may stimulate the outer layer of skin tissue to regenerate too rapidly and seal the wound closed before the subsurface portion of the wound heals and drains, leading to potential infection.

Bonus This infusion, with or without the lavender essential oil, can be used alone or added to salves or balms and used as a topical massage agent to aid in mending broken bones (comfrey isn't referred to as "knitbone" for nothing), torn ligaments, severely strained muscles, and bruises. And it makes a terrific nail growth and conditioning oil if massaged into nails once or twice daily.

DANDRUFF *(Seborrheic Dermatitis)*

Dandruff is actually seborrheic dermatitis of the scalp, somewhat similar to cradle cap in an infant. It is caused by an inflammation of the upper layers of the skin, including overactive sebaceous (oil) glands, resulting in a buildup of oily skin scales that, as they are shed from the scalp, appear as telltale white flakes in the hair and on the shoulders, and occasionally the eyebrows. Mild itching often occurs as well.

The tendency to develop dandruff often runs in families, and cold weather can make the symptoms worse. Dandruff can be triggered by hormonal disturbances, faulty diet, emotional stress, a change in climate, or a fungal infection.

If you begin to see those pesky white flakes and are not sure why, start by evaluating your hair-care regimen. The overuse of styling products, heated devices (blow dryers, curling irons, and the like), and chemical procedures can cause a flaky, dry, irritated scalp that imitates dandruff conditions. If you really do have dandruff, then try this gentle remedy to help improve the situation.

Fresh and Clean Antidandruff Scalp Treatment

With any skin disease involving the sebaceous (oil) glands, especially on the scalp, I prefer to use jojoba base oil because of its chemical similarity to human sebum and the fact that it oxygenates the follicles. It has anti-inflammatory properties and penetrates extremely well. This formula helps stimulate circulation and cell renewal, cleanses the follicles, encourages hair growth, aids in balancing sebum production (so don't be afraid to use it on an oily scalp), and fights inflammation, infection, and possible odor. Plus, it conditions dry strands beautifully!

20 drops rosemary (chemotype *verbenon*) essential oil

15 drops geranium essential oil

10 drops Atlas cedar essential oil

5 drops lemon essential oil

5 drops tea tree essential oil

5 drops thyme (chemotype *linalool*) essential oil

½ cup jojoba base oil

EQUIPMENT: *Dropper, dark glass bottle with dropper top or screw cap*
PREP TIME: *15 minutes, plus 24 hours to synergize*
YIELD: *Approximately ½ cup*
STORAGE: *Store at room temperature, away from heat and light; use within 2 years*
APPLICATION: *3 times per week*

Add the rosemary, geranium, Atlas cedar, lemon, tea tree, and thyme essential oils drop by drop directly into a storage bottle. Add the jojoba base oil. Screw the top on the bottle and shake vigorously for 2 minutes to blend. Label the bottle and place in a dark location that's between 60° and 80°F for 24 hours so that the oils can synergize.

APPLICATION INSTRUCTIONS: Shake well before using. Place 1 to 2 teaspoons of the oil blend in a small bowl. Using your fingertips, gradually massage the entire amount into your dry scalp for several minutes, making sure to rub a little down the length of your hair and onto the ends. Wrap your hair completely with plastic wrap or a plastic shower cap, then cover it with a very warm, damp towel. Replace with another warm towel once the first has cooled. Leave on for at least 1 hour, or overnight (preferably). If you leave it on overnight, remove the plastic and sleep with a dry towel on your pillow to absorb the oil.

When you're ready to shampoo, apply a gentle, chemical-free, low-sudsing shampoo directly to your hair and scalp, without wetting them first. Massage it in well, then add water, work up a lather, and rinse as usual. Follow with a conditioner, if desired. Repeat up to three times per week, if necessary, until the condition of your scalp improves.

DERMATITIS, CONTACT *(Rashes)*

The term *contact dermatitis* simply means an inflammation of the skin resulting from contact with an irritating or allergenic substance. It's a rather generic term that your health-care practitioner might assign to a skin rash whose cause is unknown. Symptoms can include intense itching, a red rash, thickening and inflammation of the skin, blisters that may break open and ooze, scales, and scabs. The rash often has clearly defined boundaries and is generally confined to a specific area of the body.

The most common causes of contact dermatitis are detergents, synthetic fragrances, preservatives, dyes, lanolin, nail polish, polish remover, formaldehyde, deodorants, irritating clothing fibers, propylene glycol (found in many cosmetics and personal-care products), industrial chemicals, lawn fertilizers, and nickel in jewelry.

What's the recommended treatment? First, remove the source of the offending substance, provided you can find it, then treat the skin with soothing remedies that will help speed healing.

Note: Though poison ivy, poison sumac, and poison oak are considered contact allergens, they are not covered in this section. See page 235 for information regarding poisonous plants and treatments for related rashes.

ALOE AND WITCH HAZEL HEALING LINIMENT

Cooling, soothing, comforting care can be so very simple to make, yet so effective in relieving the irritation of skin rashes. This herbal remedy also aids in healing all kinds of skin ailments, including blemishes, blisters, bedsores or skin ulcers, boils, sunburn, minor burns, poison plant rashes, hemorrhoids, ingrown hairs, and bug bites and stings.

½ cup commercially prepared aloe vera juice

½ cup witch hazel (commercially prepared or homemade; see the box on page 305)

½ teaspoon vegetable glycerin

EQUIPMENT: *Plastic or glass spritzer bottle*
PREP TIME: *5 minutes*
YIELD: *Approximately 1 cup*
STORAGE: *Use within 2 weeks if stored at room temperature; within 6 months if refrigerated*
APPLICATION: *3 times daily, or as needed*

Combine the aloe vera juice, witch hazel, and glycerin in a spritzer bottle and shake vigorously to blend. Label and store in the refrigerator. If you want to keep a small bottle unrefrigerated, perhaps in your purse, briefcase, gym bag, or backpack, it will last up to 2 weeks.

APPLICATION INSTRUCTIONS: Shake well before using. At least twice per day, cleanse the affected area by spraying with this formula and patting dry with a soft cloth. Spray once again and allow to air-dry.

Bonus This liniment makes a great refreshing face and underarm wash when you're in a rush and soap is unavailable. Tuck a bottle in your carry-on bag while traveling — you never know when you might get stuck in an airport!

COMFREY BLUE BALM

A gorgeous, rich, deep blue-green balm with the heavy, spicy-sweet herbal aroma of German chamomile, this treatment will counteract the itch, redness, inflammation, and heat of most generic rashes and is the ultimate skin soother for relieving pesky insect bites and stings. It soothes and calms irritated skin tissue and encourages healing.

This recipe calls for only a small amount of comfrey-infused oil, so if you have some Mend Skin: Comfrey-Infused Oil (page 140), great. If not, purchase a small bottle from your local health food store or herbal supplier. But I do recommend that you always *have at least a cup of this multipurpose infused oil on hand—fresh and homemade is best, and much less expensive!*

7 tablespoons comfrey-infused oil

1–2 tablespoons beeswax (depending on how firm you want the balm to be)

½ teaspoon menthol crystals

10 drops German chamomile essential oil

EQUIPMENT: *Small saucepan or double boiler, stirring utensil, plastic or glass jar or tin*
PREP TIME: *20 minutes to make the balm, plus 30 minutes for it to thicken*
YIELD: *Approximately ½ cup*
STORAGE: *Store at room temperature, away from heat and light; use within 1 year*
APPLICATION: *2 times per day*

Combine the oil, beeswax, and menthol crystals in a small saucepan or double boiler, and warm over low heat until the beeswax is just melted and the crystals have dissolved. Remove from the heat and allow to cool for 5 minutes, stirring a few times. Add the German chamomile essential oil and stir again to blend. Pour the mixture into the storage container, then cap and label. Set aside for 30 minutes, until the balm has thickened.

APPLICATION INSTRUCTIONS: Twice per day, wash the affected area with mild soap and water or use Aloe and Witch Hazel Healing Liniment (previous page). To help ease intense itching, you can follow this washing with an application of apple cider vinegar diluted by half with purified water, if you wish. Pat dry. Massage a small amount of balm onto the rash and surrounding area. Continue twice daily until the rash is healed.

Bonus This formula makes an incredibly beneficial treatment for *dry* eczema and psoriasis, accompanied by peeling, flaking skin.

DRY SKIN

Don't take your skin for granted; it's not there merely to make you look good. It's the largest organ you have and has more functions than you can count on both hands! If you really think about it, your skin is your "hide" that protects and regulates your inner being. When healthy, it's flexible, elastic, moist, and dewy. When dry, it lacks natural oil and moisture, the basic requirements for comfortable skin with a healthy glow. It may appear flaky or scaly and feel rough-textured, tight, or dry throughout the day. If allowed to become too damaged, your skin may admit unwelcome bacteria that can wreak havoc inside your body.

Dry skin is generally worse in cold weather, when dry heating robs the skin of moisture. Dry skin is exacerbated by excess sun exposure, air travel, alcohol consumption, an extremely low-fat diet, working outdoors without protective clothing, some medications, and living in a naturally arid climate.

To keep dry skin at bay, it's paramount to preserve the moisture already contained within your skin and supplement with daily applications of nourishing body oil blends to seal in the moisture of your daily shower or bath.

Protect your skin from the elements and condition it from the inside out by boosting your dietary intake with ample amounts of omega-3-rich natural oils such as fish oils, unrefined cod liver oil, and flaxseed oil, and add walnuts, chia seeds, and flaxseeds to your whole-foods diet. Many people find the addition of evening primrose oil or borage oil capsules to be of benefit, too. Be sure to drink plenty of water and herb teas. Avoid alcohol and keep dehydrating caffeinated beverages to a minimum.

Chicken Skin

"What is 'chicken skin' doing in a book like this?" you may ask. What I'm referring to is *keratosis pilaris*, a chronic inflammatory disorder of the area surrounding the hair follicle. It appears on the back of the upper arms and thighs and occasionally the buttocks (and outer cheeks of young children) and causes the skin to resemble that of a plucked chicken (or nutmeg grater, if that makes you feel better). The condition occurs when dead skin cells, which normally shed and fall away from the body, accumulate and form plugs at the follicle openings, leading to the formation of small, hard, pointed pimples.

There is no known cause for this cosmetic affliction, but it often runs in families who have a tendency toward rough, dry skin. Keratosis pilaris occurs mainly in winter when the humidity is low, and generally it clears up on its own in the summer.

The remedy is simple and doesn't require an herbal preparation, just regular exfoliation. To remove the buildup of dead skin from the follicle openings, practice skin brushing: Use a good-quality, natural-bristle skin brush to gently brush the affected skin surfaces for approximately 15 seconds before getting into the shower or bath. Do this daily for as long as the condition persists.

Alternatively, you could use a loofah sponge or a sugar or salt scrub on your skin while you're in the shower or bath. Pat dry and apply a thin layer of moisturizing jojoba oil to affected areas. You should see significant improvement within a few weeks.

Buttery Coconut Balm

Do you love the sweet, tropical aroma of coconuts and cocoa butter? If so, this luscious, skin-softening, deeply conditioning treat is for you. Its three edible, oil-rich ingredients have been used throughout the world for thousands of years to care for and nourish the skin. This simple formula is one of my favorites to use when I get "alligator skin," and it's wonderful for the thin, fragile skin of the elderly, keeping it soft and comfortable.

5 tablespoons extra-virgin, unrefined coconut base oil

2 tablespoons almond base oil

1 tablespoon cocoa butter

EQUIPMENT: *Small saucepan or double boiler, stirring utensil, glass or plastic jar or a tin*
PREP TIME: *20 minutes to make the balm, plus up to 24 hours for it to thicken*
YIELD: *½ cup*
STORAGE: *Store at room temperature, away from heat and light; use within 1 year*
APPLICATION: *1 or 2 times per day*

Combine the coconut oil, almond oil, and cocoa butter in a small saucepan or double boiler, and warm over low heat until all the solids are just melted. Remove from the heat and allow to cool for 5 to 10 minutes, stirring a few times. Pour into a storage container. (Since coconut oil is solid below 76°F and liquid at higher temperatures, you may prefer to store the formula in a plastic squeeze bottle in warmer weather and in a jar or tin in cooler weather.) This formula is slow to thicken and may require up to 24 hours to reach its final creamy texture.

APPLICATION INSTRUCTIONS: After bathing or showering, massage this oil-rich balm into your skin while it is still slightly damp. If your skin is very dry, you can apply it again later in the day to dry skin. Let the balm soak in for at least 5 minutes before getting dressed. Exfoliate at least twice per week to keep your skin free of the pore-clogging skin-cell buildup that inhibits moisture and oil penetration (see Exfoliate to Eliminate Dry Skin, page 151).

Bonus This ultra-penetrating formula helps prevent diaper rash and stretch marks, and a pea-size amount will condition the ends of very dry hair.

SOOTHE-ME-SESAME BODY OIL

I love skin-pampering formulas that are ultra-simple to make, are relatively inexpensive, and leave my skin feeling velvety. Sesame oil, which is the predominant base oil in this formula, contains a generous complement of vitamin E, and is often used therapeutically in Ayurvedic body-care formulations as a warming, nourishing, grounding, and deeply calming lubricating oil. It's especially recommended for individuals with extremely dry skin who have trouble relaxing and falling asleep and are mentally frazzled, burned out, scatterbrained, high-strung, and talkative. The avocado oil is rich in vitamins, minerals, protein, and lecithin, and the carrot seed essential oil serves as a tonic for regenerating and revitalizing mature or damaged skin.

50	drops carrot seed essential oil
¾	cup unrefined sesame base oil
¼	cup unrefined avocado base oil
1,000	IU vitamin E oil

EQUIPMENT: *Dropper, glass bottle or plastic squeeze bottle*
PREP TIME: *15 minutes, plus 24 hours to synergize*
YIELD: *Approximately 1 cup*
STORAGE: *Store at room temperature, away from heat and light; use within 1 year*
APPLICATION: *Once per day*

Place the carrot seed essential oil drop by drop directly to the storage bottle. Add the sesame and avocado base oils, and the vitamin E oil. Screw on the top and shake vigorously for 2 minutes to blend. Label the bottle and place in a dark location that's between 60° and 80°F for 24 hours, so that the oils can synergize.

APPLICATION INSTRUCTIONS: Shake well before using. There are two methods of application that I recommend. Try both and see which one works best for your skin.

Ayurvedic method. This method is rather stimulating, so perform it in the morning. Before your bath or shower, gently exfoliate your entire body, from head to toe, using a natural-bristle body brush or soft loofah sponge. Massage a generous portion of body oil into your *dry* skin, always massaging toward your heart.

When you are completely covered in oil, don an old bathrobe and allow the oil to sink in for 10 to 15 minutes. Then jump into the shower or bathtub and just rinse (no need to use soap except to wash underarms and intimate areas, as you've already cleansed your skin by exfoliating). The steam or hot water from your bath relaxes your pores and helps the oil penetrate your skin. Pat dry. If your skin is severely dry, follow with an application of natural body lotion, as necessary. **Cosmetology/aesthetician method.** Twice a week, gently exfoliate your entire body, from head to toe, whether dry (before bathing) or while in the tub or shower in order to keep dead skin cell build-up at bay. Every day, after bathing or showering, massage this oil blend into your skin, from head to toe, while your skin is still slightly damp in order to seal in the moisture.

Bonus Use this blend as an after-sun conditioning oil to help replenish suppleness to your baked and tanned hide.

Exfoliate to Eliminate Dry Skin

A once- or twice-daily application of a moisturizing balm, salve, or oil can work wonders in eliminating dry skin. However, dry skin tends to build up a layer of dead skin cells that inhibit oil penetration, so the balms, salves, and oils won't work as well. To keep your skin free of dead-skin-cell buildup and encourage deep penetration of moisturizers, exfoliate your entire body (or just the area where you want to apply this product) twice a week. You can use a natural-bristle body brush or soft loofah sponge on dry skin, or you can use a sugar or salt scrub, a soft loofah sponge, or an apricot kernel or jojoba wax bead scrub while in the tub or shower.

Dew-of-the-Rose Luxurious Body Oil

This is an ever-so-gentle, light- to medium-textured oil that will be adored by all rose lovers. It's perfect for pampering and softening dry skin. This simple infusion has a most delicate scent, but it can be enhanced or customized by adding essential oils. The ones listed below intensify the rose fragrance and add antiseptic, antiviral, antifungal, and skin-regenerative properties. I usually make this oil in midsummer using fresh, local, deep pink and white rugosa rose petals, but I also I like Rosa damascena and R. centifolia; in fact, you can use any wild or garden roses, but whatever variety you choose, make sure it is organic and has a strong fragrance.

Note: I prefer to use the solar infusion method and freshly wilted flowers, as it yields a sweeter and fresher scent, but dried flowers work nicely, too.

3 cups dried or 4 cups freshly wilted rose petals (see page 38 for information on wilting)

3–4 cups almond or soybean base oil (enough to completely cover the flowers)

2,000 IU vitamin E oil

60 drops essential oil(s) of choice (optional; I like 20 drops each of rose otto, palmarosa, and geranium)

EQUIPMENT: *Widemouthed 1-quart canning jar, stirring utensil, plastic wrap, strainer, fine filter, funnel, glass or plastic storage containers*
PREP TIME: *1 month*
YIELD: *Approximately 2½ cups*
STORAGE: *Store at room temperature, away from heat and light; use within 1 year*
APPLICATION: *Once per day*

Place the rose petals in a 1-quart canning jar. Drizzle the base oil over the plant matter until the oil comes to within 1 inch of the top of the jar. The flowers will settle with the weight of the oil, so don't worry if it looks as though you don't have enough plant matter in the jar. Gently stir to remove air bubbles and make sure that all the plant matter is submerged.

Place a piece of plastic wrap over the mouth of the jar (to prevent the metal lid from coming into contact with the petals) and tightly screw on the lid. Shake the jar several times to blend thoroughly. Place the jar in a warm, sunny location such as a south-facing windowsill, and allow the petals to infuse for 1 month. Shake the jar every day for 30 seconds or so.

After 1 month, carefully strain the oil through a fine-mesh strainer lined with a fine filter such as muslin or, preferably, a paper coffee filter, then strain again if necessary to remove all herb debris. Squeeze petals to extract as much of the precious oil as possible. Discard the marc. Add the vitamin E oil and the essential oil(s), if using, and stir to blend. The rose-petal-infused oil will be pale pinkish-gold in color.

Pour the finished oil into storage containers, then cap, label, and store in a dark cabinet.

APPLICATION INSTRUCTIONS: After bathing or showering, massage this fragrant oil blend into your skin while still slightly damp (though it can be applied directly to dry skin as well). Let the oil soak in for at least 5 minutes before getting dressed. Exfoliate at least twice per week to keep your skin free of the pore-clogging skin-cell buildup that inhibits moisture and oil penetration (see Exfoliate to Eliminate Dry Skin, page 151).

Bonus This oil is a wonderful skin conditioner for babies and young girls, as well as the sensitive, delicate skin of elderly women. Men may find the fragrance too feminine.

The rose distills a healing balm
The beating pulse of pain to calm.

— ODES OF ANACREON,
translated by Thomas Moore

ECZEMA

The symptoms of contact dermatitis and eczema can be quite similar: intense itching, a red rash, thickening and inflammation of the skin, blisters that may break open and ooze, scales, and scabs. The major difference is that contact dermatitis has an external cause and the rash is usually confined to the area of the body that was in contact with the irritant. This means it's possible to resolve the problem by avoiding the irritant.

Eczema, on the other hand, often is the result of multiple internal reactions to irritants and allergens, and though it can occur on its own, it often accompanies other allergic responses such as hayfever and asthma. Eczema can also be associated with poor digestion, severe constipation, low stomach acid levels, food allergies, a weak immune system, a family history of asthma or eczema, or a high level of stress. In fact, stress can be a *major* contributor toward the flare-up of eczema — keep that in mind.

The symptoms of eczema most often present on the wrists and hands (especially between the fingers and around the knuckles), in the creases of the knees and elbows, under the arms, and on the face and ears. Eczema can exhibit itself as *weeping* or *dry*, and each condition needs specific treatment to help ease the particular symptoms.

If you suffer from eczema, addressing your general health should be your first concern, including a whole-foods diet, pure water, daily exercise (but not to the point of exhaustion), stress management, enjoyable relationships and work, and sufficient rest and sleep. Additionally, regular elimination of waste is paramount in order to detoxify the body.

Though the remedies in this section will help ease the itching, promote the generation of new skin tissue, and decrease inflammation and redness, the underlying cause of your eczema needs to be identified by a qualified health-care professional. Your skin is crying out because your whole system is attempting to detoxify and rid itself of irritation.

De-Stress Tea

Many sufferers find the following helpful when eczema flares: If you are feeling stressed and anxious, regular consumption of herbal nervine-based teas (3 to 4 cups per day) may relax the peripheral nerves and your heightened emotions, thus reducing inflammation and itching to some degree.

At your local health food store, look for relaxing herb tea blends that contain such herbs as catnip, chamomile, lavender, lemon balm, licorice, skullcap, passionflower, and valerian.

EVENING PRIMROSE BLEND (FOR DRY ECZEMA)

The Crow Indians of the American West traditionally used the oil extracted from the seeds of the evening primrose to heal the symptoms of dry skin, rashes, and eczema. They applied it directly to the skin and also consumed it to help nourish the skin from the inside. Evening primrose oil is rich in anti-inflammatory gamma-linolenic acid (GLA), as well as the vitamins and minerals needed to maintain healthy skin tissue. The following is a simple remedy that will significantly ease the symptoms of redness, peeling, itching, and inflammation associated with dry eczema.

20 drops palmarosa essential oil

15 drops Moroccan blue chamomile or German chamomile essential oil

10 drops lavender essential oil

¼ cup evening primrose base oil

¼ cup jojoba base oil

EQUIPMENT: *Dropper, dark glass bottle with dropper top or screw cap*
PREP TIME: *15 minutes, plus 24 hours to synergize*
YIELD: *Approximately ½ cup*
STORAGE: *Store at room temperature, away from heat and light; use within 6 months*
APPLICATION: *2 or 3 times per day*

Add the palmarosa, chamomile, and lavender essential oils drop by drop directly into a storage bottle. Add the evening primrose and jojoba base oils. Screw the top on the bottle and shake vigorously for 2 minutes to blend. Label the bottle and place in a dark location that's between 60° and 80°F for 24 hours so that the oils can synergize.

APPLICATION INSTRUCTIONS: Shake well before using. Cleanse the affected area using a mixture of 1 part baking soda to 8 parts water; the baking soda helps ease itchiness. Pat dry. Gently massage a small amount of the herbal oil blend into the area until it is absorbed. Repeat two or three times per day.

Bonus This oil can be beneficial when massaged nightly into dry, brittle nails, and it works well to help soothe the inflammation and flaky, dry skin of psoriatic plaques.

ALOE AND PEPPERMINT CLAY PACK (FOR WEEPING ECZEMA)

If you tend to get hot, red, inflamed, weeping eczema that develops in small patches, then this is the spot treatment for you. The absorbent, cooling clay pack will tighten and soothe those areas, bringing relief to annoying irritation. This formula is best applied to eczema on flat surfaces of the skin, rather than on eczema that has formed around joints or in skin creases. This recipe may be doubled or tripled to treat large eczema patches.

Note: If a large portion of the body is affected by eczema, a baking soda bath once per day, using ½ to 1 cup of baking soda stirred into the bathwater, is recommended.

- 1 tablespoon bentonite or French green clay
- 1 teaspoon crushed dried peppermint or contents of 1 peppermint tea bag
- 5 teaspoons commercially prepared aloe vera juice

EQUIPMENT: *Small bowl, spoon or tiny whisk*
PREP TIME: *5 minutes*
YIELD: *1 or more treatments (depending on size of affected area)*
STORAGE: *Cover and refrigerate any leftovers; use within 3 days*
APPLICATION: *Once daily until weeping subsides*

In a small bowl or custard cup, use a spoon or tiny whisk to combine the clay and peppermint with the aloe vera juice to form a smooth, spreadable paste. Allow to thicken for 5 minutes. It should not have a soupy consistency; if it does, add a bit more clay to thicken it. Use immediately.

APPLICATION INSTRUCTIONS: Using your finger, spread a thick layer of clay pack onto each eczema patch and allow to dry or nearly dry for at least 45 minutes. The clay will harden and may tingle and crack as it dries. Rinse with cool water. Pat dry. Follow with a light application of plain, cold aloe vera juice and allow to air-dry.

If you have any leftover clay pack mixture, tightly cover the little bowl with plastic wrap and store in the refrigerator, where it will keep for up to 3 days. If the mixture starts to dry out, add a tad more aloe vera juice and stir well before using.

Bonus This clay pack also helps cool inflammation and relieve itching and dry oozing of skin irritated by poison plant rash.

Three Flowers Anti-Itch Spray (for Weeping or Dry Eczema)

This formula is designed specifically for those who suffer from intensely itchy eczema, be it weeping or dry. Additionally, it will deliver speedy relief to painful inflammation and stimulate the formation of new, healthy skin cells. I recommend that you keep a bottle handy in the refrigerator.

30 drops calendula essential oil

30 drops Moroccan blue chamomile or German chamomile essential oil

20 drops lavender essential oil

1 cup commercially prepared aloe vera juice

EQUIPMENT: *Dropper, glass or plastic spritzer bottle*
PREP TIME: *15 minutes, plus 24 hours to synergize*
YIELD: *Approximately 1 cup*
STORAGE: *Refrigerate; use within 6 months*
APPLICATION: *Up to 3 times per day*

Add the calendula, chamomile, and lavender essential oils drop by drop directly into a spritzer bottle. Add the aloe vera juice. Screw the top on the bottle and shake vigorously for 2 minutes to blend. Label the bottle and place in a dark location that's between 60° and 80°F for 24 hours so that the blend can synergize; then refrigerate.

APPLICATION INSTRUCTIONS: Shake well before using. Spray onto itchy patches of eczema up to three times per day. Allow to air-dry.

Bonus This spray eases the sting of a bad sunburn, aids in the repair of damaged skin tissue, and soothes the itching and swelling of hives. It also makes a good spot treatment for blemishes.

ELDER CARE CONCERNS *(70+ Years)*

The elderly often have special needs that develop with advancing years — drier and more delicate skin, slower healing of wounds, poor circulation, and declining immune health. These herbal remedies can help address these concerns.

When creating topical herbal remedies for older individuals, I always take into account that their skin generally tends to be quite papery, fragile, and porous. It can tear, bruise, and bleed easily and often reacts to even moderate ingredient concentrations when younger, thicker, healthier skin might not, so all these products are made with gentle, ultra-mild, yet effective ingredients.

Rev-Me-Up Rosemary and Geranium Rub

*A*s we age, our blood circulation tends to diminish and slow in our extremities, resulting in cold hands and feet, dry skin and nails, tingling sensations, and slow healing of cuts, scrapes, and bruises. This recipe includes two herbs that nourish, condition, and revitalize skin tissue and stimulate circulation when massaged into the hands, arms, feet, and lower legs. Both herbs also contain uplifting and balancing properties to improve your mood and enhance mental energy.

15 drops geranium essential oil

15 drops rosemary (chemotype *verbenon*) essential oil

½ cup almond, soybean, or jojoba base oil

EQUIPMENT: *Dropper, dark glass bottle with dropper top or screw cap*
PREP TIME: *15 minutes, plus 24 hours to synergize*
YIELD: *½ cup*
STORAGE: *Store at room temperature, away from heat and light; use within 1 year with soybean or almond base oil, 2 years with jojoba base oil*
APPLICATION: *1 or 2 times per day*

Add the geranium and rosemary essential oils drop by drop directly into the storage bottle. Add the base oil. Screw the top on the bottle and shake vigorously for 2 minutes to blend. Label the bottle and place in a dark location that's between 60° and 80°F for 24 hours so that the oils can synergize.

APPLICATION INSTRUCTIONS: Shake well before using. Applying the oil a tablespoon at a time, briskly massage it into your skin, using upward, circular strokes, always in the direction of the heart. Start with your feet and move up your lower legs, to the knees, followed by your hands, lower arms, and elbows. Allow the oil to soak in for 5 to 10 minutes before dressing. If a greasy residue remains, use less oil next time.

Bonus Use daily as a facial, throat, and chest moisturizing elixir to tone, tighten, and improve skin texture. Just massage several drops into the skin after cleansing and toning. It smells crisp and fresh without being harsh.

Protect and Fortify Facial Elixir

This pure, light, nourishing, protective oil can serve as your primary facial moisturizer, or you can use it in conjunction with your favorite moisturizer to intensify the level of conditioning, especially if you suffer from very dry skin. The combination of three amazing healing herbs — rosemary, comfrey, and calendula — comforts, soothes redness and irritation, encourages cell regeneration, and increases the elasticity of skin tissue.

Note: For this formula I prefer to use freshly wilted herbs harvested from my garden in summer, but dried herbs will work nicely, too. I feel the stovetop method of infusion best concentrates the sticky, resinous properties of these herbs, while evaporating their heavy moisture content (especially if you use them freshly wilted).

¼ cup dried or ½ cup freshly wilted calendula blossoms (see page 38 for information on wilting)

¼ cup dried or ½ cup freshly wilted comfrey leaves

¼ cup dried or ½ cup freshly wilted rosemary leaves

2 cups almond base oil

2,000 IU vitamin E oil

EQUIPMENT: *2-quart saucepan or double boiler, stirring utensil, candy or yogurt thermometer, strainer, fine filter, funnel, glass or plastic storage container*
PREP TIME: *5 hours*
YIELD: *Approximately 1½ cups*
STORAGE: *Store at room temperature, away from heat and light; use within 1 year*
APPLICATION: *2 times per day*

If you're using freshly wilted herbs, first cut or tear the leaves and flowers into smaller pieces to expose more surface area to the oil. Combine the calendula, comfrey, and rosemary with the almond base oil in a 2-quart saucepan or double boiler and stir thoroughly to blend. The mixture should look like a thick, leafy green and orange speckled soup. Bring the mixture to just shy of a simmer, between 125° and 135°F. Do not let the oil actually simmer — it will degrade the quality of your infused oil. *Do not* put the lid on the pot.

Allow the herbs to macerate in the oil over low heat for 5 hours. Check the temperature every 30 minutes or so with a thermometer and adjust the heat accordingly. If you're using a double boiler, add more water to the bottom pot as necessary, so it doesn't dry out. Stir the infusing mixture at least every 30 minutes or so, as the herb bits tend to settle to the bottom.

After 5 hours, remove the pan from the heat and allow to cool for 15 minutes. While the oil is still warm, carefully strain it through a fine-mesh strainer lined with a fine filter such as muslin or, preferably, a paper coffee filter, then strain again if necessary to remove all debris. Squeeze the herbs to extract as much of the precious oil as possible. Discard the marc.

Add the vitamin E oil and stir to blend. The resulting oil blend will be a greenish-orange color. Pour the finished oil into a storage container, then cap, label, and store in a dark cabinet.

APPLICATION INSTRUCTIONS: In the morning and evening, after cleansing and toning the skin, gently pat your face almost dry. Place approximately 10 drops of the oil in the palm of your hand, rub your hands together to warm the oil, then press it into your face, neck, and the chest, and gently massage it in, using upward, outward, circular strokes. Follow with sunscreen, moisturizer, or makeup, if desired.

Bonus Use this elixir to help heal minor burns (after the burn has cooled), sunburn, cuts and scrapes, dermatitis, dry eczema, psoriasis, diaper rash, stretch marks, blisters, and *new* scar tissue. It makes a comforting bath and body oil, too.

SIMPLE CALENDULA-INFUSED BODY OIL

The sunny calendula flower is strikingly beautiful and intensely colorful, and it contains simple, potent, yet gentle medicine. Calendula-infused oil is mildly antiseptic and energetically cooling, and it fights inflammation, stimulates skin cell regeneration, and conditions skin by restoring elasticity and suppleness.

This oil can be used alone or may be added to salves and balms intended to aid in the healing of all manner of skin irritations, psoriasis, eczema, stretch marks, burns, scars, cuts and scrapes, bug bites and stings, infections, dry skin, and diaper rash. I highly recommend that you grow a patch of calendula flowers and keep a jar of this "miracle oil" in your medicine cabinet.

Note: I always make this infused oil in the summer or early fall, when I can pick the flowers fresh from my garden, but if fresh blossoms are unavailable, dried ones will do nicely, too. I prefer to use the solar infusion method. Calendula flowers are very thick and sticky and need to be wilted for at least 72 hours before making this recipe so that a good portion of their moisture evaporates.

2 cups dried or 3 cups freshly wilted calendula flowers (see page 38 for information on wilting)

3–4 cups almond or soybean base oil (enough to cover flowers)

2,000 IU vitamin E oil

EQUIPMENT: *1-quart canning jar; stirring utensil, strainer, fine filter, funnel, glass or plastic storage containers*
PREP TIME: *1 month*
YIELD: *Approximately 2½ cups*
STORAGE: *Store at room temperature, away from heat and light; use within 1 year*
APPLICATION: *Once daily, or as desired*

If you're using freshly wilted calendula flowers, cut or tear the flowers into smaller pieces to expose more surface area to the oil. Place the flowers in a widemouthed 1-quart canning jar. Drizzle the base oil over the plant matter until the oil comes to within 1 inch of the top of the jar. The flowers will settle with the weight of the oil, so don't worry if it looks as though you don't have enough plant matter in the jar. Gently stir to remove air bubbles and make sure that all the plant matter is submerged.

Place a piece of plastic wrap over the mouth of the jar (to prevent the metal lid from coming into contact with the herb) and tightly screw on the lid. Shake the jar several times to blend thoroughly. Place the jar in a warm, sunny location such as a south-facing windowsill, and allow the flowers to infuse for 1 month. Shake the jar every day for 30 seconds or so.

After 1 month, carefully strain the oil through a fine-mesh strainer lined with a fine filter such as muslin or, preferably, a paper coffee filter, then strain again if necessary to remove all herb debris. Squeeze the flowers to extract as much of the precious oil as possible. Discard the marc. Add the vitamin E oil and stir to blend. The resulting calendula oil can vary in color from deep vibrant yellow to yellow-orange to bright orange.

Pour the finished oil into storage containers, then cap, label, and store in a dark cabinet.

APPLICATION INSTRUCTIONS: After a warm bath or shower, pat your skin almost dry and apply a tablespoon or two of the infused oil to your entire body, massaging in gentle, circular motions (always toward the heart) until it is completely absorbed. Let the oil soak in for 5 to 10 minutes before getting dressed. You can also massage this oil into dry skin anytime you desire — it sinks in so nicely. It's fabulous when used as your daily facial oil, too.

Bonus This favored-by-everyone floral oil can be used as a bath and facial oil. It sinks right in with nary an oily residue.

Calendula-Rose Hydrating Herbal Facial Mist

Herbal hydrosols, the watery byproducts of the steam distillation of plant materials (generally in the manufacture of essential oils), contain medicinal properties in a much less concentrated form than essential oils, yet they still deliver most of the beneficial components that the whole plant has to offer without potential irritation, plus they come in a convenient spray form.

Even though I don't fit into the elderly category just yet, I do often suffer from sensitive, dehydrated skin. I recommend the following blend to clients and friends with this skin type and have personally used it for years with good results. It's easy to make: Pour ½ cup of calendula hydrosol and ½ cup of rose hydrosol into an 8-ounce plastic or glass spritzer bottle. Shake vigorously to mix. No refrigeration is necessary, but for maximum freshness and potency, use within 6 months. To use, spray onto your face and neck immediately following your regular cleansing routine. While your skin is still damp with the hydrosol blend, apply your favorite moisturizer.

This facial mist comes in handy when you travel by plane. The recycled air on board is notoriously dehydrating and wicks your skin's moisture like a sponge. I like to keep a 2-ounce spritzer bottle in my purse and spray a layer of hydrating moisture on my face when I start to feel parched. It wakes you up and freshens your skin, too.

GARDEN WONDER BALM

This formula is the salve version of Protect and Fortify Facial Elixir (page 160), so you need to make that recipe prior to making this balm. In addition to beeswax, I've included lavender essential oil to enhance the anti-inflammatory, antiseptic, vulnerary, and skin-pampering properties. This balm, made primarily with common garden herbs, soothes redness and irritation and encourages skin cell regeneration and increased elasticity of tight, dry, mature skin tissue. It works like magic to help heal just about any minor skin irritation, even on the most sensitive of skins. I love this stuff!

7 tablespoons Protect and Fortify Facial Elixir

1–2 tablespoons beeswax (depending on how firm you want the salve to be)

25 drops lavender essential oil

EQUIPMENT: *Small saucepan or double boiler, stirring utensil, plastic or glass jar or tin*
PREP TIME: *20 minutes to make the balm, plus 30 minutes for it to thicken*
YIELD: *Approximately ½ cup*
STORAGE: *Store at room temperature, away from heat and light; use within 1 year*
APPLICATION: *2 times per day*

Combine the infused oil and beeswax in a small saucepan or double boiler, and warm over low heat until the beeswax is just melted. Remove from the heat and allow to cool for 5 minutes, stirring a few times. Add the essential oil and stir again to blend. Slowly pour the liquid mixture into the storage container, then cap and label. Set aside for 30 minutes to thicken.

APPLICATION INSTRUCTIONS: Apply a small dab twice daily to minor skin irritations to comfort and speed healing.

Bonus This balm is so gentle and mild that it can be used to treat all manner of skin irritations experienced by young children and infants.

Essential Immunity Balm

*W*ith daily application to the feet, hands, and chest, this powerful medicinal will envelop your body with an "aromatherapeutic shield" to help protect you from airborne "nasties" and surface contaminants. The soles of your feet and palms of your hands have an amazing ability to absorb topical remedies due to the plethora of sweat glands contained within their thick skin, so this formula's essential oils will quickly begin to deliver their benefits to your bloodstream. When applied to the chest area and covered with clothing, the fragrant vapors rise to your nose and mouth, fortifying the sinus and respiratory channels against illness.

Note: Use the specific essential oils called for, as they are the most skin-friendly varieties.

4 tablespoons refined shea butter (unrefined shea butter will work, but its stronger fragrance makes masks the aroma of the essential oils)

5 drops eucalyptus (species *radiata*) essential oil

5 drops spike lavender (*Lavandula latifolia*) or lavender (*L. angustifolia*) essential oil

5 drops tea tree essential oil

5 drops thyme (chemotype *linalool*) essential oil

2 drops peppermint essential oil

1 drop cinnamon essential oil

1 drop clove essential oil

EQUIPMENT: *Small saucepan or double boiler, stirring utensil, plastic or glass jar or tin*
PREP TIME: *15 minutes, plus up to 24 hours to thicken*
YIELD: *Approximately ¼ cup*
STORAGE: *Store at room temperature, away from heat and light; use within 1 year*
APPLICATION: *2 times per day*

Warm the shea butter in a small saucepan (a ¾-quart size works great) or double boiler over low heat, until it has just melted. Remove from the heat. Add the eucalyptus, lavender, tea tree, thyme, peppermint, cinnamon, and clove essential oils directly to the storage container, then slowly pour in the liquefied shea butter. Gently stir the balm to blend, then cap, label, and set aside to thicken. Unlike beeswax, shea butter takes a long time to completely thicken, and this formula may need up to 24 hours, depending on the temperature in your kitchen. When it's ready, it will be very thick, semi-hard, and white (or creamy yellow if you've used unrefined shea butter).

APPLICATION INSTRUCTIONS: Massage a small dab into your palms, the soles of your feet, including between the toes, and chest twice per day. Put on socks or hosiery after application to the feet.

ENVIRONMENTALLY DAMAGED SKIN

Environmentally damaged skin ages prematurely due to overexposure to the elements. It's been abused, and it shows! It can be oily, normal, or dry but may show any or all of the following characteristics: deep lines and wrinkles, hyperpigmentation (freckles and age spots), ruddiness, exposed "broken" capillaries, a chapped, windburned appearance, flakiness, rough texture, and uneven skin tone — telltale signs of the life you've led.

Each season brings new challenges to environmentally damaged skin. In particular, summer offers the chance for further sun abuse and winter weather makes it feel ultra-parched. In addition to gentle daily care, wear a hydrating, moisturizing, natural, preferably chemical-free sunscreen every day to prevent further damage. The following recipes offer welcome relief to this stressed-out skin type, strengthening the dermal layer and encouraging healthy cell renewal.

SAVE-MY-SKIN SALVE

A silky, buttery formula with myriad uses, this salve protects and conditions skin from exposure to the elements. It works wonders to soften and tame rough, dry cuticles and dry heels, elbows, shins, and knees. It can also be used as a nontoxic, fragrance-free salve to prevent stretch marks on pregnant bellies and breasts, and it makes a fabulous diaper rash prevention salve for infants. Use on normal to dry environmentally damaged skin.

Note: Coconut oil turns from solid to liquid at 76°F, so the salve will maintain a much softer consistency if stored in a very warm spot. If the temperature is below 76°F, the salve will be firmer especially if the temperature is quite cool.

2 tablespoons almond or soybean base oil

2 tablespoons cocoa butter

2 tablespoons extra-virgin, unrefined coconut base oil

2 tablespoons refined shea butter (unrefined shea butter will work, but its stronger fragrance will often dominate the formula.)

EQUIPMENT: *Small saucepan or double boiler, stirring utensil, plastic or glass jar or tin*
PREP TIME: *20 minutes, plus up to 24 hours to thicken*
YIELD: *½ cup*
STORAGE: *Store at room temperature, away from heat and light; use within 1 year*
APPLICATION: *2 times per day*

Combine the almond or soybean base oil, cocoa butter, coconut oil, and shea butter in a small saucepan or double boiler over low heat, and warm until the solids are just melted. Remove from the heat and allow to cool for 5 to 10 minutes. Stir a few times to blend the mixture thoroughly. Pour into a storage container, cap, and label. Set aside to thicken, which may take up to 24 hours at room temperature. Because both cocoa butter and shea butter are included, the salve may continue to change texture slightly for another 24 hours.

APPLICATION INSTRUCTIONS: In the morning and evening, after cleansing, pat your skin almost dry, then apply the appropriate toner, astringent, or herbal hydrosol for your skin type. While your skin is still damp, lightly massage a pea-size amount (or more if necessary) into your skin, beginning with the the chest and moving up to the throat and then the face, using upward, outward, and circular strokes. Wait 5 minutes before applying sunscreen, additional moisturizer (if desired), or makeup. This light salve should sink right in with no oily residue; if your skin remains oily after 5 minutes, blot off the excess and use less next time.

Bonus Rub a little dab into the ends of dry, frizzy, brittle hair to serve as a conditioning agent.

Environmental Rescue Elixir

This lightweight, "rescue remedy in a bottle" will help nourish, rejuvenate, tone, protect, and support cell membrane functions within the skin, resulting in a more elastic, supple feel with much less evident irritation. Fear not if you have oily skin; this formula will sink right in without encouraging shine and breakouts and can be used as your sole moisturizer, if desired.

8 drops German chamomile essential oil

5 drops carrot seed essential oil

5 drops palmarosa essential oil

1 tablespoon apricot kernel base oil

1 tablespoon jojoba base oil

EQUIPMENT: *Dropper, dark glass bottle with dropper top or screw cap*
PREP TIME: *15 minutes, plus 24 hours to synergize*
YIELD: *2 tablespoons*
STORAGE: *Store at room temperature, away from heat and light; use within 1 year*
APPLICATION: *2 times per day*

Add the German chamomile, carrot seed, and palmarosa essential oils drop by drop directly into a storage bottle. Add the apricot and jojoba base oils. Screw the top on the bottle and shake vigorously for 2 minutes to blend. Label the bottle and place in a dark location that's between 60° and 80°F for 24 hours so that the oils can synergize.

APPLICATION INSTRUCTIONS: Shake well before using. In the morning and evening, after cleansing, pat your skin almost dry, then apply the appropriate toner, astringent, or herbal hydrosol for your skin type. While your skin is still damp, lightly massage approximately 10 drops of elixir into it, beginning with the the chest and moving up to the throat and then the face, using upward, outward, and circular strokes. Wait 5 minutes before applying sunscreen, additional moisturizer (if desired), or makeup. The elixir should sink right in with no oily residue; if your skin remains oily after 5 minutes, blot off the excess and use less next time.

Bonus This formula, applied twice daily, soothes the itch, inflammation, and flaky skin of dry eczema and psoriasis.

LIPOSOME ELIXIR

This simply made "nourishing nectar" for your weather-beaten skin is chock-full of beneficial vitamins (A, B, D, and E) plus fatty acids, proteins, and lecithin, which together speed healing and bring comfort to environmentally ravaged skin. The bright orange calendula essential oil is a concentrated vulnerary and powerful anti-inflammatory, repairing, restoring, and rejuvenating damaged skin. This elixir is recommended for normal and dry environmentally damaged skin.

5 drops calendula essential oil

1 tablespoon avocado base oil

1 tablespoon wheat germ base oil

EQUIPMENT: *Dropper, dark glass bottle with dropper top or screw cap*
PREP TIME: *15 minutes, plus 24 hours to synergize*
YIELD: *2 tablespoons*
STORAGE: *Store at room temperature, away from heat and light; use within 3 months*
APPLICATION: *2 times per day*

Add the calendula essential oil drop by drop directly into a storage bottle. Add the avocado and wheat germ base oils. Screw the top on the bottle and shake vigorously for 2 minutes to blend. Label the bottle and place in a dark location that's between 60° and 80°F for 24 hours so that the oils can synergize. Wheat germ oil has a short shelf life, so the elixir will go rancid if not used within 3 months, but the avocado oil becomes almost solid when refrigerated.

APPLICATION INSTRUCTIONS: Shake well before using. In the morning and evening, after cleansing, pat your skin almost dry, then apply the appropriate toner, astringent, or herbal hydrosol for your skin type. While your skin is still damp, lightly massage approximately 10 drops of elixir into it, beginning with the the chest and moving up to the throat and then the face, using upward, outward, and circular strokes. Wait 5 minutes before applying sunscreen, additional moisturizer (if desired), or makeup. The elixir should sink right in with no oily residue; if your skin remains oily after 5 minutes, blot off the excess and use less next time.

Bonus This elixir makes a fabulous conditioning oil for dry, brittle fingernails and cuticles. Simply massage one drop into each nail daily.

FATIGUE

Are you in the throes of a personal energy crisis, especially in the morning? Find it difficult to get up and get going? Do cheerful "morning people" really irk you? Unlike my husband, I've never been buzzing with energy when I awaken before 6:30 A.M., but over the years I've found ways to healthfully boost my morning *chi*.

A whole-foods, vitamin- and mineral-rich diet with plenty of low- or noncaffeinated liquids, plus daily sunlight, regular exercise, ample sleep, and time to relax, is vital for recharging your batteries so that you can run on a full tank of energy. If in spite of living well, you find mornings still energetically challenging, herbs and their essential oils can help add zip to the early hours of your day.

The following herbal remedies for fatigue are some of my favorites for delivering a shot of pep to my morning, helping me start my day off on an energetic note. Try them all and see if one doesn't strike your fancy.

We can never have enough of nature. We must be refreshed by the sight of inexhaustible vigor.

— HENRY DAVID THOREAU

WAKE ME UP: TREES-OF-THE-FOREST HERBAL REFRESHER

Move over coffee! Herbs with invigorating scents and stimulating properties work amazingly well at energizing your body both mentally and physically, sans jitters and the ensuing letdown. There's a reason that the essential oils in this recipe all come from trees. Ever take a walk in an evergreen forest, breathing deeply of the crisp, resinous air, and soon feel ultra refreshed, awake, alert, and lively? These essential oils all possess properties that reduce adrenal, mental, and physical fatigue, while increasing a feeling of balanced energy.

20 drops Atlas cedar essential oil

30 drops black spruce essential oil

30 drops Scotch pine essential oil

½ cup jojoba base oil

EQUIPMENT: *Dropper, dark glass bottle with dropper top or screw cap*
PREP TIME: *15 minutes, plus 24 hours to synergize*
YIELD: *Approximately ½ cup*
STORAGE: *Store at room temperature, away from heat and light; use within 2 years*
APPLICATION: *1 or 2 times per day*

Add the Atlas cedar, black spruce, and Scotch pine essential oils drop by drop directly into a storage bottle. Add the jojoba base oil. Screw the top on the bottle and shake vigorously for 2 minutes to blend. Label the bottle and place in a dark location that's between 60° and 80°F for 24 hours so that the oils can synergize.

APPLICATION INSTRUCTIONS: Shake well before each use. Massage a few drops into the sole of each foot or onto your chest every morning after showering, or anytime during the day when you need a shot of energy. Alternatively, you can have someone massage a few drops onto your lower back, directly over your kidneys and adrenal glands, to help reduce adrenal stress. Let the oil soak in for 5 to 10 minutes before dressing.

Bonus If suffering from a cold or the flu, massage a few drops into your feet and chest to help combat the chills, body aches, and open respiratory passages, encouraging deep, oxygenating breaths.

AMAZON WOMAN BALSAM FIR-INFUSED OIL

This formula isn't just for women — men love it, too! Late in May, when the new spring growth of the balsam fir trees is at its most sticky, resinous, and aromatic, I venture into the woods and cut a small basketful of 5-inch tips. Made into an infused oil and massaged into the feet or over the entire body or used as a bath oil, the fir's essence provides your entire being with an amazing sense of fresh, balanced energy and power. It's like nothing you've ever experienced. Interestingly, in spite of fir's stimulating properties, some people find this oil to be incredibly relaxing, as it tends to open the respiratory channels, resulting in deeper breathing. The fragrance of the oil is like "Christmas in a bottle," so if you enjoy the aroma of a holiday evergreen wreath, you'll really like this. The scent slowly mellows within an hour after application.

Note: I use only the freshly wilted tips and the solar infusion method of extraction to make this strongly aromatic, delightfully green, infused fir oil. The new-growth tips are very delicate and easily release their invigorating healing properties when warmed by the sun.

3 cups freshly wilted balsam fir tips — new growth only (see page 38 for information on wilting)

3–4 cups almond, soybean, or jojoba base oil (enough to completely cover needles)

2,000 IU vitamin E oil

EQUIPMENT: *1-quart canning jar, stirring utensil, plastic wrap, strainer, fine filter, funnel, glass or plastic storage containers*
PREP TIME: *1 month*
YIELD: *Approximately 2½ cups*
STORAGE: *Store at room temperature, away from light and heat; use within 1 year*
APPLICATION: *Once per day, or as desired*

Cut or tear the wilted fir tree tips into smaller pieces to expose more surface area of the plant to the oil. Your fingers will get sticky, but they'll smell extra fresh! Place the wilted fir tips into a widemouthed 1-quart canning jar. Drizzle the base oil over the plant matter until the oil comes to within 1 inch of the top of the jar. The fir tips will settle with the weight of the oil, so don't worry if it looks as though you don't have enough plant matter in the jar. Gently stir to remove air bubbles and make sure that all the plant matter is submerged.

Place a piece of plastic wrap over the mouth of the jar (to prevent the metal lid from coming into contact with the needles) and tightly screw on the lid. Shake the jar several times to blend thoroughly. Place the jar in a warm, sunny location such as a south-facing windowsill, and allow the fir tips to infuse for 1 month. Shake the jar every day for 30 seconds.

After 1 month, carefully strain the oil through a fine-mesh strainer lined with a fine filter such as muslin or, preferably, a paper coffee filter, then strain again if necessary to remove all herb debris. Squeeze the fir tips to extract as much of the precious oil as possible. Add the vitamin E oil and stir to blend. Discard the marc. The resulting fir-infused oil will be medium green in color.

Pour the finished oil into storage containers, then cap, label, and store in a dark cabinet.

APPLICATION INSTRUCTIONS: To enliven your morning, massage 1 to 2 tablespoons of the oil over your entire body immediately following your morning shower, while your skin is still slightly damp, or simply rub a bit into your feet. Let the oil soak in for 5 to 10 minutes before getting dressed.

If you're a bath person, add approximately 1 tablespoon to your morning bath, soak for 20 minutes, then vigorously towel-dry. Massage more oil into your skin if you want a double whammy shot of energy and refreshment!

Bonus This infusion also acts as a mild sinus decongestant and respiratory antiseptic, perfect as a chest rub if you are suffering from a cold or the flu.

PEPPY PEPPERMINT AND GINGER BODY POWDER

A body powder that helps eliminate morning fatigue? Of course, why not? Here's a stimu-lating, refreshing powder to keep you cool and dry and start your day off on an energized note. The chilling effects of the powdered peppermint and the concentrated menthol send signals to your brain that energy is abundant. Powdered ginger root revitalizes circulation as well, but it is a warming stimulant. Your body and senses are being bombarded by herbal rechargers that deliver a one-two punch, leaving you rarin' to go!

¼ cup dried peppermint leaves

1 teaspoon menthol crystals

½ cup baking soda

½ cup cornstarch

½ cup white cosmetic clay

3 tablespoons ground ginger

EQUIPMENT: *Grinder or mortar and pestle, fine-mesh strainer or flour sifter, medium bowl and whisk or food processor, airtight storage container(s)*

PREP TIME: *20 minutes, plus 3 days to synergize*

YIELD: *Approximately 2 cups*

STORAGE: *Store at room temperature, away from heat and light; use within 1 year*

APPLICATION: *As desired*

Grind the dried peppermint leaves and menthol crystals into a fine powder using a coffee or spice grinder or a mortar and pestle. Sift out the larger, grainy particles using a fine-mesh strainer or flour sifter, if needed. Combine the ground peppermint and menthol crystals with the baking soda, cornstarch, clay, and ground ginger in a medium bowl or a food processor. Gently whisk together or pulse in the food processor for 15 seconds until well blended. Avoid breathing the dust, though there is no real danger of irritation as there is with cayenne powder.

Store the powder in an airtight storage container in a cool, dark place for 3 days to allow the herbal scents to permeate the mixture. Then package the powder in smaller containers, if desired.

APPLICATION INSTRUCTIONS: Apply as you would any body powder, by sprinkling or using a powder puff where needed.

Bonus This powder can double as a simple underarm deodorant for those who want to avoid the chemicals in commercial deodorants or as a foot powder for odoriferous dogs.

FOOT THERAPY

I suspect that if most feet could speak, they'd complain, and loudly. Your feet literally connect you with the earth, stabilize your being, transport you from point A to point B, and enable you to jump, run, ski, bike, swim, and enjoy life, often with grace and style. It's very difficult to get along without them.

So what do we do? Take them for granted and abuse them! We stuff them into ill-fitting shoes, wear shoes and hosiery that trap sweat and bacteria next to our skin, and more often than not put off a visit to the podiatrist if a problem does develop.

Painful, hot, sweaty, sore, odoriferous, and generally uncomfortable feet sure can make life miserable. Avoiding these problems starts with observing basic foot care, such as daily hygiene, keeping toenails trimmed and calluses pared down, wearing activity-appropriate shoes and hosiery, and visiting a podiatrist if the need arises. Personally, I think we should all go barefoot outdoors as often as possible in order to directly receive the earth's grounding energy and allow our feet to breathe and properly stretch.

Treat your feet with tender loving care and they'll reward you with years of diligent, pain-free service. Next time your "dogs" cry out for attention, try one of the following foot-care remedies and see if a little homemade TLC isn't just what the Herb Doc ordered. Your feet will thank you!

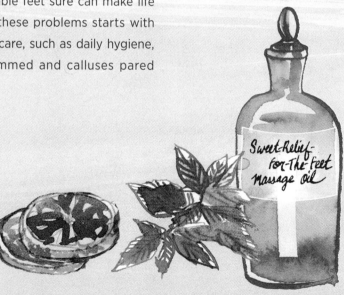

SWEET-RELIEF-FOR-THE-FEET MASSAGE OIL

Used alone, St. John's wort–infused oil, the primary ingredient in this formula, has effective cooling, analgesic, astringent, anti-inflammatory, antispasmodic, and nervine properties. Combined with birch or wintergreen essential oil, it forms an ultra-potent synergized blend with dramatic results, speeding blessed relief to sore, swollen feet, ankles, and calves.

This recipe calls for only a small amount of St. John's wort–infused oil. If you've made some at home (see the recipe on page 64), great. If not, then purchase a small bottle from your local health food store or herbal supplier. But I do recommend that you always have at least a cup of this multipurpose infused oil on hand — fresh and homemade is best, and much less expensive!

20 drops birch or wintergreen essential oil

½ cup St. John's wort–infused oil

EQUIPMENT: *Dropper, dark glass bottle with dropper top or screw cap*
PREP TIME: *15 minutes, plus 24 hours to synergize*
YIELD: *Approximately ½ cup*
STORAGE: *Store at room temperature, away from heat and light; use within 1 year*
APPLICATION: *1 or 2 times per day*

Add the birch or wintergreen essential oil drop by drop directly into a storage bottle. Add the St. John's wort–infused oil. Screw the top on the bottle and shake vigorously for 2 minutes to blend. Label the bottle and place in a dark location that's between 60° and 80°F for 24 hours so that the oils can synergize.

APPLICATION INSTRUCTIONS: Shake well before each use. Massage into feet, ankles, and calves up to twice daily. Let the oil soak in for 5 to 10 minutes before getting dressed.

Bonus Massage over the entire body to bring soothing, welcome comfort to pulled or overworked muscles or ligaments, bruises, or nerve trauma. Spinal injuries and back pain respond positively to consistent treatment with this oil as well.

ODOR-NEUTRALIZING ORANGE FOOT POWDER

*E*mbarrassing foot odor has more than the obvious symptom. It is frequently accompanied by damp skin, blisters, tenderness between the toes, and susceptibility to fungus and infection. Orange essential oil is a terrific odor fighter, tea tree and thyme essential oils can help fight fungus, and the powder helps keep your feet dry.

½ cup baking soda

½ cup cornstarch

½ cup white cosmetic clay

50 drops sweet orange essential oil

25 drops tea tree essential oil (optional)

25 drops thyme (chemotype *linalool*) essential oil (optional)

EQUIPMENT: *Medium bowl and whisk or food processor, dropper, mortar and pestle, airtight storage container(s)*
PREP TIME: *20 minutes, plus 3 days to synergize*
YIELD: *Approximately 1½ cups*
STORAGE: *Store at room temperature, away from heat and light; use within 1 year*
APPLICATION: *2 times per day, or as desired*

Combine the baking soda, cornstarch, and clay in a medium bowl or food processor. Gently whisk together or pulse in the food processor for 15 seconds until well blended. Avoid breathing the dust, though there is no real danger of irritation as there is with cayenne powder. Measure out 6 tablespoons of the powder into a mortar. Drop by drop, add the orange essential oil, and the tea tree and thyme essential oils, if using. Work them into the powder with the pestle until the oil is absorbed. Add this oil mixture to the remaining powder. Whisk the mixture together slowly, shake vigorously in a large container with a tight-fitting lid, or pulse in the food processor for 15 seconds, until blended.

Store the powder in an airtight storage container in a cool, dark place for 3 days to allow the medicinal properties of the herbal ingredients to synergize and permeate the mixture. Package the powder in smaller containers, if desired.

APPLICATION INSTRUCTIONS: Apply as you would any medicated foot powder, by sprinkling or using a powder puff.

Bonus This powder doubles as a lightly fragrant, chemical-free underarm deodorant.

Lini-Mint: Peppermint Foot Chiller

My country-living grandfather used to tell me that the fastest way to cool off and reenergize on a hot day was to immerse your hot, sweaty feet into an icy cold creek. "Literally pulls the heat right out of ya," he'd say. For most of us, though, invigorating rural creeks and mountain streams are not as close as the back forty, so what's the next best and most convenient thing to do?

Refreshing herbal relief is a quick spray away with this super-easy-to-make foot chillin' formula. Vodka and peppermint essential oil combine to form a menthol liniment of moderate intensity, with a cool to cold energy that evaporates rapidly, removing heat along with sweat and odor and leaving you feeling footloose and fancy-free. I recommend stashing a small bottle in your gym bag to use as an postworkout foot refresher — especially if there's no time to shower — it'll put some spring back in your step!

1 cup unflavored vodka

30 drops peppermint essential oil

½ teaspoon vegetable glycerin

EQUIPMENT: *Plastic or glass spritzer bottle*
PREP TIME: *5 minutes*
YIELD: *Approximately 1 cup*
STORAGE: *Store at room temperature, away from heat and light; use within 2 years*
APPLICATION: *As needed*

Combine the vodka, peppermint essential oil, and glycerin in a spritzer bottle and shake vigorously to blend. Label and store. No refrigeration is required, but chilling the formula makes it even more cooling.

APPLICATION INSTRUCTIONS: Shake well before each use. Spray on bare feet whenever they're feeling hot. Allow feet to air-dry before putting on socks or hosiery.

Bonus This spray doubles as a superior room freshener. Simply spritz into the air a few times and say good-bye to staleness and odor. The formula also works like a charm to eliminate lingering litterbox odors when spritzed in the air or on the floor near the box. (Don't spray it right in the box — some cats don't like the same smells we do and you don't want your cat to avoid the box entirely!)

GOUT

Gout develops from deposits of monosodium urate crystals in the joints that accumulate due to an abnormally high level of uric acid (hyperuricemia) in the blood Flare-ups, which can occur without warning, are characterized by extremely painful joint inflammation (arthritis) surrounded by tight, shiny red or purplish skin. The disorder most often affects the joint at the base of the big toe but also commonly the instep, ankle, knee, wrist, and elbow. These joints, being located on the periphery of the body, are cooler, so urate is more likely to crystallize in them than in the warmer joints of the spine, hips, and shoulders, which rarely are affected by gout.

The initial attacks usually affect only one joint and last only a few days, with complete joint function then returning. If the disorder is allowed to progress untreated, attacks become longer-lasting and more frequent, affecting several joints and eventually resulting in joint deformity and tissue damage. When attempting to treat the symptoms of gout, the first step is to relieve the pain by controlling the inflammation. The Herbal Aspirin Salve recipe (next page) works like magic to soothe and comfort the misery.

From a dietary standpoint, gout sufferers often feel significant and relatively rapid relief from pain and swelling when they adopt a low-fat vegetarian or vegan diet, with adequate consumption of fruits, deep green vegetables, nuts, seeds, beans, whole grains, herb teas, and water. Avoidance of alcoholic beverages, soft drinks, and coffee is recommended.

From a lifestyle standpoint, daily cardiovascular and strength-training exercise is encouraged, as many people who have gout are overweight. Ample sleep along with physical and emotional stress management is also key to alleviating symptoms.

HERBAL ASPIRIN SALVE

When you combine meadowsweet, known as "herbal aspirin," with the flowers of arnica, the "aches and pains herb," the result is a rather powerful infused oil that boasts astringent, antirheumatic, analgesic, diuretic, anti-inflammatory, and antispasmodic properties. When massaged into a joint exhibiting gout symptoms, Herbal Aspirin Salve will temporarily relieve the pain, inflammation, and stiffness. I find it to be pure "salve-ation" for my sore hands and wrists after a couple of hours spent hoeing weeds in the garden!

Note: I prefer to use the stovetop method for infusing the healing properties of these flowers into the olive oil, as it results in a very potent, effective medicinal formula.

1 cup dried or 2 cups freshly wilted meadowsweet flowers (see page 38 for information on wilting)

1 cup dried arnica flowers

3 cups extra-virgin olive base oil

2,000 IU vitamin E oil

3–4 tablespoons beeswax (depending on how firm you want the salve to be)

EQUIPMENT: *2-quart saucepan or double boiler, stirring utensil, candy or yogurt thermometer, strainer, fine filter, funnel, glass or plastic storage container (for the infused oil) glass or plastic jars or tins (for the salve)*

PREP TIME: *4 hours to infuse the oil, plus 20 minutes to make the salve and 30 minutes for it to thicken*

YIELD: *Approximately 2½ cups of infused oil and 1¼ cups of salve*

STORAGE: *Store at room temperature, away from heat and light; use within 1 year*

APPLICATION: *Up to 3 times per day*

PREPARING THE HERBAL INFUSED OIL: If you're using freshly wilted meadowsweet flowers, strip them from their stems along with the small bits of attached leaves prior to adding to the pan. Discard the stems. Combine the meadowsweet and arnica flowers with the olive base oil in a 2-quart saucepan or double boiler, and stir thoroughly to blend. The mixture should look like a thick floral soup. Bring the mixture to just shy of a simmer, between 125° and 135°F. Do not let the oil actually simmer — it will degrade the quality of your infused oil. *Do not* put the lid on the pot.

Allow the herbs to macerate in the oil over low heat for 4 hours. Check the temperature every 30 minutes or so with a thermometer and adjust the heat accordingly. If you're using a double boiler, add more water to the bottom pot as necessary, so it doesn't dry out. Stir the infusing mixture at least every 30 minutes or so, as the herb bits tend to settle to the bottom.

After 4 hours, remove the pan from the heat and allow to cool for 15 minutes. While the oil is still warm, carefully strain it through a fine-mesh strainer lined with a fine filter such as muslin or, preferably, a paper coffee filter, then strain again if necessary to remove all debris. Squeeze the herbs to extract as much of the precious oil as possible. Discard the marc.

Add the vitamin E oil and stir to blend. The resulting infused oil blend will be golden-green in color. Pour the finished oil into a storage container, then cap, label, and store in a dark cabinet.

PREPARING THE SALVE: Combine 1 cup of the infused oil with the beeswax in a small saucepan or double boiler, and warm over low heat until the beeswax is just melted. Remove from the heat and allow to cool for 5 minutes, stirring a few times to blend. Pour into plastic or glass jars or tins, cap, label, and set aside for 30 minutes to thicken.

APPLICATION INSTRUCTIONS: Massage a bit of salve into joints affected by gout. Apply up to three times per day.

Bonus This herbal "comfort in a jar" can help relieve the pain of arthritis (especially in the small joints of the fingers and wrists), muscular tension headache, backache, muscle stiffness and strains, and tendonitis.

HAND AND NAIL THERAPY

Our hands are one of our most expressive features and, sad to say, one of our most neglected and abused, aside from our feet. They're constantly exposed to the elements, not to mention dirt, grease, dry air, harsh cleansers, and excessive hand washing. No wonder they're one of the first places on our body to show age! Fingernails and cuticles become brittle and ragged; more seriously, they can become infected with disfiguring nail fungus.

Here are a few tips to fight the ravages of time and the elements on your hands:

• Frequently apply moisturizer, no matter what the season.

• Wear garden or job-appropriate gloves when working outdoors, with chemicals, or with rough materials, and wear rubber gloves when your hands will be exposed to water or cleansers.

• Apply a natural, broad-spectrum sunscreen lotion with an SPF of at least 15 whenever you're in the sun.

• Take your own thoroughly sanitized manicuring tools with you to the manicurist unless you have the utmost confidence in her sanitation habits.

The following recipes will help soften, condition, and protect your hands and nails from everyday abuse, leaving them comfortable, attractive, and soft to the touch.

Grow-My-Nails Oil

Are your fingernails slow to grow? A healthy adult fingernail grows an average of ⅛ inch per month, growing more quickly in summer than in winter. A whole-foods diet with plenty of protein, vitamins, and minerals, especially calcium, magnesium, and silica, plus ample cardio-vascular exercise to promote circulation and blood flow, will definitely encourage nail health and good nail growth. But if you'd like to speed things along and cultivate a set of magnificent talons, then this oil is just what you need. It is designed to condition nails and cuticles, stimulate circulation, and promote growth, plus it acts as an antiseptic, keeping potential infection at bay if you happen to have a nick or cut on your fingers. Comfrey-infused oil does amazing things for slow-to-grow nails that may also be brittle or weak with ragged cuticles. If you massage it into your nails daily, expect to see positive results within a couple of months.

This recipe calls for only a small amount of comfrey-infused oil. If you have some homemade Mend Skin: Comfrey-Infused Oil (page 140), great. If not, then purchase a small bottle from your local health food store or herbal supplier, but I do recommend that you always have at least a cup of this multipurpose infused oil on hand—fresh and homemade is best, and much less expensive!

5 drops ginger essential oil

5 drops lemon essential oil

2 tablespoons comfrey-infused oil

EQUIPMENT: *Dropper, dark glass bottle with dropper top or screw cap*

PREP TIME: *15 minutes, plus 24 hours to synergize*

YIELD: *2 tablespoons*

STORAGE: *Store at room temperature, away from heat and light; use within 1 year*

APPLICATION: *1 or 2 times per day*

Add the ginger and lemon essential oils drop by drop directly into a storage bottle. Add the comfrey-infused oil. Screw the top on the bottle and shake vigorously for 2 minutes to blend. Label the bottle and place in a dark location that's between 60° and 80°F for 24 hours so that the oils can synergize.

APPLICATION INSTRUCTIONS: Shake well before each use. Massage a few drops into clean, dry nails and cuticles once or twice daily. Be consistent with this ritual and you'll be rewarded with strong, flexible, healthy nails.

FARMER'S FRIEND SALVE

*S*age, rosemary, thyme, and myrrh gum — four resinous herbs with incredible vulnerary, antiseptic, anti-inflammatory, and deodorizing properties — come together in this salve specifically designed for serious gardeners and farmers. It comforts and soothes dry, rough, cracked, sun-damaged "outdoor hands" that take a serious beating.

Note: I prefer to use the stovetop method for making the infused oil in this recipe, as it provides a superior extraction of the active properties of these somewhat resinous herbs.

½ cup dried or 1 cup freshly wilted rosemary leaves (see page 38 for information on wilting)

½ cup dried or 1 cup freshly wilted sage leaves

½ cup dried or 1 cup freshly wilted thyme leaves

1 tablespoon myrrh gum powder

3 cups extra-virgin olive base oil

2,000 IU vitamin E oil

3 tablespoons beeswax

1 tablespoon cocoa butter

EQUIPMENT: *2-quart saucepan or double boiler, stirring utensil, candy or yogurt thermometer, strainer, fine filter, funnel, glass or plastic storage container (for the infused oil), glass or plastic jars or tins (for the salve)*

PREP TIME: *5 hours to infuse oil, plus 20 minutes to make the salve and 1 hour for it to thicken*

YIELD: *Approximately 2½ cups of infused oil and 1¼ cups of salve*

STORAGE: *Store at room temperature, away from heat and light; use within 1 year*

APPLICATION: *2 times per day*

PREPARING THE INFUSED OIL: If using you're wilted herbs, strip the leaves from the stems and gently cut or tear them into smaller pieces to expose more surface area to the oil. Discard the stems. Combine the rosemary, sage, thyme, and myrrh with the olive base oil in a 2-quart saucepan or double boiler, and stir thoroughly to blend. The mixture should look like a thick, chunky, green herbal soup. Bring the mixture to just shy of a simmer, between 125° and 135°F. Do not let the oil actually simmer — it will degrade the quality of your infused oil. *Do not* put the lid on the pot.

Allow the herbs to macerate in the oil over low heat for 5 hours. Check the temperature every 30 minutes or so with a thermometer and adjust the heat accordingly. If you're using a double boiler, add more water to the bottom pot as necessary, so it doesn't dry out. Stir the infusing mixture at least every 30 minutes or so, as the herb bits tend to settle to the bottom.

After 5 hours, remove the pan from the heat and allow to cool for 15 minutes. While the oil is still warm, carefully strain it through a fine-mesh strainer lined with a fine filter such as muslin or, preferably, a paper coffee filter, then strain again if necessary to remove all debris. Squeeze the herbs to extract as much of the precious oil as possible. Discard the marc.

Add the vitamin E oil and stir to blend. The resulting infused oil blend will be medium to dark green in color. Pour the finished oil into a storage container, then cap, label, and store in a dark cabinet.

PREPARING THE SALVE: Combine 1 cup of the herbal infused oil with the beeswax and cocoa butter, and warm over low heat until the solids are just melted. Remove from the heat and allow to cool for 5 to 10 minutes, stirring a few times. Pour into storage containers, cap, and label. Set aside for 1 hour to thicken.

APPLICATION INSTRUCTIONS: To aid in healing and conditioning outdoor chore-ravaged hands, massage a dab into slightly damp, clean hands and nails at least twice daily. This will seal in new moisture and prevent evaporation of existing moisture within the skin, plus it will help keep infection at bay if the skin is abraded or cracked.

Bonus This salve is wonderful for conditioning dry or rough feet, shins, elbows, and knees; for healing minor cuts and scrapes; for soothing insect bites and stings; and as a salve for baby's bum to keep diaper rash at bay.

Helping Hand at the Kitchen Sink: Lemon-Spice Oil

I really enjoy using this colorful, lemony-spicy infused oil and often keep a small bottle by my kitchen sink. It conditions and softens dishpan hands, plus it neutralizes food odors that tend to linger on your hands, such as garlic, onion, and fish. This lightly fragrant oil also acts as a mild antiseptic.

Note: I prefer the stovetop method for making this blend, as the dry, hard cinnamon bark, cracked cloves, and tough lemon rind release their medicinal properties best when processed over a steady, even heat source.

½ cup cinnamon bark chips or 10 cinnamon sticks, broken into pieces

½ cup whole cloves, crushed

Peel of 3 lemons, minced or finely chopped

2 cups almond, apricot kernel, or soybean base oil

2,000 IU vitamin E oil

EQUIPMENT: *2-quart saucepan or double boiler, stirring utensil, candy or yogurt thermometer, strainer, fine filter, funnel, glass or plastic storage container*
PREP TIME: *6 hours*
YIELD: *Approximately 1¾ cups*
STORAGE: *Store at room temperature, away from heat and light; use within 1 year*
APPLICATION: *As desired*

Combine the cinnamon, cloves, and lemon peel with the base oil in a 2-quart saucepan or double boiler, and stir thoroughly to blend. The mixture should look like a thick, chunky lemon-spice soup. Bring the mixture to just shy of a simmer, between 125° and 135°F. Do not let the oil actually simmer — it will degrade the quality of your infused oil. *Do not* put the lid on the pot.

Allow the peel and spices to macerate in the oil over low heat for 6 hours. Check the temperature every 30 minutes or so with a thermometer and adjust the heat accordingly. If you're using a double boiler, add more water to the bottom pot as necessary, so it doesn't dry out. Stir the infusing mixture at least every 30 minutes or so, as the peel and spices tend to settle to the bottom.

After 6 hours, remove the pan from the heat and allow to cool for 15 minutes. While the oil is still warm, carefully strain it through a fine-mesh strainer lined with a fine filter such as muslin or, preferably, a paper coffee filter, then strain again if necessary to remove all debris. Squeeze the ingredients to extract as much of the precious oil as possible. Discard the marc.

Add the vitamin E oil and stir to blend. The resulting infused oil blend will be light to medium amber in color. Pour the finished oil into a storage container, then cap, label, and store in a dark cabinet.

APPLICATION INSTRUCTIONS: If you don't like to wear dishwashing gloves when you wash dishes, massage a small amount of the oil into your hands and nails before and after washing dishes. This helps protect your hands during their exposure to hot, soapy water and conditions them afterward. Also, after handling garlic, onions, seafood, or other stinky ingredients, wash your hands, then massage a bit of this oil into them to neutralize the odor.

Not-So-Nice Nail Fungus

Nail fungus, otherwise known as *onychomycosis* or *tinea unguium*, is a disfiguring, unsightly fungal infection of the nail that results in the nail thickening, discoloring, and peeling, with white patches that can be scraped off the surface or long yellowish streaks within the nail itself. The infection often invades the free edge of the nail and spreads toward the root, causing detachment from the nail bed.

Like athlete's foot, this fungus is difficult to eradicate and must be consistently treated. Fungus-Be-Gone Oil Drops (page 68) work well against nail fungus, on both fingernails and toenails. Simply massage 2 drops thoroughly into all 10 nails and the surrounding skin (even if only one nail is infected). Let the oil soak in for 5 minutes. Do this two or three times daily for several months until you see improvement.

Keep your nails cut short and well groomed during this treatment, and *do not share your grooming implements with anyone*, as the fungus is highly contagious. Sanitize all utensils by soaking in hot, soapy water infused with a splash of bleach after each use, then allow to air-dry.

BRITTLE NAIL AND CUTICLE BUTTERY CONDITIONING OIL

This formula makes a very thick, soft, shiny oil with incredible staying power to aid in protecting the nail surface and cuticle from the elements and everyday wear and tear. It adds a natural sheen and promotes strength and flexibility in brittle nails. This rich butter conditions severely dry skin on the hands, feet, knees, shins, and elbows, and it makes a superb stretch-mark prevention ointment when massaged twice daily into ever-expanding pregnant bellies and breasts. (Though if you're making the formula for this last use, use only lavender essential oil, or omit the essential oil entirely.)

5 tablespoons castor base oil

3 tablespoons refined shea butter (unrefined shea butter will work, but its stronger fragrance will often mask the aroma of the essential oils)

25 drops of one of the following essential oils: carrot seed, grapefruit, lavender, lemon, orange, peppermint, *or* rosemary (chemotype *verbenon*), or any combination thereof

EQUIPMENT: *Small saucepan or double boiler, stirring utensil, plastic or glass jar or tin*
PREP TIME: *20 minutes, plus up to 12 hours to thicken*
YIELD: *½ cup*
STORAGE: *Store at room temperature, away from heat and light; use within 1 year*
APPLICATION: *2 times per day, or as desired*

Combine the castor base oil and shea butter in a small saucepan or double boiler, and gently warm over low heat until the shea butter is just melted. Remove from the heat and allow to cool for 5 to 10 minutes. Stir a few times to blend thoroughly. Add essential oil(s) and stir again. Pour the mixture into a storage container, then cap and label. Set this buttery oil aside to thicken, which may take up to 12 hours, depending on the temperature in your kitchen. When it's ready, it will be thick and white (or creamy yellow if you used unrefined shea butter).

APPLICATION INSTRUCTIONS: Once or twice a day, massage a tiny dab of butter into each nail until the butter is absorbed. Gently push back the cuticles with an orange stick. To add sheen, finish by buffing each nail surface with a hand-held nail buffer or soft, flannel cloth, taking care not to buff too hard or fast, which causes the nail surface to become hot.

Bonus This oil is particularly effective in preventing scar tissue formation if formulated with carrot seed, lavender, or rosemary essential oil and consistently applied to fresh cuts and scrapes.

HEADACHES *(Tension)*

In today's modern world, with its incessant noise, barrage of electronic media, near-constant stimulation, emotional upheavals, and incredibly stressful demands on your time and energy, many people suffer from tension headaches, and who can blame them? In general, tension headaches are caused by excessive stress, resulting in tight muscles, throbbing nerves, and constricted circulation. They affect the temple region on either side of the head, the forehead, and the back of the head at the base of the skull. People who have experienced trauma to the neck region tend to experience headaches most frequently in this region.

Analgesic, anti-inflammatory, antispasmodic, and nervine herbs release tension, especially when combined with the aromatically relaxing effect of essential oils. So before you reach for an over-the-counter NSAID (nonsteroidal anti-inflammatory drug), such as ibuprofen, to combat your pain, try a plant-based remedy first. Often a short nap, a little quiet time, a refreshing beverage, and a soothing herbal headache massage oil or balm are just what's needed to obtain significant relief and well-being.

Pay attention to your stress level and your body's reaction to it and learn how to manage your stress or you may find yourself suffering from frequent headaches. My favorite tried-and-true methods of dealing with tension headaches are long, slow walks along a woodland trail; 15 minutes of flowing yoga; a nap with a cold compress or gel pad on my forehead or a chilled lavender and buckwheat eye pillow laid across my eyes and cheeks; or simply weeding in my garden. The stress just melts away as my focus is on something else entirely and the environment is exquisitely quiet.

Constipation and Headaches

I feel I must say this . . . make sure that your bowels move regularly, at least twice per day, as often the cause of chronic headaches, of whatever variety, is simply constipated bowels. Constipation causes the colon to swell and put pressure on your spine, various organs, and major blood vessels and nerves, which can result in aches and pain of all kinds, including headaches.

SERIOUS HEADACHE HELPER

This is serious medicine here — Mother Nature at her finest. Once again, the aromatic lavender flower comes to the rescue, delivering powerful pain relief with a gentle, relaxing hand. Combine that with the analgesic, cooling refreshment of peppermint and the anti-inflammatory and antispasmodic properties of birch and you have an effective natural formula that is very concentrated yet extremely safe.

Note: This is an aromatherapeutically concentrated formula, so use only by the drop as directed.

8 drops peppermint essential oil

8 drops birch essential oil

1 tablespoon lavender essential oil

1 tablespoon jojoba base oil

EQUIPMENT: *Dark glass bottle with dropper top or screw cap*
PREP TIME: *15 minutes, plus 24 hours to synergize*
YIELD: *2 tablespoons*
STORAGE: *Store at room temperature, away from heat and light; use within 2 years*
APPLICATION: *2 or 3 times per day*

Add the peppermint and birch essential oils drop by drop directly into a storage bottle. Add the lavender essential oil and jojoba base oil. Screw the top on the bottle and shake vigorously for 2 minutes to blend. Label the bottle and place in a dark location that's between 60° and 80°F for 24 hours so that the oils can synergize.

APPLICATION INSTRUCTIONS: Shake well before each use. Massage 1 drop into each temple, 2 drops into the base of the neck, and 2 drops into the forehead region. Next, place 3 drops in one palm, rub your palms together to warm the oil, then close your eyes and inhale the vapors from your cupped hands. Breathe slowly and deeply for a few minutes. Your tension headache should begin to melt away.

Bonus This potent antiseptic and anti-inflammatory formula can be applied by the drop to cuts and scrapes, insect bites and stings, blisters, boils, ingrown hairs, ingrown toenails, hangnails, puncture wounds, and bedsores and skin ulcers.

Herbal Foot Soak for Headache Relief

Want a quick and utterly simple remedy for a tension headache? Take a load off and soak your feet in cold water for a spell. It draws blood from your head, easing the heat and muscular tightness that are causing your headache. With the addition of peppermint plus lavender or geranium essential oil to your foot soak, you'll receive energetically balancing and cooling aromatherapeutic benefits throughout your body, all the while softening and deodorizing your rough, tired feet.

2 teaspoons vegetable glycerin

5 drops lavender or geranium essential oil

3 drops peppermint essential oil

EQUIPMENT: *Small bowl, stirring utensil, plastic foot tub*
PREP TIME: *5 minutes*
YIELD: *1 treatment*
STORAGE: *Do not store; mix as needed*
APPLICATION: *As desired*

Combine the glycerin with the essential oils in a small bowl, such as a custard cup, and stir thoroughly to mix.

APPLICATION INSTRUCTIONS: Pour the oil blend into a foot tub with enough very cold water (and maybe a few ice cubes) to cover your feet and ankles. Swish with your feet to blend. Soak your feet for 10 to 15 minutes, with your eyes closed, and breathing deeply and regularly. Briskly dry your feet with a thick, rough towel and follow with an application of a peppermint foot lotion or your favorite moisturizer. Both Save-My-Skin-Salve (page 167) and Buttery Coconut Balm (page 149) work wonders to help keep feet soft and comfortable.

St. John's Wort Blessed Relief Drops

For those of you who get throbbing headaches that concentrate in the neck region, this formula is your herbal blessing of relief. Fresh and aromatic St. John's wort–infused oil combines with slightly camphorous spike lavender essential oil, with its antispasmodic, anti-inflammatory, analgesic and nervine properties, to deliver welcome comfort to tense muscles and spasmodic nerves.

This recipe calls for only a small amount of St. John's wort–infused oil. If you've made some at home (see the recipe on page 64), great. If not, then purchase a small bottle from your local health food store or herbal supplier. But I do recommend that you always have at least a cup of this multipurpose infused oil on hand — fresh and homemade is best, and much less expensive!

30 drops spike lavender essential oil

¼ cup St. John's wort–infused oil

EQUIPMENT: *Dropper, dark glass bottle with dropper top or screw cap*
PREP TIME: *15 minutes, plus 24 hours to synergize*
YIELD: *Approximately ¼ cup*
STORAGE: *Store at room temperature, away from heat and light; use within 1 year*
APPLICATION: *2 or 3 times per day*

Add the spike lavender essential oil drop by drop directly into a storage bottle. Add the St. John's wort–infused oil. Screw the top on the bottle and shake vigorously for 2 minutes to blend. Label the bottle and place in a dark location that's between 60° and 80°F for 24 hours so that the oils can synergize.

APPLICATION INSTRUCTIONS: Shake well before each use. When you feel a tension headache coming on, massage several drops of this oil blend into the nape of your neck, your shoulders, and top of your spine, or better yet, have someone else do it combined with 5 minutes of gentle massage. Lie down, close your eyes, and breathe deeply for 20 minutes, if possible.

Bonus This blend can be applied to arthritic fingers and wrists, bedsores or skin ulcers, blisters, shingles, hemorrhoids, sciatica, spinal injuries, bruises, and inflamed muscles, joints, and tendons. It's a truly multipurpose formula that should be in everyone's medicine chest.

HEMORRHOIDS *(External)*

Hemorrhoids are swollen veiny tissues. They're located in the wall of the rectum and anus and may become inflamed, bleed (especially after a bowel movement), discharge mucous, itch and burn, develop a blood clot (thrombus), or become enlarged and protrude. Those that remain in the anus are called *internal hemorrhoids*, and those that protrude are called *external hemorrhoids*. The formulas offered here are for treating the external variety.

Hemorrhoids may result from repeated straining during bowel movements; constipation makes the straining worse. They often develop to various degrees during pregnancy due to the expanding uterus pressing on the colon and the tendency toward constipation.

The treatment of external hemorrhoids depends on the severity of the symptoms, not the extent of the hemorrhoids. In most instances, the only therapy required is improvement in anal hygiene and administration of a stool softener, psyllium, or mild laxative to prevent straining during bowel movements. Avoiding constipation is of utmost importance so that the condition doesn't persist or return.

Sitz Salve

For more comfort when you "sitz" down, this herbal salve offers astringent, anti-inflammatory, cooling, soothing, and antiseptic properties to help heal irritated hemorrhoidal tissue, stop bleeding, and relieve swelling and pain. The salve doesn't require all the infused oil that this recipe makes; you can use the leftover infused oil to make Great Green Goop (page 210), which is useful for treating insect stings and bites as well as all manner of cuts, scrapes, and other skin irritations.

Note: I prefer to use the stovetop method for infusing the healing properties of the herbs into the olive oil, as this process yields a very potent, effective medicinal formula.

½ cup dried or 1 cup freshly wilted yarrow flowers and leaves (see page 38 for information on wilting)

¼ cup dried or ½ cup freshly wilted chickweed leaves and stems

¼ cup dried or ½ cup freshly wilted plantain leaves

¼ cup dried or ½ cup freshly wilted Oregon grape root

¼ cup powdered black walnut hulls or ½ cup fresh black walnut hulls

3 cups extra-virgin olive base oil

2,000 IU vitamin E oil

3–4 tablespoons beeswax (depending on how firm you want the salve to be)

EQUIPMENT: *2-quart saucepan or double boiler, stirring utensil, candy or yogurt thermometer, strainer, fine filter, funnel, glass or plastic storage container (for the infused oil), glass or plastic jars or tins (for the salve)*

PREP TIME: *6 hours to infuse the oil, plus 20 minutes to make the salve and 30 minutes for it to thicken*

YIELD: *Approximately 2½ cups of infused oil and 1¼ cups of salve*

STORAGE: *Store at room temperature, away from heat and light; use within 1 year*

APPLICATION: *As desired*

PREPARING THE INFUSED OIL: If you're using freshly wilted yarrow, chickweed, or plantain, first cut or tear the herb into smaller pieces to expose more surface area to the oil. If you're using freshly wilted Oregon grape roots or fresh black walnut hulls, coarsely or finely chop them. They're tough — do the best you can. Combine the yarrow, chickweed, plantain, Oregon grape root, and black walnut hulls with the olive base oil in a 2-quart saucepan or double boiler, and stir thoroughly to blend. The mixture should look like a thick, leafy-woody slurry. Bring the mixture to just shy of a simmer, between 125° and 135°F. Do not let the oil actually simmer — it will degrade the quality of your infused oil. *Do not* put the lid on the pot.

Allow the herbs to macerate in the oil over low heat for 6 hours. Check the temperature every 30 minutes or so with a thermometer and adjust the heat accordingly. If you're using a double boiler, add more water to the bottom pot as necessary, so it doesn't dry out. Stir the infusing mixture at least every 30 minutes or so, as the herb bits tend to settle to the bottom. Walnut hull powder will form a paste in the bottom of the pan, so you may need to stir more often.

After 6 hours, remove the pan from the heat and allow to cool for 15 minutes. While the oil is still warm, carefully strain it through a fine-mesh strainer lined with a fine filter such as muslin or, preferably, a paper coffee filter, then strain again if necessary to remove all debris. Squeeze the herbs to extract as much of the precious oil as possible. Discard the marc.

Add the vitamin E oil and stir to blend. The resulting infused oil blend will be dark greenish-brown with a hint of gold. Pour the finished oil into a storage container, then cap, label, and store in a dark cabinet.

PREPARING THE SALVE: Combine 1 cup of the herbal infused oil with the beeswax in a small saucepan or double boiler, and warm over low heat until the beeswax is just melted. Remove from the heat and allow to cool for 5 minutes, stirring a few times to blend. Pour into storage containers, cap, and label. Set aside for 30 minutes to thicken.

APPLICATION INSTRUCTIONS: Cleanse affected area with a cool, soapy, soft washcloth, chemical-free cleansing wipe, or your own Preparation "B": Astringent Aloe Wipes (next page). Pat dry. Apply ½ teaspoon or so of this salve to the irritated area as desired, but especially before bedtime, in the morning, and after each bowel movement.

Bonus This salve can be used to aid in healing bruises, blisters, bedsores and skin ulcers, cuts and scrapes, poison plant rashes, insect bites and stings, eczema, dermatitis, psoriasis, and cracked, fissured skin. It's also wonderfully therapeutic when massaged into postpartum surgical incisions and perineal tears.

Preparation "B": Astringent Aloe Wipes

In addition to the itching and burning of irritated rectal tissue, swollen hemorrhoids will occasionally discharge blood and mucous, leaving you feeling less than fresh and quite uncomfortable. Aloe vera, witch hazel, and lavender essential oil work together to firm tissue, reduce secretions, cool the burn, and calm the itch, while effectively cleansing and deodorizing the anal area. This remedy also aids in healing all manner of other minor infections and skin irritations — blemishes, blisters, boils, contact dermatitis, sunburn, minor burns, ingrown hairs, and bug bites and stings.

½ cup commercially prepared aloe vera juice

½ cup witch hazel (commercially prepared or homemade; see the box on page 305)

1 teaspoon vegetable glycerin

75 drops lavender essential oil

EQUIPMENT: *Plastic or glass bottle*

PREP TIME: *5 minutes*

YIELD: *Approximately 1 cup*

STORAGE: *Use within 2 weeks if stored at room temperature; within 6 months if refrigerated*

APPLICATION: *Up to 5 times per day*

Combine the aloe vera juice, witch hazel, glycerin, and lavender essential oil in a bottle and shake vigorously to blend. Label and store in a dark cabinet.

APPLICATION INSTRUCTIONS: Shake well before each use. Soak a soft flannel cloth, chemical-free and unscented baby wipe, or square cotton cosmetic pad with the wash, and use it to wipe the affected area. Use up to five times per day, but especially before bedtime, in the morning, and after each bowel movement to leave you with a fresh, clean, more comfortable feeling. Follow with Sitz Salve (previous recipe) if desired.

Bonus Use these wipes as a refreshing facial and underarm cleansing wash when you're in a rush and soap is unavailable. Tuck a bottle in your carry-on bag while traveling — you never know when you might get stuck in the airport!

Soothing Comfort Herbal Hemorrhoid Powder

Most hemorrhoidal medicines come in the form of an ointment, salve, or balm, but this is a unique remedy in that it is in the form of a medicated powder. All of the herbs included here have astringent, antiseptic, tissue-tightening, deodorizing, and anti-inflammatory properties with an overall cooling energy to help bring welcome relief while keeping you dry and sanitary.

Note: It's important to purchase these herbs pre-powdered, as they are practically impossible to powder finely enough using common kitchen equipment.

½ cup baking soda

½ cup cornstarch

½ cup white cosmetic clay

3 tablespoons powdered Oregon grape root

3 tablespoons powdered witch hazel bark

2 tablespoons powdered myrrh gum

EQUIPMENT: *Medium bowl and whisk or food processor, airtight storage container(s), flour sifter (optional)*
PREP TIME: *20 minutes, plus 3 days to synergize*
YIELD: *Approximately 2 cups*
STORAGE: *Store at room temperature, away from heat and light; use within 1 year*
APPLICATION: *As desired*

Combine the baking soda, cornstarch, clay, Oregon grape root, witch hazel, and myrrh in a medium bowl or food processor. Slowly whisk together, or pulse in the food processor for 15 seconds, until well blended. Avoid breathing the dust, though there is no real danger of irritation as there is with cayenne powder. Store the powder in an airtight storage container in a cool, dark place for 3 days to allow the medicinal properties of the herbal ingredients to synergize and permeate the mixture. If the mixture is too granular for your liking, sift it through a flour sifter to remove the larger particles. Then package the powder in smaller containers, if desired.

APPLICATION INSTRUCTIONS: Apply with a large cotton ball or cosmetic cotton square to the affected area.

Bonus This powder makes an effective astringent underarm or foot deodorant, especially for people who tend to sweat a lot.

HIVES *(Urticaria)*

Generally appearing as pale or reddened wheals or irregularly shaped swollen patches, hives, also called *urticaria*, are a transient reaction in the skin to a food or drug allergy, infections, or extreme or prolonged stress. The wheals can vary in size from as small as a pea to as large as 8 inches in diameter, in which case the center area may be clear, forming a ring. Hives are characterized by intense itching and burning that can become quite maddening.

Hives can, in addition to manifesting on the skin, result in the release of large amounts of histamines. Histamines are natural chemicals located in the skin that, when activated by an injury, allergic reaction, or other stressor, can cause flushing of the skin, swelling, tightness in the chest, wheezing, and a feeling of faintness.

The most common type of hives, *acute urticaria,* typically lasts less than 6 weeks, and in the majority of cases hives appear suddenly and then disappear within minutes, hours, or a few days. *Chronic urticaria* refers to outbreaks lasting for more than 6 weeks; often the cause is more difficult to pinpoint. *Physical urticaria* refers to hives that develop from pressure, insect bites, vibration, cold, heat, exercise, or sunlight.

Hives are a very common malady, affecting 10 to 20 percent of the population at least once. Prevention can be difficult, because you never know if you will be allergic to a new food or drug or if a new stressful situation in your life will cause an outbreak. The best preventive is to avoid foods and drugs that are known systemic irritants and to minimize stress in your life.

The best topical treatments for hives are those that soothe the itch, cool the burn, and reduce inflammation. I hope you find one of the following remedies helpful the next time you or a loved one suffer from this most irritating of skin maladies.

CHICKWEED JUICE

It doesn't get any fresher than the juice of a common summer weed straight from an organic lawn or garden. Fresh, diluted chickweed juice is cooling, slightly astringent, antiseptic, and anti-inflammatory. It delivers emollient, demulcent properties to soothe irritated, sensitive skin and take the heat and itch out of a case of hives.

Note: Be aware that this formula may slightly sting raw skin and will stain light-colored clothing.

2 cups fresh chickweed leaves and stems

½ cup purified water

¼ cup unflavored vodka

½ teaspoon vegetable glycerin

EQUIPMENT: *Blender, spatula, fine-mesh strainer, fine filter, funnel, glass or plastic bottle*
PREP TIME: *15 minutes*
STORAGE: *Refrigerate; use within 2 weeks*
YIELD: *Approximately 1 cup*
APPLICATION: *3 or 4 times per day*

Chop or tear the chickweed into small pieces before putting it in a blender along with the water, vodka, and glycerin. Blend at low speed for about 10 seconds, then at medium speed for 20 seconds or so. Use a spatula to scrape down the sides of the blender (and free the blades, if they're clogged with plant matter). Add a bit more water if needed to thin the mixture. Blend again for approximately 15 seconds, until the mixture becomes a bright green slurry.

Strain the liquid through a fine-mesh strainer or strainer lined with a fine filter such as muslin or, preferably, a paper coffee filter. Press or squeeze the herb to release all the valuable liquid. Discard the marc. Pour the liquid into a storage container. Label and refrigerate. You will notice that after 2 days of storage, a brownish-green liquid will separate out from the otherwise murky liquid. That's normal, so no worries.

APPLICATION INSTRUCTIONS: Shake well before using. Soak a small cotton pad or square of cotton flannel with the juice and gently dab onto the affected skin. Allow to air-dry. Repeat this procedure 3 or 4 times per day.

Bonus Fresh chickweed juice can be applied directly to any hot, red abscessed tissue such as boils, bedsores or skin ulcers, and blemishes, as well as infections, cuts and scrapes, insect bites and stings, poison plant rashes, dermatitis, weeping eczema, and psoriasis.

PEPPERMINT & LEMON BALM ITCH RELIEF SPRAY

Herbal hydrosols are the watery byproduct of steam-distilling plant materials, most often resulting from the manufacture of essential oils. They contain medicinal properties in a much less concentrated form than essential oils, yet deliver most of the beneficial components of the whole plant without potential irritation, plus they come in a convenient spray form. I use them for all manner of skin problems.

My nerves tend to get jangled by anxiety and anticipation, so I often get an irritating case of itchy, red hives on my chest just before I have to do a lot of traveling and speaking. To help calm my skin, I have used the following hydrosol blend for years with good results.

½ cup lemon balm hydrosol
½ cup peppermint hydrosol

EQUIPMENT: *Spritzer bottle*
PREP TIME: *5 minutes*
YIELD: *1 cup*
STORAGE: *Store at room temperature, away from heat and light; use within 6 months*
APPLICATION: *As desired*

Combine the lemon balm and peppermint hydrosols in a sprizer bottle. Cap, label, and store in a dark cabinet. There's no need to refrigerate, but it feels even better when chilled.

APPLICATION INSTRUCTIONS: Spray on affected area as often as necessary for instant relief.

Bonus This remedy brings great cooling relief when you're experiencing hot flashes or you're in need of a pick-me-up on a hot afternoon!

INFECTIONS OF THE SKIN *(Minor to Moderate)*

It's just a fact of life that sometimes a cut, scrape, burn, or other skin injury becomes infected to some degree, with the attendant redness, swelling, pus, pain, and itchiness. Mother Nature offers us plenty of botanical infection fighters to choose from to help prevent infection or to heal a wound that has already begun to fester.

The herbs used in the following formulas are relatively gentle on the skin yet offer quite potent antiseptic, vulnerary, and anti-inflammatory agents to help the healing process while keeping bacteria at bay. All four formulas should be in everybody's medicine cabinet, ready to use at a moment's notice.

WOUND MAGIC SALVE

*W*ound Magic Salve was so named because it cools, calms, and speeds healing of damaged tissue almost as if by magic. This creamy golden-orange-green salve includes Oregon grape root and calendula blossoms, both with bitter and cooling energies, which aid in tightening tissue and reducing inflammation, while providing antimicrobial protection that ward against and fight off infection. It's strong skin medicine but is gentle enough to use on children over 2 years of age.

Note: I prefer to use the stovetop method for infusing the healing properties of tough, woody Oregon grape root and resinous, sticky, sap-filled calendula flowers into the olive oil, as it results in a very potent, effective formula.

¾ cup dried or 1½ cups freshly wilted Oregon grape root (see page 38 for information on wilting)

¾ cup dried or 1½ cups freshly wilted calendula flowers

3 cups extra-virgin olive base oil

2,000 IU vitamin E oil

3 tablespoons beeswax

1 tablespoon cocoa butter

100 drops lavender essential oil

EQUIPMENT: *2-quart saucepan or double boiler, stirring utensil, candy or yogurt thermometer, strainer, fine filter, funnel, glass or plastic storage container (for the infused oil), glass or plastic jars or tins (for the salve)*

PREP TIME: *5 hours to infuse the oil, plus 20 minutes to make the salve and 1 hour for it to thicken*

STORAGE: *Store at room temperature, away from heat and light; use within 1 year*

YIELD: *Approximately 2½ cups of infused oil and 1¼ cups of salve*

APPLICATION: *2 or 3 times per day*

PREPARING THE INFUSED OIL: If you're using wilted Oregon grape root, chop or grate the root to expose more surface area to the oil. If you're using wilted calendula flowers, gently cut or tear the flowers into smaller pieces. Combine the Oregon grape root and calendula flowers with the olive base oil in a 2-quart saucepan or double boiler, and stir thoroughly to blend. The mixture should look like a thick, chunky yellow-orange herbal soup. Bring the mixture to just shy of a simmer, between 125° and 135°F. Do not let the oil actually simmer — it will degrade the quality of your infused oil. *Do not* put the lid on the pot.

Allow the herbs to macerate in the oil over low heat for 5 hours. Check the temperature every 30 minutes or so with a thermometer and adjust the heat accordingly. If you're using a double boiler, add more water to the bottom pot as necessary, so it doesn't dry out. Stir the infusing mixture at least every 30 minutes or so, as the herb bits tend to settle to the bottom.

After 5 hours, remove the pan from the heat and allow to cool for 15 minutes. While the oil is still warm, carefully strain it through a fine-mesh strainer lined with a fine filter such as muslin or, preferably, a paper coffee filter, then strain again if necessary to remove all debris. Squeeze the herbs to extract as much of the precious oil as possible. Discard the marc.

Add the vitamin E oil and stir to blend. The color of the resulting infused oil blend will be a lovely mix of gold, orange, and green. Pour the finished oil into a storage container, then cap, label, and store in a dark cabinet.

PREPARING THE SALVE: Combine 1 cup of the herbal infused oil with the beeswax and cocoa butter in a small saucepan or double boiler, and warm over low heat until the solids are just melted. Remove from the heat and allow to cool for 5 minutes, stirring a few times. Add the lavender essential oil and stir again. Pour into plastic or glass jars or tins, cap, and label. Set aside for 1 hour to thicken.

APPLICATION INSTRUCTIONS: Cleanse the affected area with soap and water, your favorite natural antiseptic cleanser, Super Herbal Antimicrobial Liniment (next recipe), or Stinking Rose Liniment (page 206). Pat dry, then apply this salve so that it just covers the wound. Gently massage into skin and surrounding area. Do this two or three times per day.

Bonus This salve works miracles when massaged into severely dry, cracked hands and heels, slow-to-heal wounds, patches of psoriasis or eczema, poison plant rashes, and skin that is suffering from a new bruise.

SUPER HERBAL ANTIMICROBIAL LINIMENT

This is an alcoholic extract of seven herbs frequently used to treat skin conditions that need astringent and antiseptic attention plus relief from inflammation. This liniment also makes an excellent wash for removing debris from fresh wounds and a fabulous follow-up wash to clear out any pus that is weeping from a wound.

Note: This liniment *will sting* open wounds and raw flesh, but it is amazingly effective.

½ cup dried or 1 cup freshly wilted echinacea root (see page 38 for information on wilting)

½ cup dried or 1 cup freshly wilted Oregon grape root

¼ cup cloves, crushed

¼ cup myrrh gum powder

1 teaspoon ground cayenne

1 teaspoon vegetable glycerin

50 drops palmarosa essential oil

50 drops thyme (chemotype *linalool*) essential oil

3–4 cups unflavored vodka

EQUIPMENT: *1-quart canning jar, plastic wrap, fine-mesh strainer, fine filter, funnel, glass or plastic storage containers*
PREP TIME: *8 weeks*
STORAGE: *Store at room temperature, away from heat and light; use within 2 years*
YIELD: *Approximately 2½ cups*
APPLICATION: *2 or 3 times per day*

If you are using freshly wilted echinacea or Oregon grape root, chop or grate them to expose more surface area during maceration. Combine the echinacea root, Oregon grape root, cloves, myrrh, and cayenne with the glycerin and the palmarosa and thyme essential oils in a 1-quart canning jar. Pour the vodka over all, so that it comes to within ½ inch of the top of the jar. The herbs should be completely covered. Place a piece of plastic wrap over the mouth of the jar (to prevent the metal lid from coming into contact with the jar's contents), then screw on the lid. Shake the mixture for about 30 seconds to blend the contents thoroughly. After 24 hours, top up with more vodka if necessary. The herbs will settle a bit in the jar, but that's okay.

Store the jar in a cool, dark place for 8 weeks so that the vodka can extract the valuable chemical components from the herbs. Shake the jar several times each day for 15 to 30 seconds in order to prevent the myrrh gum and cayenne powders from forming a paste at the bottom of the jar.

At the end of the 8 weeks, strain the herbs through a fine-mesh strainer lined with a fine filter such as muslin or, preferably, a paper coffee filter. Press or squeeze the herbs to release all the valuable herbal extract. Strain again, if necessary, to remove all of the fine herb particulate matter. Discard the marc. Pour the liquid into a storage container. Cap, label, and store in a dark cabinet.

APPLICATION INSTRUCTIONS: Shake well before each use. Using a soft cloth or cotton pad, dab the liniment onto the affected area two or three times daily. Allow to air-dry, preferably, or gently pat dry. Follow with an application of Wound Magic Salve (previous recipe) or Super Herbal Antibacterial Drops (page 208).

Bonus This liniment can be applied by the drop, twice daily, to blemishes, ingrown toenails, and ingrown hairs to help soothe inflammation, reduce redness, and kill bacteria.

The man who has planted a garden feels that he has done something for the good of the world.

— CHARLES DUDLEY WARNER

STINKING ROSE LINIMENT

What's a stinking rose? Garlic, of course! Some people may hesitate to use this formula due to the lingering garlic aroma. But when you have a minor to moderate infection that is slow to heal, and all else has failed, garlic liniment more often than not will come to the rescue. With its powerful antiviral, antifungal, broad-spectrum antibacterial, and anthelmintic properties, garlic is a potent warrior in the war against infection! This liniment also makes an excellent wash for removing debris from fresh wounds and a fabulous follow-up wash to clear out any pus that is weeping from a wound.

Note: Be aware that this liniment *will sting* raw skin and open wounds, but it is oh-so-effective at encouraging healing in damaged and infected skin tissue.

2 cups peeled garlic cloves

1 teaspoon vegetable glycerin

3–4 cups unflavored vodka

EQUIPMENT: *1-quart canning jar, plastic wrap, fine-mesh strainer, fine filter, funnel, glass or plastic storage containers*
PREP TIME: *20 minutes, plus 4 weeks for extraction*
STORAGE: *Store at room temperature, away from heat and light; use within 2 years*
YIELD: *Approximately 3 cups*
APPLICATION: *2 or 3 times per day*

Crush or finely chop the garlic cloves to expose more surface area during maceration. Add the garlic and glycerin to a 1-quart canning jar, then pour the vodka over them, so that it comes to within ½ inch of the top of the jar. The garlic should be completely covered. Place a piece of plastic wrap over the mouth of the jar (to prevent the metal lid from coming into contact with the jar's contents), then screw on the lid. Shake the mixture for about 30 seconds to blend the contents. After 24 hours, top up with more vodka if necessary.

Store the jar in a cool, dark place for 4 weeks so that the vodka can extract the valuable chemical components from the garlic. Shake the jar every day for 15 to 30 seconds.

At the end of the 4 weeks, strain the garlic through a fine-mesh strainer lined with a fine filter such as muslin or, preferably, a paper coffee filter, then strain again if necessary to remove all herb debris. Press or squeeze the garlic to release all the valuable extract. Discard the marc. Pour the liquid into storage containers. Cap, label, and store in a dark cabinet.

APPLICATION INSTRUCTIONS: Shake well before each use. Using a soft cloth or cotton pad, dab the liniment onto the affected area two or three times daily. Allow to air-dry, preferably, or gently pat dry. Follow with an application of Wound Magic Salve (page 202) or Super Herbal Antibacterial Drops (next page).

Russian Penicillin

During World War I, British, French, and Russian army physicians treated infected battle wounds with garlic juice. They also prescribed garlic to prevent and treat amoebic dysentery.

Alexander Fleming's discovery of penicillin in 1928 launched the Age of Antibiotics, and by World War II, penicillin and sulfa drugs had largely replaced garlic as the treatment of choice for infected wounds. But Russia's more than 20 million World War II casualties overwhelmed its antibiotic supply. Red Army physicians relied heavily on garlic, which came to be called Russian penicillin.

— MICHAEL CASTLEMAN, *The Healing Herbs: The Ultimate Guide to the Curative Power of Nature's Medicines*

Super Herbal Antibacterial Drops

Extremely easy to make, this concentrated formula has a cooling energy and powerful antiseptic, anti-inflammatory, and skin-cell-regenerating properties. It also helps relieve the itch that so often accompanies the healing of a wound. It has an intense "green medicine" fragrance. You can use it by the drop on any skin affliction to prevent or fight off infection. I recommend keeping a small bottle with you at all times, because you never know what your skin might encounter over the course of a day.

Note: This is an aromatherapeutically concentrated formula, so use only by the drop as directed.

25 drops Moroccan blue chamomile or German chamomile essential oil

25 drops tea tree essential oil

1 tablespoon lavender essential oil

2½ teaspoons jojoba base oil

EQUIPMENT: *Dropper, dark glass bottle with dropper top or screw cap*
PREP TIME: *15 minutes, plus 24 hours to synergize*
YIELD: *Approximately 2 tablespoons*
STORAGE: *Store at room temperature, away from heat and light; use within 2 years*
APPLICATION: *2 times per day*

Add the chamomile and tea tree essential oils drop by drop directly into a storage bottle. Add the lavender essential oil and jojoba base oil. Screw the top on the bottle and shake vigorously for 2 minutes to blend. Label and place the bottle in a dark location that's between 60° and 80°F for 24 hours so that the oils can synergize.

APPLICATION INSTRUCTIONS: Cleanse the affected area with soap and water, your favorite natural antiseptic cleanser, Super Herbal Antimicrobial Liniment (page 204), or Stinking Rose Liniment (previous recipe). Pat dry, then apply this formula by the drop, so that it just covers the wound. Gently tap into the skin and surrounding area with your finger. Do this twice daily.

Bonus These drops can be applied twice daily to blemishes, ingrown toenails, and ingrown hairs to help soothe inflammation, reduce redness, and kill bacteria.

INSECT BITES AND STINGS

Summertime — don't you love just about every-thing it has to offer? Everything, that is, except the crawling, buzzing, flying nuisance insects that can inject misery into an almost perfect day. When an insect stings or bites, its venom enters the skin, causing the familiar sensations of burning and itching accompanied by inflammation, heat, and localized swelling. What you need is an herbal remedy that delivers cooling plant energy with astringent and anti-inflammatory properties to calm the itch. The following formulas offer rapid and effective relief from bites and stings that are driving you mad with the need to scratch.

Not My Grandma's Remedy

I have to share this tidbit with you regarding my great-grandmother Ashe. She had this nasty habit of chewing tobacco — complete with the requisite brass spittoons scattered about the house, their edges spattered with brown slime. She grew a personal tobacco patch in her backyard, as many rural folks did in the southeastern United States. My grandfather told me that she used to apply chewed-tobacco "spit paste" to the occa-sional bee stings that he and his many sib-lings would get, to help relieve the pain. It does work, but at the time I heard this story I was about 8 years old, and the thought of someone putting their slimy tobacco "chaw" on my skin grossed me out.

Nowadays, when I get a burning ant bite or bee sting, I find a common plantain leaf growing nearby, chew it to a pulp, and apply my own "spit paste" to the affliction. Yes, it works as well as tobacco. Plantain's inherent astringency and bitterness cool the red heat or inflammation of the bite or sting, allowing its tissue-healing properties to work. Pretty neat, isn't it? A potent remedy from a simple, common weed — and no need for spittoons!

GREAT GREEN GOOP

The final product looks like a very dark green tar — rather icky, but I promise that it will deliver loads of relief for many minor skin ailments. It acts as a fabulous anti-inflammatory, astringent, vulnerary, and antiseptic, plus the German chamomile essential oil delivers antihistamine benefits.

This recipe calls for a small amount of the oil from Sitz Salve (page 194). If you've made that salve and have leftover infused oil, great! If not, then make the infused oil for that recipe (not the entire recipe, just the infused oil!).

7 tablespoons Sitz Salve infused oil

1–2 tablespoons beeswax (depending on how firm you want the salve to be)

20 drops German chamomile or Moroccan blue chamomile essential oil

EQUIPMENT: *Small saucepan or double boiler, stirring utensil, plastic or glass jar or tin*
PREP TIME: *20 minutes to make the salve, plus 30 minutes to thicken*
YIELD: *Approximately ½ cup*
STORAGE: *Store at room temperature, away from heat and light; use within 1 year*
APPLICATION: *As desired*

Combine the infused oil and the beeswax in a small saucepan or double boiler, and warm over low heat until the beeswax is just melted. Remove from the heat and allow to cool for 5 minutes, stirring a few times. Add the chamomile essential oil and stir again to thoroughly blend. Slowly pour the liquid salve into the storage container, then cap and label. Set aside for 30 minutes to thicken.

APPLICATION INSTRUCTIONS: Apply a tiny dab to insect bites and stings, as desired.

Quick and "Neat" Insect Bite and Sting Relief

Lavender and tea tree are two of only a handful of essential oils that can be safely applied to the skin "neat" or undiluted. To gain quick relief from the itch, pain, and swelling of bites and stings, apply a drop of either essential oil directly to the affected area up to three times per day until the discomfort has subsided. *Always* keep a small bottle of both essential oils in your medicine cabinet. Between the two, they can cure and comfort almost any malady!

CALENDULA JUICE

A simple recipe made from fresh-picked, sticky, resinous calendula flowers, this diluted juice is a potent anti-inflammatory, astringent, antiseptic, and vulnerary that will deliver relief to the irritation of insect bites and stings. If your mishaps with insects have a tendency to get infected, perhaps because you pick at them or scratch too much, this brownish-orange flower juice is for you, as it really helps fight infection and speeds skin cell regeneration.

Note: This brownish-orange juice will stain light-colored clothing and slightly sting raw skin.

2 cups freshly picked calendula flowers

½ cup unflavored vodka

½ cup purified water

½ teaspoon vegetable glycerin

EQUIPMENT: *Blender, spatula, fine-mesh strainer, fine filter, funnel, glass or plastic bottle*
PREP TIME: *15 minutes*
YIELD: *Approximately 1¼ cup*
STORAGE: *Refrigerate; use within 2 weeks*
APPLICATION: *3 or 4 times per day*

First, cut or tear the calendula flowers into smaller pieces so that they blend more easily. Place the flowers in the blender along with the vodka, water, and glycerin. Blend at low or medium speed for about 10 seconds. Use a spatula to scrape down the sides of the blender and free the blades, if they're clogged with plant matter. Add a bit more water if necessary. Repeat, until the mixture becomes a frothy, pale yellow-orange slurry.

Strain the thick liquid through a fine-mesh strainer or strainer lined with a fine filter such as muslin or, preferably, a paper coffee filter. Press or squeeze the herb to release all the valuable liquid. Discard the marc. Pour the liquid into a storage container. Label and refrigerate. You will notice that after 2 days of storage, a dark brownish-orange liquid will separate out from the otherwise murky liquid. That's normal, so no worries.

APPLICATION INSTRUCTIONS: Shake well before each use. Soak a small cotton pad or square of cotton flannel with the juice and gently dab onto bites or stings. Allow to air-dry. Repeat this procedure three or four times per day.

Bonus This herbal juice make a great spot treatment for drying up blemishes, when applied up to three times per day with a cotton swab.

INSOMNIA

Insomnia is extremely common; up to one-third of the population suffers from it, some chronically. According to the National Sleep Foundation, though most experts recommend at least 7 to 9 hours of sleep per night, most adults in the United States get significantly less. On average, working adults sleep almost an hour less than they need to.

Sleep robbers include anxiety, illness and certain medical conditions (such as sleep apnea and restless legs syndrome), depression, stress, pain, hormonal changes, poor sleep habits, nontraditional working hours, and parenting young children. Plus, changes in sleep patterns are part of the normal aging process. As we age we tend to have a more difficult time falling and staying asleep.

Sleep is critical to good health and well-being, and being sleep-deprived takes its toll on our looks, mood, and overall health and comfort. Getting adequate sleep should become a priority for everyone, treasured as the true health and beauty treatment that it is! Here are some tips for blissful sleep as well as aromatically pleasing herbal formulas that I hope will have you feeling and looking fabulous in 40 winks.

Useful Tips to Pave the Way for Better Sleep

According to the National Sleep Foundation, doing the following can help you achieve a good night's rest:

- Establish consistent sleep and wake schedules, even on weekends.
- Create a regular, relaxing bedtime routine such as soaking in a hot bath or listening to soothing music — begin an hour or more before the time you expect to fall asleep.
- Create a sleep-conducive environment that is dark, quiet, comfortable, and cool.
- Sleep on a comfortable mattress and pillows.
- Use your bedroom only for sleep and sex (keep "sleep stealers" out of the bedroom — avoid watching TV, using a computer, or reading in bed).
- Finish eating at least 2 to 3 hours before your regular bedtime.
- Exercise regularly, but not for at least a few hours before bedtime.
- Avoid caffeine and alcohol close to bedtime, and give up smoking.

INSOMNIACS' FRIEND: HERBAL PILLOW DROPS

As I'm sure you've noticed by now, lavender essential oil appears in a myriad of my formulas. I use it so often because it is considered the most universally useful essential oil produced today, not to mention its consistent availability and affordability. Lavender is known for its relaxing, soothing, and calming effects and is an age-old, gentle, yet powerful aid toward balancing the central nervous system. It promotes deep, restful sleep with nary a side effect. These highly aromatic pillow drops contain lavender as their primary ingredient plus other calming and balancing essential oils that will help you get some much needed shut-eye.

Note: This is an aromatherapeutically concentrated formula, so use only by the drop as directed.

5 drops Roman chamomile essential oil

5 drops sweet marjoram essential oil

1 tablespoon lavender essential oil

EQUIPMENT: *Dropper, dark glass bottle with dropper top or screw cap*
PREP TIME: *15 minutes, plus 24 hours to synergize*
YIELD: *1 tablespoon*
STORAGE: *Store at room temperature, away from heat and light; use within 2 years*
APPLICATION: *Once a day, immediately before bedtime*

Add the Roman chamomile and sweet marjoram essential oils drop by drop directly into a storage bottle. Add the lavender essential oil. Screw the top on the bottle and shake vigorously for 2 minutes to blend. Label the bottle and place the bottle in a dark location that's between 60° and 80°F for 24 hours so that the oils can synergize.

APPLICATION INSTRUCTIONS: Place 2 to 4 drops on your pillowcase, or on a tissue or handkerchief you'll hold in your hand or tuck under your head. Lie down, pull up the covers, and breathe deeply as you drift off into a more peaceful place.

Bonus These drops work wonders to relieve tension headaches. Apply a drop to each temple, a drop behind each ear, and two drops to the nape of your neck. Lie down with your eyes closed for 20 minutes, breathing deeply of the vapors.

SLEEPY TIME BALM

In the summer, when fresh herbs are available, I make several jars of this sleep-enhancing balm in preparation for winter, when I like to slather myself with its soothing, aromatic goodness just prior to bedtime. It works double-duty to lull me to sleep while moisturizing my winter-dry skin. This is my wintertime "beauty rest in a jar" balm. If you have trouble falling asleep when traveling, tuck a small jar of Sleepy Time Balm in your overnight bag and rest easy.

Note: I prefer to use the stovetop method of extraction and freshly wilted herbs to brew this infused oil blend, as I like the more potent, relaxing aroma that results. Dried herbs will work nicely, too, though, with the exception of lemon balm, which must always be used fresh.

¾ cup freshly wilted lemon balm leaves (see page 38 for information on wilting)

⅓ cup dried or ⅔ cup freshly wilted mugwort leaves

⅓ cup dried or ⅔ cup freshly wilted chamomile flowers

⅓ cup dried or ⅔ cup freshly wilted lavender buds

3 cups almond or soybean base oil

2,000 IU vitamin E oil

3–4 tablespoons beeswax (depending on how firm you want the balm to be)

40 drops lavender essential oil

20 drops sweet orange or bergamot essential oil

10 drops rose otto essential oil (optional)

EQUIPMENT: *2-quart saucepan or double boiler, stirring utensil, candy or yogurt thermometer, strainer, fine filter, funnel, glass or plastic storage container (for the infused oil), glass or plastic jars or tins (for the balm)*

PREP TIME: *4 hours to infuse the oil, plus 20 minutes to make the balm and 30 minutes for it to thicken*

YIELD: *Approximately 2½ cups of infused oil and 1¼ cups of balm*

STORAGE: *Store at room temperature, away from heat and light; use within 1 year*

APPLICATION: *As desired*

PREPARING THE HERBAL INFUSED OIL: Cut or tear the leaves of the lemon balm into smaller pieces, to expose more surface area to the oil. If you're using freshly wilted mugwort, do the same. If using you're using freshly wilted chamomile or lavender flowers, strip the flowers from the stems; discard stems. Combine the lemon balm, mugwort, chamomile, and lavender in a 2-quart saucepan or double boiler. Add the base oil and stir thoroughly to blend. The mixture should look like a thick, leafy-floral slurry. Bring the mixture to just shy of a simmer, between 125° and 135°F. Do not let the oil actually simmer — it will degrade the quality of your infused oil. *Do not put the lid on the pot.*

Allow the herbs to macerate in the oil over low heat for 4 hours. Check the temperature every 30 minutes or so and adjust the heat accordingly. If you're using a double boiler, add more water to the bottom pot as necessary, so it doesn't dry out. Stir the infusing mixture at least every 30 minutes or so, as the herb bits tend to settle to the bottom.

After 4 hours, remove the pan from the heat and allow to cool for 15 minutes. While the oil is still warm, carefully strain it through a fine-mesh strainer lined with a fine filter such as muslin or, preferably, a paper coffee filter, then strain again if necessary to remove all debris. Squeeze the herbs to extract as much of the precious oil as possible. Discard the marc.

Add the vitamin E oil and stir to blend. The resulting infused oil blend will be golden-green in color. Pour the finished oil into a storage container, then cap, label, and store in a dark cabinet.

PREPARING THE BALM: Combine 1 cup of the herbal infused oil and the beeswax in a small saucepan or double boiler, and warm over low heat until the beeswax is just melted. Remove from the heat and allow to cool for 5 minutes, stirring a few times. Add the lavender, sweet orange or bergamot, and rose otto essential oils and stir thoroughly. Pour into storage containers, cap, label, and set aside for 30 minutes to thicken.

APPLICATION INSTRUCTIONS: Gently massage a little dab of balm into your chest, back, and temples, around your ears, under your nose, and on your throat. It can be applied at any time of day to induce a sense of serenity and relaxation.

Sleep-Enhancing Herbal Spray

Some people, especially those who are sensitive to intense fragrance, prefer to use essential oils diluted in a spray rather than inhaling the concentrated essential oil vapors directly. Either way, the benefits of serenity, peacefulness, and sound sleep will be received by all. To create a calming, mildly aromatic pillow or linen mist or room spray, simply make Insomniacs' Friend: Herbal Pillow Drops (page 213) and combine 20 drops of that blend with ¼ cup of purified or distilled water and ¼ cup of unflavored vodka in a spray bottle. The total yield will be ½ cup.

Shake well before each use. Prior to bedtime, generously spray your bedroom or lightly mist your pillow or bed linens. Good night . . . sleep tight . . . and here's hoping your sweet dreams come true!

Note: Avoid spraying directly on or over furniture or plastics.

DREAM WEAVER'S RELAXING RUB

*T*he essential oils in this formula were chosen for their relaxing and sedative properties and soothing aromas. When massaged into strategic places on your body, this sleep-enhancing oil blend will lull you into a peaceful state of mind and lead you down the tranquil path to the Land of Nod.

This recipe calls for a small amount of Chamomile Baby Massage Oil (page 106). If you've made that oil and have some left over, great! If not, you can use almond or soybean oil, though the final fragrance, texture, and relaxing properties will be somewhat diminished.

25 drops lavender essential oil

15 drops bergamot essential oil

15 drops grapefruit essential oil

15 drops sweet orange essential oil

1 cup Chamomile Baby Massage Oil or almond or soybean base oil

EQUIPMENT: *Dropper, dark glass bottle with dropper top or screw cap*
PREP TIME: *15 minutes, plus 24 hours to synergize*
YIELD: *Approximately 1 cup*
STORAGE: *Store at room temperature, away from heat and light; use within 2 years*
APPLICATION: *As desired*

Add the lavender, bergamot, grapefruit, and sweet orange essential oils drop by drop directly into a storage bottle. Add the base oil. Screw the top on the bottle and shake vigorously for 2 minutes to blend. Label the bottle and place it in a dark location that's between 60° and 80°F for 24 hours so that the oils can synergize.

APPLICATION INSTRUCTIONS: Gently massage a little dab of oil into your chest, back, and temples, around your ears, under your nose, and on your throat. Apply at any time of day to induce a sense of serenity and relaxation.

> **Bonus** This oil blend can be used as a most relaxing bath oil and conditioning body massage oil; it is especially blissful if made with chamomile-infused oil as the base. It's perfect for easing tense muscles and calming irritable or overexcited young children over 2 years of age.

Rest, rest, perturbed spirit.

— WILLIAM SHAKESPEARE, *Hamlet*

LIP THERAPY

Your lips, unlike the rest of your skin, do not contain any sebaceous (oil) or sweat glands and therefore cannot moisturize themselves; they constantly need lubrication from an outside source. Normally, a small amount of saliva combined with natural oil that seeps in from the surrounding skin is sufficient to keep them moist. However, if the lip tissue is damaged from heat, cold, matte lipsticks, dry air, smoking, sunburn, windburn, herpes, infection, or topical or oral medications, your natural supplies of lubrication will not be sufficient to prevent your lips from becoming dry, cracked, or rough.

To keep your smoocher soft, kissable, comfortable, and protected from the elements, try one of the following totally natural lip-pampering formulas. Take heart, all of the ingredients are actually edible, without a slick of petroleum jelly in sight.

Healthy Lip Tips

Little quarter- or half-ounce jars of homemade lip gloss or balm make welcome holiday or anytime gifts for friends and family. From experience in crafting scads of them over the years, I've noticed that children tend to like sweet and fruity flavors, and occasionally anise or fennel. Men mostly like the mints, sweet orange, eucalyptus, and plain flavor, and women tend to favor the mints, sweet orange, tangerine, lime, rose, and vanilla. Personally, I like to combine lime, orange, tangerine, or peppermint with vanilla, as it softens the sharpness of those four flavors.

Here are a couple of tips if you don't have a pot of lip balm handy:

- Dab honey on your lips to soothe and protect. Honey acts as a humectant — it draws moisture from the air to your skin, thus keeping lips soft and plump. It tastes great, too.
- Castor oil, the first ingredient in most lipsticks, can be applied straight out of the bottle for a glossy look with real staying power! Castor oil is super thick and shiny.

PURE AND SIMPLE FLAVORED LIP GLOSS

This is a very basic, protective lip gloss to which I've added viscous, shiny castor oil to provide real staying power. Make it plain or with the optional essential oils for flavoring — it's up to you. Feel free to experiment with natural, oil-based food flavorings such as coconut, almond, cherry, apricot, apple, or peach, as they can add more exciting, luscious tastes.

6 tablespoons almond, apricot kernel, or soybean base oil

1 tablespoon castor base oil

1 tablespoon beeswax (plus 1–3 additional teaspoons if you prefer a firmer gloss)

¼ teaspoon vegetable glycerin

30 drops of one of the following essential oils: anise, fennel, lemon, lime, peppermint, rose otto, spearmint, sweet orange, tangerine, or vanilla, or a combination thereof

VARIATION: Use 30 drops carrot seed, rosemary (chemotype *verbenon*), or myrrh essential oil to revitalize dry, chapped lips *or* 30 drops of tea tree or eucalyptus (species *radiata*) essential oil to treat cold sores and cracked, bleeding lips.

EQUIPMENT: *Small saucepan or double boiler, stirring utensil, small glass or plastic jars or tins*
PREP TIME: *Approximately 30 minutes, plus 2 hours to synergize and thicken*
YIELD: *Approximately ½ cup (eight ½-ounce containers)*
STORAGE: *Store at room temperature, away from heat and light; use within 1 year*
APPLICATION: *As desired*

Combine the base oils, beeswax, and glycerin in a small saucepan (a ¾-quart size works great) or double boiler, and warm over low heat until the wax is just melted. Remove from the heat and allow to cool for 5 minutes, stirring a few times to blend. Add the essential oils (if desired), and stir again to thoroughly blend. Slowly pour the liquid lip gloss into storage containers, cap, and label. Set aside for 2 hours for the flavor and consistency to synergize and the balm to thicken.

APPLICATION INSTRUCTIONS: To keep lips in tiptop condition, apply throughout the day, as desired.

COCONUT-HONEY BLISS LIP BUTTER

Restore comfort and softness to chapped, dry, weatherbeaten lips with this thick, rich, emollient, lip butter. This formula is loaded with natural moisturizers, including honey, which adds both luscious flavor and humectants. Completely edible and quite yummy — everyone loves this lip treatment.

- 2 tablespoons extra-virgin, unrefined coconut base oil
- 3 tablespoons almond base oil
- 3 tablespoons cocoa butter
- 1 tablespoon beeswax
- 1 tablespoon refined shea butter, (unrefined shea butter will work, but its stronger fragrance will tend to mask the coconut-honey aroma and taste)
- 1 teaspoon raw honey

EQUIPMENT: *Small saucepan or double boiler, stirring utensil, small plastic or glass jars or tins*
PREP TIME: *30 minutes, plus up to 48 hours to synergize and thicken*
YIELD: *Approximately 10 tablespoons (10 ½-ounce containers)*
STORAGE: *Store at room temperature, away from heat and light; use within 1 year*
APPLICATION: *As desired*

Combine the coconut base oil, almond base oil, cocoa butter, beeswax, shea butter, and honey in a small saucepan (a ¾-quart size works great) or double boiler, and warm over low heat until the solids are just melted. Remove from the heat and allow to cool for 5 minutes, stirring a few times to blend. Over the next 15 minutes, as the mixture continues to cool and begins to turn opaque and thicken a bit, vigorously stir the mixture for 10 seconds every minute or so to thoroughly incorporate the water-based honey.

Slowly pour the thick mixture into storage containers. Cap and label. This particular blend of ingredients may require up to 48 hours at room temperature for the consistency and flavor to synergize and to properly thicken. You can speed the thickening process along, if you wish, by putting the containers in the refrigerator for 1 hour. (Let the balm return to room temperature before use.) Due to the inclusion of coconut oil, this "butter" will have a harder consistency at cooler temperatures and softer consistency at temperatures over 76°F.

APPLICATION INSTRUCTIONS: To keep lips in tip-top condition, apply throughout the day, as desired.

Bonus This skin-nourishing butter is highly recommended for the prevention of stretch marks before, during, and after pregnancy. It is also wonderful for conditioning brittle nails, softening dry, cracked heels and feet, and protecting heels from blisters.

MEMORY ENHANCEMENT

In addition to the typical memory changes that come with aging (most of which are normal, not indicative of encroaching dementia!), high stress, a sedentary lifestyle, and high blood pressure are associated with poor memory. Sad to say, these are typical conditions of today's modern times. But they don't have to be. It's important to find time to exercise daily, in the fresh air and sunshine, if possible. Keep stress to a minimum or learn to manage it through practicing yoga, meditation, and regular physical activity, and, with the help of a qualified herbalist, nutritionist, or other health professional, find a natural way to lower your blood pressure through diet and lifestyle modifications.

A whole-foods, low- to moderate-fat diet plays a very important role in maintaining the health of your mind. The brain needs optimal nourishment, especially from the omega-3 fatty acids found in cold-water fish, flax seeds, walnuts, and chia seeds; complex carbohydrates, with their slow-release natural sugars; and antioxidants from colorful fruits and vegetables, including lots of vibrant berries, plus black and green teas.

Keeping the mind stimulated and active by regularly solving puzzles, reading, practicing creative hobbies, taking classes and learning new skills, and simply being social goes a long way toward maintaining maximum function of your brain, including having a sharp memory.

Many studies have shown that there is a strong connection between memory and scent, and we all know that certain odors can trigger specific memories in a flash. Stimulating, strongly scented herbs can not only trigger past memories but can aid in the retention of new information. Herbs such as rosemary, peppermint, balsam fir, basil, pine, black pepper, clary sage, cardamom, and geranium, along with the peels of lemon and grapefruit, are often included in topical memory-enhancing formulations, not only because of their strong aromas, but also because they act as circulatory stimulants, increasing blood flow throughout the body.

To awaken the full potential of your brain, follow these suggestions and try the two brain-power-boosting recipes on the next page, and you'll soon notice an improvement in your cognitive abilities.

Rain's Rosemary Remembrance Balm

*T*his formula is dedicated to a lovely friend of mine named Rain, who adores rosemary. This refreshing, stimulating, uplifting, rejuvenating, resinous, clarifying herb is just the thing to awaken your brain and help you recall and retain what you seem to have forgotten! If you love rosemary, then you'll appreciate this fragrant balm.

7 tablespoons almond or soybean base oil

1–2 tablespoons beeswax (depending on how firm you want the balm to be)

60 drops rosemary (chemotype *verbenon* or non-chemotype-specific) essential oil

EQUIPMENT: *Small saucepan or double boiler, stirring utensil, glass or plastic jar or tin*
PREP TIME: *20 minutes to make the balm, plus 30 minutes to thicken*
YIELD: *Approximately ½ cup*
STORAGE: *Store at room temperature, away from heat and light; use within 1 year*
APPLICATION: *2 or 3 times per day*

Combine the base oil and beeswax in a small saucepan or double boiler, and warm over low heat until the beeswax is just melted. Remove from the heat and allow to cool for 5 minutes, stirring a few times. Add the rosemary essential oil and stir again to thoroughly blend. Slowly pour the liquid balm into a storage container. Cap and label. Set aside for 30 minutes to thicken.

APPLICATION INSTRUCTIONS: For memory enhancement, up to three times per day, apply a little dab of this balm to each temple, the nape of your neck, the base of your throat, and behind each ear. Breathe deeply.

Bonus This balm also aids in healing dry, cracked feet, hands, nails, shins, elbows, and knees. I use it occasionally to condition the ends of my very dry, curly hair and as a blister balm when I'm hiking. It even helps heal oozing poison plant rashes and dermatitis.

There's rosemary, that's for remembrance; pray, love, remember. And there is pansies, that's for thoughts.

— WILLIAM SHAKESPEARE, *Hamlet*

Memory and Concentration "Study Aid" Balm

This is the perfect formula for anyone, no matter what his or her age, who is attempting to learn a new skill or hobby, as it helps keep the mind fresh and alert and aids in the retention of new knowledge. High school or college students who need a natural study aid will benefit from this invigorating, sharply fragrant balm, rather than relying on too much caffeine to keep them awake. Be sure to send them off to school with a little jar tucked into their bag.

This formula includes three of my favorite stimulating essential oils: lemon, for its mentally uplifting, fresh scent; basil, which offers energizing and clarifying properties to an overworked brain; and rosemary, to enhance remembrance, of course.

Note: This is a highly concentrated formula, so only use as directed below. Do not slather it all over your body.

4 tablespoons refined shea butter (unrefined shea butter will work, but its stronger fragrance will often mask the aroma of the essential oils)

30 drops rosemary (chemotype *verbenon* or non-chemotype-specific) essential oil

20 drops lemon essential oil

10 drops basil essential oil

EQUIPMENT: *Small saucepan or double boiler, stirring utensil, glass or plastic jar or tin*
PREP TIME: *15 minutes, plus up to 24 hours to thicken*
YIELD: *Approximately ¼ cup*
STORAGE: *Store at room temperature, away from heat and light; use within 1 year*
APPLICATION: *1 or 2 times per day*

Warm the shea butter in a small saucepan (a ¾-quart size works great) or double boiler over low heat, until it has just melted. Remove from the heat. Add the rosemary, lemon, and basil essential oils directly to your storage container, then slowly pour in the liquefied shea butter. Gently stir the balm to blend. Cap and label the container, and set it aside until the balm has thickened. Unlike beeswax, shea butter takes a long time to completely thicken, and this formula may need up to 24 hours, depending on the temperature in your kitchen. When it's ready, it will be very thick, semi-hard, and white (or creamy yellow if you've used unrefined shea butter).

APPLICATION INSTRUCTIONS: Apply a tiny dab — no more — of this balm to each temple, the nape of your neck, the base of your throat, and behind each ear once or twice per day. Breathe deeply.

Bonus This balm makes the perfect conditioner and growth stimulator for dry, brittle nails and cuticles. Every evening, simply massage a little dab into your nails and they'll soon become healthier and more flexible.

MEN'S CONCERNS

Men's personal-care and health concerns are often omitted from herbal healing books in favor of remedies focusing on the care of women and children. I'm not quite sure why. Perhaps men are perceived as too macho to be helped by the simplicity of herbal remedies, or perhaps it's assumed that they can't be bothered to make a fuss about their appearance or well-being — neither of which is true. Well, I'd like to change this trend. Men do indeed have their own set of concerns that can be naturally treated using topical remedies with much success. What follows are a handful of formulas that men of all ages will find useful and relatively easy to make, I promise. And never fear, they don't smell like froufrou flowers.

The first two recipes cover that masculine ritual of shaving, which in itself is not harmful to the skin. On the contrary, just like using masks and scrubs, it thoroughly exfoliates the face and neck and reveals smooth, new skin. But little nicks and cuts and patches of inflamed skin can result, and ingrown hairs are a particular hazard for men with stiff, heavy, curly facial hair who shave regularly.

Unlike *folliculitis,* which is an infection of the hair follicles caused by staphylococcus bacteria, *pseudofolliculitis barbae* — a tongue-twister of a term — happens when the tip of a growing hair curves under the skin's surface instead of exiting the follicle orifice. The condition appears as inflamed, red bumps than can easily be mistaken for acne and will persist for as long as the man continues to shave, possibly leaving scars.

Many aestheticians, myself included, recommend a gentle facial scrub two or three times per week, after a warm shower or hot towel application to the face, to help loosen embedded hairs and remove surface buildup of dead skin. Alternatively, you could always grow a beard and the condition will take care of itself. For the clean shaven, the Myrrh Clay Pack and Exfoliant (next page) and Myrrh and Aloe Anti-inflammatory Aftershave (page 225) are useful for soothing the unsightly and often painful inflammation of this particular shaving irritation. They are not cures but palliative treatments only.

Myrrh Clay Pack and Exfoliant

This unique clay pack, with its masculine, resinous aroma, serves double duty, first as a gentle exfoliating facial scrub, and second, when allowed to dry on the skin, as a mask to soothe inflamed follicles.

Note: Do not use this clay pack on sensitive, sunburned, windburned, or acneic skin.

2 tablespoons white cosmetic clay or French green clay

1 teaspoon myrrh gum powder

5–6 teaspoons commercially prepared aloe vera juice

EQUIPMENT: *Small bowl, spoon or tiny whisk*
PREP TIME: *5 minutes*
YIELD: *1 treatment*
STORAGE: *Do not store; mix as needed*
APPLICATION: *2 or 3 times per week — on non-shaving days only*

In a small bowl or custard cup, use a spoon or tiny whisk to combine the clay and myrrh powder with enough of the aloe vera juice to form a smooth, spreadable paste. Allow to thicken for 5 minutes. It should not be soupy in consistency; if it is, add a tiny bit more clay and stir again. If too thick, stir in a bit more aloe vera juice. Use immediately.

APPLICATION INSTRUCTIONS: Use first as a mild facial scrub by spreading a thin layer over your beard growth area, including the neck, and gently massaging for 1 minute, using circular motions. Do not rinse. Apply the remaining mixture over the same area and allow to dry or nearly dry for at least 30 minutes, preferably while you are lying down. The clay will harden and may tingle and crack as it dries. Rinse with cool water. Pat dry. Follow with a light application of plain, cold aloe vera juice and allow the skin to air-dry, then apply a light facial moisturizer, if desired.

Bonus This clay pack can be applied to weeping eczema to calm and dry affected areas, or used as a spot treatment to help heal blemishes.

MYRRH AND ALOE ANTI-INFLAMMATORY AFTERSHAVE

This low-alcohol, soothing facial liniment is specifically designed to be used after shaving. It has mild astringent, antiseptic, and anti-inflammatory properties that help prevent potential infection while healing irritated tissue. It also tones and tightens skin tissue and is highly recommended for skin that tends to suffer from ingrown hairs, as a natural alternative to the harsh, drying, alcohol-based commercial products that merely sting the face and offer no real healing and conditioning benefits.

½ cup commercially prepared aloe vera juice

½ cup witch hazel (commercially prepared or homemade; see the box on page 305)

½ teaspoon vegetable glycerin

25 drops myrrh essential oil

10 drops carrot seed essential oil

EQUIPMENT: *Plastic or glass bottle*
PREP TIME: *5 minutes*
YIELD: *Approximately 1 cup*
STORAGE: *Use within 2 weeks if stored at room temperature; within 6 months if refrigerated*
APPLICATION: *Immediately after shaving*

Combine the aloe vera juice, witch hazel, glycerin, and myrrh and carrot seed essential oils in a bottle and shake vigorously to blend. Label and store. This remedy is quite refreshing when chilled.

APPLICATION INSTRUCTIONS: Shake well before each use. Apply generously immediately after shaving as a facial splash or with cotton pads. Follow with your favorite light moisturizer, if desired.

Bonus This herbal liniment can also be used to help heal shaving nicks and razor burn, as well as other minor skin injuries or irritations.

MUSCLE SHEEN "BUFF" BUTTERY BODY OIL

Proud of all your hard work at the gym? Here's the perfect rich, emollient, conditioning skin butter with which to accentuate your muscular contours. It sinks right in with nary an oily slick, only a light attractive sheen. The rosemary and sage essential oils add a subtle masculine fragrance along with skin-revitalizing properties, but they can be left out, if desired.

6 tablespoons almond or soybean base oil

2 tablespoons refined shea butter (unrefined shea butter will work, but its stronger fragrance will often mask the aroma of the essential oils)

20 drops rosemary (chemotype *verbenon*) essential oil (optional)

10 drops sage essential oil (optional)

EQUIPMENT: *Small saucepan or double boiler, stirring utensil, plastic squeeze bottle*
PREP TIME: *20 minutes, plus 24 hours to thicken*
YIELD: *½ cup*
STORAGE: *Store at room temperature, away from heat and light; use within 1 year*
APPLICATION: *As desired*

Combine the base oil and shea butter in a small saucepan or double boiler, and warm over low heat until the shea butter is just melted. Remove from the heat and allow to cool for 15 minutes. Add the rosemary and sage essential oils, if desired, and gently stir for 1 minute to thoroughly blend. Pour the mixture into a storage bottle. Cap and label the container, then it set aside until the blend has thickened. Unlike beeswax, which hardens rather quickly, shea butter can take quite a while to thicken, and this formula may need up to 24 hours, depending on the temperature of your kitchen. When it's ready, it will be very thick and white (or creamy yellow if you've used unrefined shea butter).

APPLICATION INSTRUCTIONS: Shake well before each use. Immediately following a bath or shower, while your skin is still slightly damp, slather this oil blend onto your body — really massage it in. Because it is very concentrated, begin with 1 teaspoon at a time. Let the product soak in for 10 minutes before getting dressed.

Bonus This butter can be used to moisturize and condition rough, cracked, or leathery hands, feet, elbows, knees, and shins, as well as brittle nails and dry cuticles. It's great for softening chapped lips, too.

SCALP NOURISHER: HERBAL BALD HEAD RUB

Just because your head is void of hair doesn't mean that it doesn't need care. Consider a bare scalp an extension of your face and treat it in the same manner by regularly cleansing, exfoliating, and moisturizing.

This simple, mild, masculine-scented herbal oil blend is designed to polish and shine your dome while stimulating circulation to encourage a healthy scalp. The ingredients lubricate, oxygenate, and nourish hair follicles, leaving your scalp feeling fresh, clean, and comfortable. It not only feels great but will enliven your senses as well.

Note: The Protect and Fortify Facial Elixir (page 160) and Simple Calendula-Infused Body Oil (page 162) would also work wonderfully as daily scalp treatments and don't smell "girly."

20 drops Atlas cedar
   essential oil

20 drops cardamom
   essential oil

20 drops myrrh essential oil

 1 cup jojoba base oil

EQUIPMENT: *Dropper, dark glass bottle with dropper top or screw cap*
PREP TIME: *15 minutes, plus 24 hours to synergize*
YIELD: *Approximately 1 cup*
STORAGE: *Store at room temperature, away from heat and light; use within 2 years*
APPLICATION: *Daily*

Add the Atlas cedar, cardamom, and myrrh essential oils drop by drop directly into a storage bottle. Add the jojoba base oil. Screw the top on the bottle and shake vigorously for 2 minutes to blend. Label the bottle and place in a dark location that's between 60° and 80°F for 24 hours so that the oils can synergize.

APPLICATION INSTRUCTIONS: Shake well before using. Massage a few drops into a clean, slightly damp scalp once daily.

Bonus This formula can be used to moisturize and condition rough, leathery hands and feet, elbows, knees, and shins, as well as brittle nails and dry cuticles.

HERBAL JOCK ITCH RELIEF POWDER

*J**ock itch** (tinea cruris), also called "groin ringworm," is a fungal skin disease that affects the scrotal, crural (thigh), anal, and genital areas; it is characterized by irritating, itchy, red, ring-like areas, sometimes with small blisters on the skin. It develops more frequently in warm weather and more often occurs in men than in women. Recurring bouts are common, as the fungi can survive indefinitely on the skin. The herb combination in this powder offers effective, nontoxic antifungal, astringent, and antiseptic properties to help soothe the skin and eradicate associated fungi and yeasts.*

Note: Purchase all these herbs pre-powdered, as most are very tough materials and practically impossible to powder using common kitchen equipment.

½ cup baking soda

½ cup cornstarch

½ cup white cosmetic clay

2 tablespoons black walnut hull powder

2 tablespoons lavender bud powder

2 tablespoons myrrh gum powder

2 tablespoons Oregon grape root powder

50 drops tea tree essential oil

25 drops sage essential oil

25 drops thyme (chemotype *linalool*) essential oil

EQUIPMENT: *Medium bowl and whisk or food processor, mortar and pestle, airtight storage container(s)*
PREP TIME: *20 minutes, plus 3 days to synergize*
YIELD: *Approximately 2 cups*
STORAGE: *Store at room temperature, away from heat and light; use within 1 year*
APPLICATION: *2 or 3 times per day*

Combine the baking soda, cornstarch, clay, black walnut, lavender, myrrh, and Oregon grape root in a medium bowl or food processor. Slowly whisk together, or pulse in the food processor for 15 seconds, until well blended. Avoid breathing the dust, though there is no real danger of irritation as there is with cayenne powder. Measure out 6 tablespoons of the powder into a mortar. Drop by drop, add the tea tree, sage, and thyme essential oils, working them into the powder with the pestle, until the oil is absorbed. Add this oil mixture to the remaining powder. Whisk the mixture together slowly, shake vigorously in a large container with a tight-fitting lid, or pulse in the food processor for 15 seconds, until blended.

Store the powder in an airtight storage container in a cool, dark place for 3 days to allow the medicinal properties of the herbal ingredients to synergize and permeate the mixture. Then package the powder in smaller containers, if desired.

APPLICATION INSTRUCTIONS: Apply as you would any medicated body powder, by sprinkling or using a large cotton ball or cotton square to apply it over affected area(s).

Bonus This powder doubles as a treatment for athlete's foot.

MENTAL FATIGUE

Ever feel like your brain is drained? You're not alone. It's a common complaint. Most of us tend to do too much and are pulled in many directions during the day, demanding that our brain be at peak performance at all times. Even a single task requiring intense concentration, whether a serious, job-related task or an enjoyable hobby such as sewing, knitting, canning vegetables, painting, or writing, can be mentally exhausting.

There are several things you can do to recharge your brain power. Perhaps most importantly, your brain requires a higher amount of energizing carbohydrates or natural sugars than any other organ. So, one way to help prevent mental fatigue is to stoke the brain's fire with a fortifying complex-carbohydrate snack such as fruit, granola, oatmeal spiked with dried fruit, vegetable sticks, nuts, or seeds.

Adding spices such as cayenne, ginger, jalapeños, and cinnamon to your diet will stimulate both your digestion and your circulation. A few cups of green tea with fresh ginger slices go a long way toward keeping you wide-eyed and bushy-tailed, plus they provide your brain and body with a boatload of anti-aging antioxidants.

A 5-minute exercise break several times a day is a great way to reoxygenate your brain and stimulate mental circulation. Simply take a quick walk around your workspace or around the block, or walk up and down a few flights of stairs, or bend and stretch a few times and then do a dozen squats and a dozen push-ups — anything that will get fresh blood pumping to your brain.

Another thing you can do to enliven your mind is to take full advantage of the stimulating scents offered by the herb world. For example, crush a few fresh peppermint or scented geranium leaves between your fingers and inhale their crisp fragrance to instantly feel mentally and emotionally uplifted. Refreshing, revitalizing essential oils, in particular, can have an amazing energizing effect. The following aromatically pleasing recipes will help rejuvenate your tired brain, so give them a try the next time you're feeling foggy and mentally drained.

Brain-Charger Aroma Mist

If, at any point during your busy day, you experience an inability to focus or lack of mental clarity, this sparkling, ultra-fresh aromatic room mist is just the product you'll want to reach for to rev up your brain power. By their very light, refreshing nature, most citrus oils tend to be rather uplifting to the psyche and particularly good at stimulating a sluggish mind accompanied by stagnant circulation, which is why I chose them for the basis of this formula. I added rosemary essential oil for the sharp, energizing, mind-clearing properties that it lends.

Note: You can spray your environment several times per day, but take care not to spray directly on plastic or lacquered surfaces.

½ cup unflavored vodka

½ cup purified or distilled water

15 drops grapefruit essential oil

15 drops lemon essential oil

15 drops petitgrain or sweet orange essential oil

10 drops rosemary (chemotype *verbenon* or non-chemotype-specific) essential oil

EQUIPMENT: *Plastic or glass spritzer bottle*
PREP TIME: *5 minutes*
YIELD: *Approximately 1 cup*
STORAGE: *Store at room temperature, away from heat and light; use within 1 year*
APPLICATION: *3 or 4 times per day*

Combine the vodka, water, and grapefruit, lemon, petitgrain or orange, and rosemary essential oils in a spritzer bottle and shake vigorously to blend. Label and store.

APPLICATION INSTRUCTIONS: Shake well before using. When in need of mental stimulation, lightly mist your surrounding area and breathe deeply.

Bonus This mist is the perfect herbal disinfectant to use during cold and flu season. All of its essential oils contain general antiseptic properties that will help keep your work area and home free of sickness. Use it as a hand sanitizer as well.

"Fog Lifter" Mind Stimulation Drops

Clean, green, sharp, and invigorating—this is exactly the type of aromatherapy your brain needs when "pea-soup brain fog" moves in. A mere few drops of this refreshing formula go a long way toward boosting mental activity and your ability to focus on the task at hand.

Note: This is an aromatherapeutically concentrated formula, so use only by the drop as directed.

20 drops balsam fir essential oil

20 drops peppermint essential oil

20 drops rosemary (chemotype *verbenon* or non-chemotype-specific) essential oil

¼ cup jojoba base oil

EQUIPMENT: *Dropper, dark glass bottle with dropper top or screw cap*
PREP TIME: *15 minutes, plus 24 hours to synergize*
YIELD: *Approximately ¼ cup*
STORAGE: *Store at room temperature, away from heat and light; use within 2 years*
APPLICATION: *1 or 2 times per day*

Add the balsam fir, peppermint, and rosemary essential oils drop by drop directly into a storage bottle. Add the jojoba base oil. Screw the top on the bottle and shake vigorously for 2 minutes to blend. Label the bottle and place in a dark location that's between 60° and 80°F for 24 hours so that the oils can synergize.

APPLICATION INSTRUCTIONS: Shake well before using. Once or twice a day, when in need of mental stimulation and clarity of thought, apply a drop of this oil blend to each temple, the nape of your neck, the base of your throat, and behind each ear. Breathe deeply.

Bonus Use these aromatic drops as an aid in healing cuts, scrapes, bug bites, blemishes, infected ingrown hairs, blisters, rashes, boils, minor burns, or any minor to moderate skin infection. A wonderful addition to your herbal first aid kit!

MUSCLE STIFFNESS AND SORENESS

When a body has been sedentary for too long, an unaccustomed task such as raking leaves, tilling the garden, hiking up a mountain, or playing an impromptu game of backyard football can lead to muscle soreness, fatigue, and stiffness. And occasional muscular pain is just part of life. To minimize the potential for muscular pain, always observe correct posture for whatever activity you are engaged in and begin any new physical activity slowly, so that your muscles can become acclimated and strengthened. It's wise to exercise on a regular basis, including strength and cardiovascular training, as well as to have a good stretching routine, so that when life asks you to perform the annual spring cleanup of your lawn or a friend wants to hike up Mt. Yahoo, you won't have several days of painful downtime spent recovering.

Many muscular complaints can be greatly relieved by simple massage combined with the application of herbal liniments, massage oils, or balms that increase circulation, removing inflammatory wastes such as lactic acid while bringing fresh oxygen- and nutrient-rich blood to the affected area. Herbs with anti-inflammatory, antispasmodic, analgesic, and vulnerary properties are typically chosen.

Many people, myself included, find that after a long day of physical activity, taking a hot bath with 2 to 3 cups of Epsom salts added to the water dramatically decreases muscle pain and swelling. Follow this with the application of a good sore muscle remedy (a friend comes in handy for this) and a day or two of taking it easy and you're golden! See your physician or chiropractor if pain and swelling persist for more than 48 hours.

Be sure to read the "Backache" section (see page 69), as many of the recipes there can help with sore, stiff, strained muscles in other areas of the body, as well.

SORE MUSCLE RELIEF LINIMENT

All of the herbs included in this formula are specific for treating muscles in spasm, quickly relieving the pain, swelling, and potential residual achiness and tension. Every summer I make up a new batch of this liniment using fresh sage, peppermint, and mullein from my garden. The cooling vodka base quickly evaporates once applied, leaving the herbal properties to penetrate the tissue.

½ cup dried or 1 cup freshly wilted peppermint leaves (see page 38 for information on wilting)

½ cup dried or 1 cup freshly wilted sage leaves

½ cup dried or 1 cup freshly wilted mullein flowers

½ cup fresh ginger, grated, sliced, or finely chopped

1 teaspoon vegetable glycerin

3–4 cups unflavored vodka

EQUIPMENT: *1-quart canning jar, plastic wrap, fine-mesh strainer, fine filter, funnel, glass or plastic storage containers*
PREP TIME: *10 minutes, plus 4 weeks for extraction*
YIELD: *Approximately 2½ cups*
STORAGE: *Store at room temperature, away from heat and light; use within 2 years*
APPLICATION: *Up to 3 times per day*

Bonus This remedy makes a most effective spot treatment for blemishes, minor cuts and scrapes, and insect bites and stings. It even performs quite well as an underarm deodorant spray.

If you're using freshly wilted peppermint or sage leaves, first cut or tear them into smaller pieces to expose more surface area during the maceration. Wilted mullein flowers need no further processing. Combine the peppermint, sage, mullein, and ginger with the glycerin in a 1-quart canning jar and pour the vodka over them, so that it comes to within ½ inch of the top of the jar. The herbs should be completely covered. Place a piece of plastic wrap over the mouth of the jar (to prevent the metal lid from coming into contact with the jar's contents), then screw on the lid. Shake for about 30 seconds to blend the contents. After 24 hours, top up with more vodka if necessary.

Store the jar in a cool, dark place for 4 weeks so that the vodka can extract the valuable chemical components from the herbs. Shake the jar every day for 15 to 30 seconds.

At the end of the 4 weeks, strain the herbs through a fine-mesh strainer lined with a fine filter such as muslin or, preferably, a paper coffee filter, then strain again if necessary to remove all herb debris. Press or squeeze the herbs to release all the valuable herbal extract. Discard the marc. Pour the extract into storage containers, then cap, label, and store in a dark cabinet.

APPLICATION INSTRUCTIONS: Briskly massage a generous amount of liniment into any area where muscles are stiff, sore, tense, tight, or achy. Rub it in well. Apply up to three times per day until your muscles feel better.

BOBCAT BALM #2

This balm is a variation of Bobcat Balm #1 (page 70), and like the original formula, it contains an infusion of nature's finest plant healers to repair damaged tissue, relieve the pain of muscular tension, and ease the achiness that can linger for days. This soothing balm contains an "irritant" essential oil — your choice between birch or wintergreen, which are two of the best anti-inflammatories and antispasmodics for overworked muscles. When massaged into the affected area, they will bring blood to the skin's surface, boosting circulation and easing discomfort.

This recipe calls for a small amount of the infused oil used to make Bobcat Balm #1. If you've made that balm and have some of the infused oil left over, great. If not, then make the infused oil for that recipe (not the entire recipe, just the infused oil!).

7 tablespoons infused oil from Bobcat Balm #1

1–2 tablespoons beeswax (depending on how firm you want the balm to be)

40 drops birch or wintergreen essential oil

EQUIPMENT: *Small saucepan or double boiler, stirring utensil, plastic or glass jar or tin*
PREP TIME: *20 minutes to make the balm, plus 30 minutes for it to thicken*
YIELD: *Approximately ½ cup*
STORAGE: *Store at room temperature, away from heat and light; use within 1 year*
APPLICATION: *2 or 3 times daily*

Combine the infused oil and the beeswax in a small saucepan or double boiler and warm over low heat until the beeswax is just melted. Remove from the heat and allow to cool for 5 minutes, stirring a few times. Add the birch or wintergreen essential oil and stir again to thoroughly blend. Slowly pour the liquid balm into the storage container. Cap, label, and set aside for 30 minutes to thicken.

APPLICATION INSTRUCTIONS: Have a friend or partner massage this remedy into achy areas two or three times per day. Massaging into skin that is pre-warmed from a bath, shower, or heating pad encourages penetration of the medicinal qualities.

Bonus This balm can be used to soothe backache, arthritic joints, gout, tendonitis, and sore feet, plus it can relieve the blood stagnancy in bruises.

POISON PLANT RASHES

Poison ivy, poison oak, poison sumac — this trio is the menace of summer woodlands! Depending upon the sensitivity of your skin and the amount of exposure, symptoms of your encounter with one of these plants may take a few hours or as long as a few days to appear. Minor itching and burning along with a red, slightly raised rash are the first signs, followed by the formation of small blisters that eventually rupture and form a crust.

The itchiness and irritation is caused by *urushiol*, the toxic oily resin common to all three plants. Some people are immune to its effects, while in others it quickly produces dermatitis. Typically, severe reactions occur only if the plant resin comes in contact with your eyes, throat, feet, fingers, or groin, or if you constantly scratch the irritation.

Run-ins with poison ivy, oak, and sumac usually occur during the warmer months, but that's not to say that you're completely safe during the winter, as the plants can be difficult to identify without their leaves. An ounce of prevention is definitely worth a pound of cure, so learn to identify the plants in both summer and winter. If you know you're going to be walking through areas where these plants are common, protect yourself by wearing long sleeves, long pants, and boots.

If you do have a run-in with any of them, wash your clothing in hot water immediately upon arriving home so they don't come in contact with other clothes and spread the poisonous agent. Thoroughly wash your hands with hot soapy water after handling the affected clothes, followed by rinsing them with either vodka or isopropyl alcohol.

Simple Remedies for Dealing with Poison Plant Rashes

Here are some simple at-home treatments as well as recommendations for remedies in this book that will offer soothing comfort to your rashy skin:

SOAP AND WATER. A good scrub in a hot shower immediately after contact with a poisonous plant will help remove urushiol from your skin. The hot water also often brings dramatic symptomatic relief that can last for hours. For soap, I recommend using a full-strength, undiluted eucalyptus or peppermint castile liquid soap. This type of soap is relatively gentle to your skin in the short term, but strong in action against the urushiol. Apply a light, chemical-free body lotion after bathing, if your skin feels parched from the soap.

VODKA OR RUBBING ALCOHOL. Unflavored, unsweetened vodka and rubbing alcohol both act as solvents for urushiol and can be applied to the affected area immediately after contact with the plant to help remove the irritating plant oil.

OATMEAL BATH. For most minor reactions, health professionals and herbalists recommend soaking for 20 to 30 minutes in a tepid bath to which you have added ½ to 1 cup finely ground or colloidal oatmeal.

ANTI-ITCH POTIONS. Commercial aloe vera juice or gel, or the gel scraped from the inside of a fresh aloe leaf, can be applied several times per day to help heal the blisters and alleviate itching. The good old standby, calamine lotion, can be used in the same way. Professional arborists, tree cutters, and loggers have long used straight witch hazel to help dry up oozing poison plant rashes; see the box on page 305 for a homemade version or try one of the following remedies:

- Witch Hazel and Yarrow Astringent (page 79)
- Preparation "B": Astringent Aloe Wipes (page 196)
- Sitz Salve (page 194)

STAY COOL. If possible, stay as cool and dry as possible, as hot, humid weather seems to exacerbate the itching (and your irritability).

DIET SUPPLEMENTS. As a child growing up in Georgia, I rambled among poison ivy plants all the time with nary an itch, but as an adult, I am now highly sensitive to both poison ivy and oak and must take precautions when walking through the woods or fields. I find that taking 500 to 1,000 milligrams of vitamin C, as soon as I notice a rash developing and continuing with a daily dose until my skin heals, helps prevent infection and the spread of the rash. The blisters seems to dry up faster, too!

CAUTION

In its advanced stage, a poison ivy, oak, or sumac rash can be so irritating that it consumes every waking hour of your mental energy. If you develop a rash in your eyes, throat, or groin region, or if your rash — no matter the location — becomes raw, severely blistered, or infected, consult with your health professional immediately. Aside from being intensely uncomfortable, a bad rash can be a threat to your health.

PSORIASIS

This unpleasant disease is characterized by sharply defined, thick, raised, pinkish red patches of skin, often covered with dry silvery gray scales, appearing on any part of the body, but particularly the scalp, knees, elbows, fingers, and lower back. Psoriatic patches can itch, burn, or sting, depending on the severity of the disease. The disease generally develops slowly, typically followed by unexplained remissions and recurrences.

The symptoms can vary in severity from very mild, where an individual doesn't realize he or she actually has the disease, to extremely debilitating, in which the skin's protective functions are destroyed, allowing the skin to lose fluids and nutrients and to no longer control body temperature, making patients susceptible to infection.

Psoriasis is caused by abnormal skin cell production. Normal skin cells mature every 28 to 35 days and are sloughed off unnoticed. With psoriasis, skin cells mature in just 3 to 4 days, causing them to pile up and create thick skin plaques. Their red appearance is due to the rich blood supply feeding the rapidly multiplying new skin cells.

If your parents suffered from psoriasis, chances are that you will, too. But you can take measures to help prevent the disease from progressing. Eat a whole-foods, anti-inflammatory diet high in vitamins A, B, C, D, and E, zinc, and sulfur (from onions and garlic). Emphasize cooling foods, such as watery fruits and vegetables (especially greens), as well as grains, rice milk, fermented soy products, beans, and fish. Avoid warming spices and stimulating beverages. Minimize sour and salty foods and all refined foods, especially sugar. Evening primrose oil or borage oil, fish oil (unrefined, low-temperature-extracted), and flaxseed oil are often beneficial for reducing inflammation.

Many professionals suggest using stress reduction methods such as hypnosis, exercise, deep breathing, and yoga on a regular basis. Additionally, regular elimination of waste is paramount in order to detoxify the body.

Avoid using soap on your skin; instead, use a soap-free body cleanser. Cold aloe vera juice, applied twice daily with a soft cloth, makes a refreshing, soothing cleanser for psoriasis plaques.

The following two remedies do not offer a cure for this condition, which is often frustratingly difficult to treat, but they generally deliver blessed symptomatic relief from the discomfort and dryness. The underlying cause(s) of your psoriasis need to be identified by a qualified health professional. Your external skin is crying out because your internal body is irritated and attempting to detoxify itself.

3 Cs Calming Salve

Chamomile, calendula, and comfrey — the three ultra-calming "Cs" of the herb world are energetically cooling when applied to metabolically overactive psoriasis plaques. This blend contains vulnerary, anti-inflammatory, ever-so-gently astringent, yet emollient properties that offer comfort to psoriasis sufferers.

Note: I prefer to use freshly wilted herbs to make this infused oil blend, but dried herbs will work nicely, too. I use the stovetop method of infusion, as I feel it best concentrates the sticky, resinous properties of these herbs, while evaporating their heavy moisture content (especially if you use them freshly wilted).

½ cup dried or 1 cup freshly wilted calendula blossoms (see page 38 for information on wilting)

½ cup dried or 1 cup freshly wilted chamomile flowers

½ cup dried or 1 cup freshly wilted comfrey leaves

3 cups extra-virgin olive base oil

2,000 IU vitamin E oil

3 tablespoons beeswax

1 tablespoon cocoa butter

EQUIPMENT: *2-quart saucepan or double boiler, stirring utensil, candy or yogurt thermometer, strainer, fine filter, funnel, glass or plastic storage container (for the infused oil), glass or plastic jars or tins (for the salve)*

PREP TIME: *5 hours to infuse oil, plus 20 minutes to make the salve and 1 hour for it to thicken*

YIELD: *Approximately 2½ cups of infused oil and 1¼ cups of salve*

STORAGE: *Store at room temperature, away from heat and light; use within 1 year*

APPLICATION: *2 or 3 times per day, or as desired*

PREPARING THE HERBAL INFUSED OIL: If you're using wilted herbs, first cut or tear them into smaller pieces to expose more surface area to the oil (though the chamomile flowers need no further processing as they are quite small). Combine the calendula, chamomile, and comfrey with the olive base oil in a 2-quart saucepan or double boiler and stir thoroughly to blend. The mixture should look like a thick, chunky yellow-orange-green herbal soup. Bring the mixture to just shy of a simmer, between 125° and 135°F. Do not let the oil actually simmer — it will degrade the quality of your infused oil. *Do not* put the lid on the pot.

Allow the herbs to macerate in the oil over low heat for 5 hours. Check the temperature every 30 minutes or so with a thermometer and adjust the heat accordingly. If you're using a double boiler, add more water to the bottom pot as necessary, so it doesn't dry out. Stir the infusing mixture at least every 30 minutes or so, as the herb bits tend to settle to the bottom.

After 5 hours, remove the pan from the heat and allow to cool for 15 minutes. While the oil is still warm, carefully strain it through a fine-mesh strainer lined with a fine filter such as muslin or, preferably, a paper coffee filter, then strain again if necessary to remove all debris. Squeeze the herbs to extract as much of the precious oil as possible. Discard the marc.

Add the vitamin E oil and stir to blend. The resulting infused oil blend will be a lovely hue of greenish gold-orange. Pour the finished oil into a storage container, then cap, label, and store in a dark cabinet.

PREPARING THE SALVE: Combine 1 cup of the infused oil with the beeswax and cocoa butter in a small saucepan or double boiler, and warm over low heat until the solids are just melted. Remove from the heat and allow to cool for 5 minutes, stirring a few times. Pour the liquid salve into glass or plastic jars or tins, and cap and label. Set aside for 1 hour to thicken.

APPLICATION INSTRUCTIONS: If the psoriatic plaques itch, gently cleanse the affected areas two or three times per day using a mixture of 1 part baking soda to 8 parts water. The baking soda helps ease itching. Alternatively, you can cleanse the plaques with cold aloe vera juice. Pat the skin dry, then gently massage a small amount of the salve into the irritated areas, until the salve is absorbed.

Bonus This salve is quite beneficial for healing diaper rash, minor cuts and scrapes, poison plant rashes, blisters, dermatitis, and dry eczema. It also conditions brittle nails and cuticles, rough elbows, knees, and shins, and cracked or fissured heels. It makes a soothing salve for chapped lips and an excellent skin conditioner for the prevention of stretch marks during pregnancy.

De-Stress Tea

If you are feeling stressed and anxious, regular consumption of herbal nervine-based teas (3 to 4 cups per day) may relax the peripheral nerves and your heightened emotions, thus reducing inflammation and itching to some degree. At your local health food store, look for relaxing herb tea blends that contain such herbs as lavender, valerian, catnip, lemon balm, licorice, chamomile, skullcap, and passionflower.

ULTRA-NOURISHING SKIN REVITALIZER

This blend of rich, skin-nourishing oils is chock-full of valuable antioxidants such as vitamins A, D, and E, flavonoids, gamma-linolenic acid, and punicic acid, plus lecithin, proteins, and squalene. It often works like magic to control the excessive discomfort of psoriasis while softening and adding flexibility to the dry, thick, flaky plaques.

½ cup jojoba base oil

3 tablespoons evening primrose base oil

3 tablespoons pomegranate seed base oil

2 tablespoons wheat germ base oil

EQUIPMENT: *Glass or plastic storage container*
PREP TIME: *15 minutes, plus 24 hours to synergize*
YIELD: *Approximately 1 cup*
STORAGE: *Refrigerate; use within 6 months*
APPLICATION: *2 or 3 times per day*

Add the jojoba, evening primrose, pomegranate seed, and wheat germ base oils directly into a storage bottle. Screw the top on the bottle and shake vigorously for 2 minutes to blend. Label the bottle and place in a dark location that's between 60° and 80°F for 24 hours so that the oils can synergize. After the first 24 hours, refrigeration is required.

APPLICATION INSTRUCTIONS: Shake well before using. If the psoriatic plaques itch, gently cleanse the affected areas two or three times per day using a mixture of 1 part baking soda to 8 parts water. The baking soda helps ease itching. Alternatively, you can cleanse the plaques with cold aloe vera juice. Pat the skin dry, then gently massage a small amount of the herbal oil blend into the irritated areas, until the oil is absorbed.

Bonus This conditioning oil is beneficial when applied nightly to dry fingernails and cuticles, cracked and fissured skin, slow-to-heal wounds, patches of dry skin or dry eczema, chapped lips, and blisters.

RESPIRATORY CONGESTION

Healthy respiration depends greatly on the ability to take a deep, comfortable breath without tightness, pain, and congestion in the chest or head. The remedies that follow contain herbs and essential oils with mucolytic, expectorant, antiseptic, and antiviral properties that will go a long way toward soothing irritation and congestion in the respiratory tract. They're guaranteed to help bring comfort and ease symptoms to make you feel better soon. Combine these treatments with more-than-ample bed rest, bowls of steaming organic chicken or vegetable-garlic-onion soup, lots of herb tea and water, hot relaxing baths with purifying herbal oils, and possibly the use of a saline nasal irrigation system such as a neti pot, and you've got the recipe for healing!

Fending Off Germs

Always remember to take preventive measures to keep potential infectious nasties from taking up residence. During and after visiting places where people congregate, such as airports, bus and train stations, schools, churches, public bathrooms, and grocery stores, wash your hands or use a sanitizing gel as many times as you feel is necessary. I like to tote along a packet of disposable, moist sanitizing sheets so that I can wipe down surfaces that perhaps a thousand other people have touched before me, especially grocery cart handles, arm rests, and food tray tables on airplanes. No need to be obsessive, just proactive.

Deep Herbal Lung Release Massage Oil

This gentle formula contains herbs traditionally used as mucolytics, respiratory antiseptics, and antivirals to help fight infection, ease your wheezing, and open and relax the entire respiratory tract. The lungs truly benefit from receiving a chest and back massage with this remedy, especially when the oil is warmed and your skin is still warm from taking a hot bath.

Note: I typically make this herbal oil blend with fresh herbs, but if dried herbs are your only option, don't worry — they'll work, too. I prefer to use the stovetop method for making the infused oil for this recipe, as it results in a superior extraction of the resinous properties of these somewhat sticky herbs.

½ cup dried or 1 cup freshly wilted mugwort leaves (see page 38 for information on wilting)

¼ cup dried or ½ cup freshly wilted mullein flowers

¼ cup dried or ½ cup freshly wilted rosemary leaves

¼ cup dried or ½ cup freshly wilted sage leaves

¼ cup dried or ½ cup freshly wilted thyme leaves

3 cups extra-virgin olive base oil

2,000 IU vitamin E oil

40 drops eucalyptus (species *radiata*) essential oil

40 drops rosemary (chemotype *verbenon*) essential oil

EQUIPMENT: *2-quart saucepan or double boiler, stirring utensil, candy or yogurt thermometer, strainer, fine filter, funnel, glass or plastic storage containers*
PREP TIME: *4 hours to infuse the oil, plus 10 minutes to make the massage oil*
YIELD: *Approximately 2½ cups of infused oil and 1 cup of massage oil*
STORAGE: *Store at room temperature, away from heat and light; use within 1 year*
APPLICATION: *3 or 4 times per day*

PREPARING THE INFUSED OIL: If you are using freshly wilted herbs, first cut or tear them into smaller pieces to expose more surface area to the oil (though the mullein flowers need no further processing, as they are quite tiny.) Combine the mugwort, mullein, rosemary, sage, and thyme with the olive base oil in a 2-quart saucepan or double boiler, and stir thoroughly to blend. The mixture should look like a thick, leafy greenish yellow soup. Bring the mixture to just shy of a simmer, between 125° and 135°F. Do not let the oil actually simmer — it will degrade the quality of your infused oil. *Do not put the lid on the pot.*

Allow the herbs to macerate in the oil over low heat for 4 hours. Check the temperature every 30 minutes or so with a thermometer and adjust the heat accordingly. If you're using a double boiler, add more water to the bottom pot as necessary, so it doesn't dry out. Stir the infusing mixture at least every 30 minutes or so, as the herb bits tend to settle to the bottom.

After 4 hours, remove the pan from the heat and allow to cool for 15 minutes. While the oil is still warm, carefully strain it through a fine-mesh strainer lined with a fine filter such as muslin or, preferably, a paper coffee filter, then strain again if necessary to remove all debris. Squeeze the herbs to extract as much of the precious oil as possible. Discard the marc.

Add the vitamin E oil and stir to blend. The resulting infused oil will be deep green in color. Pour the finished oil into a storage container, then cap, label, and store in a dark cabinet.

PREPARING THE MASSAGE OIL: Pour 1 cup of the infused oil into a storage container and add the eucalyptus and rosemary essential oils. Cap and label the container, then shake well to blend and store in a dark cabinet.

APPLICATION INSTRUCTIONS: Shake well before each use. Warm 1 to 2 tablespoons of the massage oil, whether in the microwave (for 10 seconds or so) or in a saucepan on the stove. Don't allow it to get too hot, just very warm. Massage an ample amount into your chest and throat, and ask a friend or significant other to massage some into your mid- and upper back. Lie down, relax, and cover up with a blanket. Hopefully your lungs will open up enough so that you can inhale the vapors, but if they don't, know that the medicinal herbal properties will successfully penetrate via the sweat glands and follicles within your skin.

Bonus This blend makes a terrific soothing massage oil for tired, achy legs and feet.

AGE-OLD ONION AND GARLIC POULTICE FOR LUNG CONGESTION

This remedy dates back hundreds, if not thousands, of years. It's what our grandparents and great-grandparents relied upon to help open tight lungs and sinuses, thin and expectorate mucous, and keep infection at bay. Sure, you'll smell of onions and garlic, but being sick and miserable stinks, too. Onions and garlic are chock-full of infection-fighting sulfur compounds, plus garlic is a potent antiviral. Ginger contains stimulating, circulation-enhancing, anti-inflammatory properties that ease aches and pains. And when the poultice is applied to your chest, the heat and vapors penetrate your chest cavity and sinuses, breaking up congestion and making breathing easier.

Note: This remedy is *not recommended* if you are running a fever and sweating, as the ingredients are too energetically hot and stimulating and could possibly make you feel worse. Use it if you have the chills combined with mucous that is thick and congestive.

4 large onions, finely chopped

8 garlic cloves, finely chopped

¼ cup finely chopped or grated ginger

1–2 tablespoons water

EQUIPMENT: *Sauté pan, spatula, fork or potato masher*
PREP TIME: *25 minutes*
YIELD: *1 treatment*
STORAGE: *Do not store; prepare as needed*
APPLICATION: *Up to 3 times a day*

Combine the onions, garlic, and ginger with a tablespoon or so of water in a medium pan over medium heat — covered — and gently sauté for 15 to 20 minutes, until soft and glossy. Remove the pan from the heat and allow to cool slightly. Mash to form a soft pulp. Strain off any excess juice.

APPLICATION INSTRUCTIONS: You'll need to be reclining to apply this poultice or have someone else apply it for you, as the pulp can be a bit gloppy. My favorite method is to place the poultice in a very small pillowcase, with the open end folded over so the pulp can't ooze out, and lay the pillowcase on your bare chest. A drawstring bag made of light cloth also works well, or you can lay a square of soft material, such as flannel, on your chest, apply the poultice, and cover with another square of material. Pull a light blanket up and over your head, relax, and breathe deeply of the healing vapors. Discard the entire poultice when it cools. Repeat up to three times per day, as needed.

Be Clear Sinus Vapor Rub

This vapor rub is an essential oil blend that contains strong respiratory antiseptics to help fight infection and mucolytics to aid in dissolving and loosening mucous congestion. Antiviral, decongestant, and analgesic properties help heal the source of your stuffiness, shrink swollen mucous membranes, and alleviate tightness in your chest.

This particular remedy calls for a wide variety of essential oils, but they can be used in many other recipes in this book and I recommend having them all.

Note: This is an aromatherapeutically concentrated formula, so use only as directed.

25 drops cajeput essential oil

20 drops eucalyptus (species *radiata*) essential oil

10 drops balsam fir essential oil

10 drops lavender essential oil

10 drops peppermint essential oil

10 drops sage essential oil

5 drops clove essential oil

5 drops tea tree essential oil

5 drops thyme (chemotype *linalool*) essential oil

½ cup jojoba base oil

EQUIPMENT: *Dropper, dark glass storage bottle with dropper top or screw cap*

PREP TIME: *15 minutes, plus 24 hours to synergize*

YIELD: *Approximately ½ cup*

STORAGE: *Store at room temperature, away from heat and light; use within 2 years*

APPLICATION: *2 or 3 times per day*

Add the cajeput, eucalyptus, balsam fir, lavender, peppermint, sage, clove, tea tree, and thyme essential oils drop by drop directly into a storage bottle. Add the jojoba base oil. Screw the top on the bottle and shake vigorously for 2 minutes to blend. Label the bottle and place it in a dark location that's between 60° and 80°F for 24 hours so that the oils can synergize.

APPLICATION INSTRUCTIONS: Shake well before using. Apply a drop or two of this aromatic oil under your nose, on your throat, on your temples, and behind your ears. If your skin is not too sensitive, place a drop on each cheekbone as well. Spread several drops on your chest and even on the soles of your feet so they can be absorbed via all those sweat glands. Be sure to massage the oil drops in well, until they are totally absorbed into your skin with nary an oil slick in sight.

After you've rubbed the oil into the skin, inhale the essences from your hands by cupping them over your mouth and nose. Close your eyes and breathe deeply.

Bonus Acts as an aid in fighting athlete's foot and nail fungus. Simply massage into your clean feet and nails twice daily. It also acts as an antiseptic for minor to moderate skin ailments and as a spot treatment for blemishes.

EUCALYPTUS, PINE, AND THYME RESPIRATORY VAPORS BALM

Eucalyptus, pine, and thyme essential oils are traditionally used to help ease respiratory conges-tion, thereby encouraging deep, oxygenating breaths while fortifying resistance and general immunity. They also offer powerful antiviral, anti-inflammatory, analgesic, and antiseptic proper-ties accompanied by a stimulating energy. The base ingredients soothe and soften the dry, raw skin in and around your nose.

This recipe calls for a small amount of Amazon Woman Balsam Fir–Infused Oil (page 172). If you have some, do use it; it adds amazing fragrance and has respiratory-opening properties.

Note: This is an aromatherapeutically concentrated formula, so use only as directed.

- 5 tablespoons infused oil from Amazon Woman — Balsam Fir–Infused Oil or soybean or almond base oil
- 1 tablespoon beeswax
- 1 tablespoon cocoa butter
- 1 tablespoon refined shea butter (unrefined shea butter will work, but its stronger fragrance will often mask the aroma of the essential oils)
- 40 drops eucalyptus (species *radiata*) essential oil
- 40 drops Scotch pine essential oil
- 20 drops thyme (chemotype *linalool*) essential oil

EQUIPMENT: *Small saucepan or double boiler, stirring utensil, plastic or glass jar or tin*
PREP TIME: *20 minutes to make the balm, plus 12 hours to thicken*
YIELD: *½ cup*
STORAGE: *Store at room temperature, away from heat and light; use within 1 year*
APPLICATION: *3 or 4 times per day*

Combine the base oil, beeswax, cocoa butter, and shea butter in a small saucepan or double boiler, and gently warm over low heat until all the solids are just melted. Remove from the heat and allow to cool for 5 to 10 minutes. Stir a few times to blend the mixture thoroughly. Add the eucalyptus, Scotch pine, and thyme essential oils and stir again. Pour into a storage container. Cap and label, and set the balm aside to thicken overnight at room tempera-ture. Because both cocoa butter and shea butter are included, the balm may continue to change texture slightly for another 24 hours.

APPLICATION INSTRUCTIONS: Apply a tiny dab or two of this aromatic balm under your nose, on your throat, on your temples, and behind your ears. If your skin is not too sensitive, place a tiny amount on each cheekbone as well. Spread a little bit onto your chest and even on the soles of your feet. Massage the balm in well. After you've rubbed the balm into your skin, inhale the essences from your hands by cupping them over your mouth and nose.

"Ouch . . . My Nose Hurts" Salve

Your poor nose can really suffer when you have a cold, sinus congestion, or allergy. Constantly wiping your nose with dry tissues can leave it rough, sore, raw, and oh-so-unattractively red. What you need is an extremely gentle, moisturizing salve to soothe and heal the damaged tissue. Basic shea butter with the addition of an antiseptic, anti-inflammatory essential oil such as lavender, myrrh, German chamomile, or palmarosa will gently stimulate skin cell regeneration, while conditioning and softening the skin in and around your nose so that you soon feel comfortable again. If you don't want to add an essential oil to this simple remedy, plain shea butter can be used as an effective treatment on its own, as can extra-virgin coconut oil.

4 tablespoons refined shea butter (unrefined shea butter will work, but its stronger fragrance will often mask the aroma of the essential oils)

20 drops German chamomile, lavender, myrrh, *or* palmarosa essential oil

EQUIPMENT: *Small saucepan or double boiler, stirring utensil, glass or plastic jar or tin*
PREP TIME: *15 minutes, plus up to 24 hours to thicken*
YIELD: *Approximately ¼ cup*
STORAGE: *Store at room temperature, away from heat and light; use within 1 year*
APPLICATION: *As desired*

Warm the shea butter in a small saucepan (a ¾-quart size works great) or double boiler over low heat, until it has just melted. Remove from the heat. Add the essential oil directly to your storage container, then slowly pour in the liquefied shea butter. Gently stir to blend. Cap and label. Unlike beeswax, shea butter takes a long time to completely thicken, and this formula may need up to 24 hours, depending on the temperature in your kitchen. When it's ready, it will be very thick, semi-hard, and white (or creamy yellow, if you've used unrefined shea butter).

APPLICATION INSTRUCTIONS: As needed, smear a small dab of this salve slightly inside and around the nostrils, completely covering all irritated skin. If your lips are dry, spread a dab there, too.

Bonus This salve works wonders to condition dry, brittle nails and cuticles and also helps heal blisters and cracked skin on your feet. It also makes a protective balm for your skin during winter, when you'll be exposed to the harsh, dry, cold air.

SCARS

A scar forms as your skin repairs a wound that has penetrated the dermal layer or second layer of your skin. Scars can result from cuts, scabbing diseases such as chickenpox or acne, serious burns, or a severe rash. They are part of the natural healing processes of your body. Scars can be raised or flat, long, short, or round, and flesh-toned, pink, purple, or brown in color.

Some people are more likely than others to develop more pronounced scars. A scar's formation and appearance depend on general health, age, skin type, condition of skin, skin color, location of the injury (body or face), and the particulars of the initial trauma. The degree to which a scar develops greatly depends on the severity of the damage to the skin and the length of time it takes to heal. The longer the healing process and the greater the damage to the skin, the increased likelihood of a noticeable scar.

A *hypertrophic* scar is elevated above the surface of the skin, and the tissue forms in direct proportion to the size of the wound. A *keloid* is similar to a hypertrophic scar, except that the scar tissue forms out of proportion to the amount of scar tissue normally required for repair and healing. In other words, it extends beyond the boundaries of the original wound site and into the surrounding skin. Black skin is particularly prone to the development of keloids.

To avoid scars entirely, you'd need to live in a bubble. Life happens. Once you do have an injury, the best way to minimize scarring is to begin proper care of the wound at once and avoid further injury to the wound site. It pays to keep skin in tip-top shape by conditioning it regularly with nourishing oils, body creams, and lotions and by eating a whole-foods diet to ensure that the skin remains flexible, elastic, and able to heal rapidly.

When treating scars with home remedies, keep in mind that everyone's skin is unique and reacts differently to different products. For additional assistance, consult with your local pharmacist about nonprescription topical scar treatments. Scars older than a year or two, raised scars, long surgical scars, burn scars, or those that develop and deepen over time, such as acne and chickenpox scars, can be difficult to treat with home remedies and should be addressed by a dermatologist if they cause discomfort or negatively impact your self-esteem.

ROSEHIP AND ROSEMARY RECOVERY OIL BLEND

Rosehip seed oil, rich in essential fatty acids, is highly regenerative, promoting the growth of fresh, healthy new skin. With continued application, it dramatically increases the elasticity of the skin and stimulates the formation of new collagen fibrils, resulting in a smoother, more toned appearance. Combined with skin-conditioning wheat germ oil, plus rosemary and lavender essential oils, this blend synergizes to form a superior scar-preventive treatment when applied to new injuries and a scar-fading treatment when applied to existing scars less than 2 years old.

15 drops lavender essential oil

15 drops rosemary (chemotype *verbenon*) essential oil

3 tablespoons rosehip seed base oil

1 tablespoon vitamin E oil or wheat germ base oil

EQUIPMENT: *Dropper, dark glass bottle with dropper top or screw cap*
PREP TIME: *15 minutes, plus 24 hours to synergize*
YIELD: *Approximately ¼ cup*
STORAGE: *Refrigerate; use within 6 months*
APPLICATION: *2 times per day*

Add the lavender and rosemary essential oils drop by drop directly into a storage bottle. Add the base oils. Screw the top on the bottle and shake vigorously for 2 minutes to blend. Label the bottle and place in a dark location that's between 60° and 80°F for 24 hours so that the oils can synergize. After 24 hours, refrigeration is required.

APPLICATION INSTRUCTIONS: Shake well before each use. If possible, immediately after incurring an injury, clean the area and then massage several drops (or more, depending upon the size of the injury) of this formula into the surrounding skin. Massage several drops into the entire wound twice daily as it begins to heal to prevent or at least minimize scarring.

Additionally, twice-daily application for at least 6 months can dramatically fade and soften existing scars that are less than two years old. Consistency with application is key.

Bonus This remedy can be applied twice daily, by the drop, to areas of your face and neck where you notice new wrinkles forming as well as to deeper, existing wrinkles to help plump and nourish the underlying tissue. If you are consistent with application and proper care of your skin, expect to see noticeable results within 6 months.

CALENDULA AND CALOPHYLLUM REJUVENATIVE DROPS

Homemade calendula-infused oil is frequently my go-to herbal remedy base for treating injuries that have the potential for scarring. With calendula and calophyllum oils, along with carrot seed and lavender essential oils, this formula has analgesic, anti-inflammatory, antiseptic, and skin-cell-regenerative properties, and an amazing ability to assist the skin in successful rejuvenation while restoring elasticity and suppleness.

This recipe calls for only a small amount of calendula-infused oil. If you have some homemade Simple Calendula-Infused Body Oil (page 162), great. If not, then purchase a small bottle from your local health food store or herbal supplier. But I do recommend that you always have at least a cup of this multipurpose infused oil on hand — fresh and homemade is best, and much less expensive!

15 drops carrot seed essential oil

15 drops lavender essential oil

3 tablespoons calendula-infused oil

1 tablespoon calophyllum base oil

EQUIPMENT: *Dropper, dark glass bottle with dropper top or screw cap*
PREP TIME: *15 minutes, plus 24 hours to synergize*
YIELD: *Approximately ¼ cup*
STORAGE: *Store at room temperature, away from heat and light; use within 1 year*
APPLICATION: *2 times per day*

Add the carrot seed and lavender essential oils drop by drop directly into a storage bottle. Add the calendula and calophyllum base oils. Screw the top on the bottle and shake vigorously for 2 minutes to blend. Label the bottle, and place in a dark location that's between 60° and 80°F for 24 hours so that the oils can synergize.

APPLICATION INSTRUCTIONS: Shake well before each use. If possible, immediately after incurring an injury, clean the area and then massage several drops (or more, depending upon the size of the injury) of this formula into the surrounding skin. Massage several drops into the entire wound twice daily as it begins to heal to prevent or at least minimize the potential for scarring.

Bonus When applied by the drop, this blend speeds healing to minor cuts and scrapes, blisters, bruises, dermatitis, and dry eczema, plus it soothes and moisturizes patches of severely dry or cracked skin anywhere on the body.

SKIN-BE-SMOOTH: LAVENDER AND COCOA BUTTER BALM

Lavender essential oil and cocoa butter have long been used to help prevent scarring after an injury. This formula combines these traditional herbal ingredients into one potent blend with antiseptic, vulnerary, anti-inflammatory, analgesic, and skin-cell-regenerating properties that will aid in healing the injury and rejuvenating the skin so that scarring is minimized. It is gentle enough to be used on children over 6 years old. The blend has a lovely lavender-cocoa cream smell and is readily absorbed into the skin upon application.

Note: This is an extremely mild, yet aromatherapeutically concentrated formula, so use only as directed.

2 tablespoons cocoa butter

2 tablespoons jojoba base oil

50 drops lavender essential oil

EQUIPMENT: *Small saucepan or double boiler, stirring utensil, glass or plastic jar or tin*
PREP TIME: *20 minutes to make the balm, plus up to 36 hours to synergize and thicken*
YIELD: *Approximately ¼ cup*
STORAGE: *Store at room temperature, away from heat and light; use within 1 year*
APPLICATION: *2 times per day*

Bonus This gentle yet highly effective balm is wonderfully healing for minor to moderate cuts and scrapes, blisters, and poison plant rashes.

Combine the cocoa butter and jojoba oil in a very small saucepan (a ¾-quart size works great) or double boiler, and warm over low heat until the cocoa butter is just melted. Remove from the heat and allow to cool for 5 minutes, stirring a few times. Add the lavender essential oil and stir again to thoroughly blend. Slowly pour the liquid balm into the storage container. Cap and label.

This particular blend of ingredients can take up to 36 hours to synergize and properly thicken, depending on the temperature in your kitchen. If after 36 hours it has not thickened to at least a soft salve consistency, then give it a good, gentle stir and place the container in the refrigerator for 1 hour. Remove the container after that time, and allow the product to return to room temperature before use.

APPLICATION INSTRUCTIONS: If possible, immediately after incurring an injury, clean the area and then massage a small dab (or more depending on the size of the injury) of this formula into the surrounding skin. Massage a small dab into the entire wound twice daily as it begins to heal to prevent or at least minimize the potential for scarring.

SPLINTERS

Everyone has experienced splinters at some point, usually embedded in a finger or the sole of the foot. They can be difficult to remove, often breaking off at the surface of the skin. Herbal clay pack recipes can aid in the withdrawal of small wooden and metal splinters (no longer than ¼ inch) that are lodged near the surface of the skin. When thickly applied and allowed to dry, a clay pack increases circulation and temperature in the skin and helps draw out any infection present while gently pulling the splinter toward the surface. Once the clay pack is washed off, the splinter should be easier to remove with a pair of tweezers.

BLACK WALNUT CLAY PACK

This clay pack is nearly black in color from the combination of bentonite clay and black walnut hull powder. Due to its astringent and antiseptic properties and its cold, bitter energy, as it dries it tones and tightens skin tissue, cools inflammation surrounding the splinter, and helps fight potential infection.

Note: This clay pack will stain light-colored fabrics, so be careful during application and removal. I always use a navy blue or black washcloth to remove it.

1 tablespoon bentonite clay

1 teaspoon black walnut hull powder

5–6 teaspoons commercially prepared aloe vera juice or purified water

EQUIPMENT: *Small bowl, spoon or tiny whisk*

PREP TIME: *5 minutes*

YIELD: *1 or more treatments*

STORAGE: *Refrigerate any left-overs; use within 3 days*

APPLICATION: *As desired*

In a small bowl or custard cup, use a spoon or tiny whisk to combine the clay and black walnut hull powder with enough aloe vera juice or water to form a smooth, spreadable paste. Bentonite clay tends to become lumpy, so make sure to stir thoroughly. Allow to thicken for 5 minutes. If the mixture is soupy, add a bit more clay. If too thick, add a bit more liquid. Use immediately.

APPLICATION INSTRUCTIONS: Using your finger, simply spread a thick layer of clay pack over the splinter and allow to dry for at least 45 minutes. The clay will harden and may tingle and crack as it dries. Rinse with warm water.

If you are now able to grip the tip of the splinter with a pair of sterilized tweezers, attempt to carefully remove it from the same angle at which it went into your skin. You may repeat the clay pack application as often as necessary until the splinter becomes easier to remove.

If you have any leftover clay pack mixture, tightly cover the little bowl with plastic wrap and store in the refrigerator, where it will keep for up to 3 days. If the mixture starts to dry out, add a tad more aloe vera juice or water and stir well before using.

Oregon Grape Root Anti-Infection Clay Pack

The yellow pigment in this clay pack comes from the Oregon grape root, which is highly anti-septic, anti-inflammatory, astringent, tissue-toning, energetically cold, and bitter. I use this clay pack when I see pus forming around an embedded splinter.

Note: This clay pack will stain light-colored fabrics, so be careful during application and removal. I always use a navy blue or black washcloth to remove it.

1 tablespoon bentonite clay

1 teaspoon Oregon grape root powder

5–6 teaspoons commercially prepared aloe vera juice or purified water

EQUIPMENT: *Small bowl, spoon or tiny whisk*
PREP TIME: *5 minutes*
YIELD: *1 or more treatments*
STORAGE: *Refrigerate any left-overs; use within 3 days*
APPLICATION: *As desired*

In a small bowl or custard cup, use a spoon or tiny whisk to combine the clay and Oregon grape root powder with enough aloe vera juice or water to form a smooth, spreadable paste. Bentonite clay tends to become lumpy, so make sure to stir thoroughly. Allow to thicken for 5 minutes. If the mixture is soupy, add a bit more clay. If too thick, add a bit more liquid. Use immediately.

APPLICATION INSTRUCTIONS: Using your finger, simply spread a thick layer of clay pack over the splinter and allow to dry for at least 45 minutes. The clay will harden and may tingle and crack as it dries. Rinse with warm water.

If you are now able to grip the tip of the splinter with a pair of sterilized tweezers, attempt to carefully remove it from the same angle at which it went into your skin. You may repeat the clay pack application as often as necessary until the splinter becomes easier to remove.

If you have any leftover clay pack mixture, tightly cover the little bowl with plastic wrap and store in the refrigerator, where it will keep for up to 3 days. If the mixture starts to dry out, add a tad more aloe vera juice or water and stir well before using.

STRESS

In today's world of texting, faxing, cell phones and landlines, beepers, e-mails, and social media, there's often no peace, no time to yourself. If you're like most people these days, you're pulled in too many directions, doing too much and giving too much. I can almost guarantee that you're stressed to some degree, my friend.

Uncontrolled, long-term stress can manifest itself in many ways, mentally and physically: high blood pressure, short temper, bad attitude, depression, low energy or exhaustion, muscle aches, acne, eczema, weight gain, lowered immunity, and hormonal imbalances. Poor eating habits tend to accompany unabated stress since junk food is generally high in simple, refined carbohydrates that quickly, albeit temporarily, lift your mood and soothe your nerves.

To put it simply, excess stress drains our mental and physical capacities! So, what's a person to do? For starters, make yourself a priority. Learn to say "no" to demanding people, chill out, and reserve some precious "me" time. It's not an indulgence to get 8 hours of sleep each night either; it's a requirement. With some of your newly allotted "health and wellness time," take up a fun hobby, find a mode of daily exercise that you enjoy, get sunlight on your skin and fresh air in your lungs, drink plenty of water and herb teas, eat a tasty, whole-foods diet, and by all means, take advantage of the soothing properties of herbs. Mother Nature shares with us her healing herbs for when we're sick, her energizing herbs for when we need a little boost, and her calming herbs for when we need relaxation and tranquility.

The following two recipes will help you to de-stress and unwind, delivering you to a more serene, comfortable place. I partake of them quite frequently.

LEMON BALM AND ST. JOHN'S WORT BODY OIL

This oh-so-relaxing herbal body oil has nervine, antiviral, anti-inflammatory, and analgesic properties. It's the perfect end-of-the-day massage or bath oil to help relieve tight, sore, fatigued muscles and joints, and to ease your stressed and frazzled nerves, restoring your calm demeanor. This formula is one of my favorites; I especially enjoy the light, pleasing sweet-tart aroma. The addition of lavender essential oil is optional, but it will enhance the sedative effects and fragrance.

Note: These herbs *must* be processed when fresh to ensure medicinal potency. Dried herbs will not do. I prefer the solar infusion method for these herbs, as I feel that they release their best medicinal properties when processed in this gentle manner.

1½ cups freshly wilted lemon balm leaves (see page 38 for information on wilting)

1½ cups freshly wilted St. John's wort flowering tops

3–4 cups almond or soybean base oil (enough to completely cover the herbs)

2,000 IU vitamin E oil

80 drops lavender essential oil (optional)

EQUIPMENT: *Rubber or latex gloves, 1-quart canning jar, stirring utensil, plastic wrap, strainer, fine filter, funnel, glass or plastic storage containers*
PREP TIME: *1 month*
YIELD: *Approximately 2½ cups*
STORAGE: *Store at room temperature, away from heat and light; use within 1 year*
APPLICATION: *As desired, preferably before bedtime*

First, if you don't want your hands stained a deep purplish-red by the St. John's wort, put on rubber or latex gloves. Then cut or tear the wilted lemon balm and St. John's wort into smaller pieces to expose more surface area to the oil. Place the wilted herbs in a widemouthed 1-quart canning jar. Drizzle the base oil over the plant matter, until the oil comes to within 1 inch of the top of the jar. The wilted herb matter will settle with the weight of the oil, so don't worry if it looks as though you don't have enough plant matter in the jar. Gently stir to remove air bubbles and make sure that all the plant matter is submerged.

Place a piece of plastic wrap over the mouth of the jar (to prevent the metal lid from coming into contact with the herbs), and tightly screw on the lid. Shake the jar several times to blend the herbs and oil thoroughly. Place the jar in a warm, sunny location such as a south-facing windowsill, and allow the herbs to infuse for 1 month. Shake the jar every day for 30 seconds.

After 1 month, carefully strain the oil through a fine-mesh strainer lined with a fine filter such as muslin or, preferably, a paper coffee filter, then strain again if necessary to remove all herb debris. Squeeze the herbs to extract as much of the precious oil as possible. Discard the marc. Add the vitamin E oil and lavender essential oil, if using, and stir to blend. The resulting oil blend will be a deep reddish-green in color.

Pour the finished oil into storage containers, then cap, label, and store in a dark cabinet.

APPLICATION INSTRUCTIONS: Shake well before using. Massage this oil all over your body (it's especially comforting applied to slightly damp, warm skin after a hot bath or shower) or just in places where you feel tense and stressed, such as your legs and feet, back, or neck. It makes a wonderfully relaxing bath oil, too. Allow the oil to soak in for 5 to 10 minutes before getting dressed.

Bonus This blend can be used on infants and small children (and you, too!) to help lull them to sleep at night. Simply massage their entire body, or just their legs and feet, prior to bedtime (after a hot bath, if possible). Your loving touch combined with the relaxing herbal properties will have them nodding off in no time.

STATE-OF-BLISS BODY OIL

In an increasingly tense world, lavender and lemon balm are welcome companions. Combined, they offer a much needed tonic for the overly stressed mind and body. We owe Mother Nature a debt of gratitude for these relaxing, calming, soothing, gentle herbs that help balance the central nervous system and ease physical tension. The addition of lavender essential oil is optional, but it will enhance the sedative effects and fragrance, while lemon essential oil will add a hint of citrusy aroma.

Note: Lemon balm leaves *must* be processed when fresh, not dried, to ensure medicinal potency. Harvest them straight from the garden, preferably before the plant goes into bloom. I prefer the solar infusion method for this formula, as I feel that the herbs release their best medicinal properties when processed in this gentle manner.

1½ cups freshly wilted lemon balm leaves (see page 38 for information on wilting)

1 cup dried or 1½ cups freshly wilted lavender buds

3–4 cups almond or soybean base oil (enough to completely cover the herbs)

2,000 IU vitamin E oil

80 drops lavender essential oil (optional)

40 drops lemon essential oil (optional)

EQUIPMENT: *1-quart canning jar, stirring utensil, plastic wrap, strainer, fine filter, funnel, glass or plastic storage containers*
PREP TIME: *1 month*
YIELD: *Approximately 2½ cups*
STORAGE: *Store at room temperature, away from heat and light; use within 1 year*
APPLICATION: *As desired, preferably before bedtime*

Cut or tear the lemon balm leaves into smaller pieces. If you're using wilted lavender, first strip the buds and bits of greenery from the stems; discard the stems. This will mash the buds a bit to release more of their essential oil into the infusion. (Feel free to add the bits of greenery to the jar.) Place the lemon balm and lavender in a widemouthed 1-quart canning jar. Drizzle the base oil over the plant matter until the oil comes to within 1 inch of the top. The herbs will settle with the weight of the oil, so don't worry if it looks as though you don't have enough plant matter in the jar. Gently stir to remove air bubbles and make sure that all the plant matter is submerged.

Place a piece of plastic wrap over the mouth of the jar (to prevent the metal lid from coming into contact with the herbs), and tightly screw on the lid. Shake the jar several times to blend the herbs and oil thoroughly. Place the jar in a warm, sunny location such as a south-facing windowsill, and allow the herbs to infuse for 1 month. Shake the jar every day for 30 seconds or so.

After 1 month, carefully strain the oil through a fine-mesh strainer lined with a fine filter such as muslin or, preferably, a paper coffee filter, then strain again if necessary to remove all herb debris. Squeeze the herbs to extract as much of the precious oil as possible. Discard the marc. Add the vitamin E oil and the essential oils, if using, and stir to blend. The resulting infused oil will be a pale golden-green to green in color.

Pour the finished oil into storage containers, then cap, label, and store in a dark cabinet.

APPLICATION INSTRUCTIONS: Shake well before using. Massage this oil all over your body or just in places that you feel tense and stressed, such as on your legs and feet, back, or neck. It's especially comforting applied to slightly damp skin that is still warm from a bath or shower and it makes a wonderfully relaxing bath oil, too. Allow the oil to soak in for 5 to 10 minutes before getting dressed.

Bonus If you omit the lemon essential oil, which is potentially irritating to tender skin, this blend can be used on infants and small children to help lull them to sleep at night. Simply massage their entire body, or just their legs and feet, prior to bedtime (after a hot bath, if possible). Your loving touch combined with the relaxing herbal properties will have them nodding off in no time.

A life of retreat offers various joys; none, I think, will compare with the time one employs in the study of herbs, or in striving to gain some practical knowledge of nature's domain.

— ABBOTT WALAFRID STRABO

STRETCH MARKS

What exactly are stretch marks? These lovely skin stripes, earned in this experience we call life, are generally wavy or curved, and often slightly shimmery; they may be reddish or pale reddish-purple when new, becoming white or pale silver as they mature. The striations appear on the breasts, buttocks, abdomen, thighs, and occasionally lower back and backs of upper arms as a result of rapid weight gain, usually in excess of 20 to 30 pounds, as experienced in pregnancy. Repeated weight gain and loss from yo-yo dieting typically leaves skin flabby and scarred by stretch marks. Avid sun worshippers are prone to stretch marks due to the cumulative environmental sub-surface skin damage.

The marks appear when the skin's underlying supportive matrix of fibers has broken down, overstretched, dried out, and torn. They're generally permanent once they appear, but as a rule they become less noticeable over time. The key to minimizing the potential for stretch marks is to keep skin healthy, hydrated, and elastic by adhering to good dietary and lifestyle habits and observing proper skin care.

If and when you do find yourself gaining weight, for whatever reason, be especially consistent about applying nurturing, skin-compatible herbal oils, salves, or balms to your entire body on a daily basis so that your skin remains supple and moist. Skin that is dry and dehydrated while being constantly stretched and strained is an open invitation for stretch mark formation.

ESSENTIAL SKIN CONDITIONER

Rich, luxurious, and emollient, this oil blend derived from a fruit, a nut, and a seed is highly compatible with human skin. It penetrates readily, nourishing skin from the outside in. Chock-full of essential fatty acids, monounsaturated fats, vitamins (especially vitamin E), minerals, and proteins, this protective formula, applied daily, smoothes and conditions normal to dry skin, promoting elasticity and protecting your skin as it stretches during weight gain. I like to use it as a full-body massage and bath oil during the winter when my skin has a tendency to get super-dry; it leaves me feeling velvety soft.

⅓ cup avocado base oil

⅓ cup jojoba base oil

⅓ cup macadamia nut base oil

1,000 IU vitamin E oil

EQUIPMENT: *Glass or plastic storage bottle*

PREP TIME: *10 minutes*

YIELD: *Approximately 1 cup*

STORAGE: *Store at room temperature, away from heat and light; use within 6 months*

APPLICATION: *1 or 2 times per day, or as desired*

Combine the avocado, macadamia nut, and jojoba oils with the vitamin E oil in a storage bottle. Tightly cap the bottle and shake vigorously. Label and store in a dark cabinet.

APPLICATION INSTRUCTIONS: Shake well before using. Once or twice a day, preferably after bathing or showering, massage this oil blend into your skin, from head to toe if you wish, while your skin is still slightly damp (though it can be applied directly to dry skin as well, as it is highly absorptive). Let the oil soak in for at least 5 minutes before getting dressed. The oil should sink right in with no oily residue; if your skin remains oily after 5 minutes, blot off the excess and use less next time. Exfoliate at least twice per week to keep your skin free of the pore-clogging skin-cell buildup that inhibits moisture and oil penetration (see Exfoliate to Eliminate Dry Skin, page 151).

Bonus This formula is the ultimate conditioning oil for dry, brittle, slow-to-grow nails and ragged cuticles. Massage a drop into each nail once or twice daily.

Bee Flexible Salve

Rich in emollient, ultra-healing, anti-inflammatory, vulnerary, skin-cell-regenerating, and slightly astringent extracts of comfrey root, Solomon's seal root, and myrrh resin, this salve was developed specifically for the prevention of stretch marks accompanied by dry skin irritation. It's designed to seal in moisture, maintain elasticity, and soothe when slathered onto skin that is stretching due to weight gain. With these properties, it can also be used to soften dry hands and nails, chapped lips, cracked feet, and scaly knees, elbows, and shins. It also helps heal blisters, dry eczema, and dermatitis, and reduces scarring. It makes an excellent protective diaper rash barrier for baby's bottom.

Note: I prefer to use the stovetop method of extraction for this formula, as I feel that these particular herbs release their best medicinal properties when processed in this manner.

½ cup dried or 1 cup freshly wilted comfrey root (see page 38 for information on wilting)

½ cup dried Solomon's seal root

¼ cup myrrh gum powder

3 cups extra-virgin olive base oil

2,000 IU vitamin E oil

3–4 tablespoons beeswax (depending on how firm you want the salve to be)

EQUIPMENT: *2-quart saucepan or double boiler, stirring utensil, candy or yogurt thermometer, strainer, fine filter, funnel, glass or plastic storage container (for the infused oil), glass or plastic jars or tins (for the salve)*

PREP TIME: *6 hours to infuse the oil; 20 minutes to make the salve; 30 minutes for it to thicken*

YIELD: *Approximately 2½ cups of infused oil and 1¼ cups of salve*

STORAGE: *Store at room temperature, away from heat and light; use within 1 year*

APPLICATION: *1 or 2 times daily, or as desired*

PREPARING THE INFUSED OIL: If using you're freshly wilted comfrey root, grate or finely chop it to expose more surface area to the oil. Combine the comfrey root, Solomon's seal root, and myrrh gum powder with the olive base oil in a 2-quart saucepan or double boiler, and stir thoroughly to blend. The mixture should look like a thick, chunky herbal soup. Bring the mixture to just shy of a simmer, between 125° and 135°F. Do not let the oil actually simmer — it will degrade the quality of your infused oil. *Do not put the lid on the pot.*

Allow the herbs to macerate in the oil over low heat for 6 hours. Check the temperature every 30 minutes or so with a thermometer, and adjust the heat accordingly. If you're using a double boiler, add more water to the bottom pot as necessary, so it doesn't dry out. Stir the infusing mixture at least every 30 minutes or so, as the herb bits tend to settle to the bottom.

After 6 hours, remove the pan from the heat and allow to cool for 15 minutes. While the oil is still warm, carefully strain it through a fine-mesh strainer lined with a fine filter such as muslin or, preferably, a paper coffee filter, then strain again if necessary to remove all debris. Squeeze the herbs to extract as much of the precious oil as possible. Discard the marc.

Add the vitamin E oil and stir to blend. The resulting infused oil blend will be brownish golden green in color. Pour the finished oil into a storage containers, then cap, label, and store in a dark cabinet.

PREPARING THE SALVE: Combine 1 cup of the infused oil with the beeswax in a small saucepan or double boiler, and warm over low heat until the beeswax is just melted. Remove from the heat and allow to cool for 5 minutes, stirring a few times to blend. Pour into glass or plastic jars or tins, cap, label, and set aside for 30 minutes to thicken.

APPLICATION INSTRUCTIONS: Once or twice a day, preferably after bathing or showering, massage a judicious amount of this salve into your skin, from head to toe if you wish, while your skin is still slightly damp (though it can be applied directly to dry skin as well, as it is highly absorptive). Let the salve soak in for at least 5 minutes before getting dressed. The salve should sink right in with no greasy residue; if your skin remains oily after 5 minutes, blot off the excess and use less next time. Exfoliate at least twice per week to keep your skin free of the pore-clogging skin-cell buildup that inhibits moisture and oil penetration (see Exfoliate to Eliminate Dry Skin, page 151).

Bonus In the winter, I've been known to use this formula as a nightly eye cream to keep the delicate skin around my eyes soft and lubricated. Plus, this salve can be used as a topical massage agent to aid in mending torn ligaments, severely strained muscles, and bruises.

SUNBURN

Sunburn results from overexposure to ultraviolet B (UVB) rays. Depending on the amount of sun exposure and the type of skin pigment, the skin becomes red, tender, swollen, and painful anywhere from 1 to 24 hours after exposure. Blisters may form and the skin may peel. A severe sunburn might be accompanied by chills, fever, headache, and weakness.

Maybe you're one of those people who, after even a brief amount of sun exposure, develops a golden tan and thinks nothing of it, but sorry, there are no safe tans. Eventually a suntan or sunburn fades, perhaps giving the impression that any damage that was done is gone forever. But skin records light exposure and stores it, just like camera film registers and saves light images. With the passage of time as the developer, the skin's memory of that sunlight may emerge decades later in the form of hyperpigmentation (such as brown liver spots), wrinkles, hypopigmentation (white unpigmented spots), or other sun damage, such as cancer.

I'm not suggesting that we need to be sunphobic — all living things require some sunlight to live and thrive — but common sense and a daily application of natural, chemical-free sunscreen and/or protective clothing is your best bet for preventing sunburn and premature aging of the skin, plain and simple. Avoiding the sun during the peak "burning hours" — from 10:00 A.M. to 4:00 P.M. or so, depending on the time of year and where you live — makes good sense, too.

Following are a couple of my favorite recipes for cooling the burn, easing the pain, and hydrating your dried-out hide if you do get sunburned, and for restoring the vitality and suppleness of your damaged skin as it strives to return to normal.

ALOE, CARROT, AND ROSEMARY HYDRATING SKIN RESCUE SPRAY

This remedy is a nonalcoholic liniment spray with energetically cooling, tissue-healing aloe vera juice as its base. When carrot seed and rosemary essential oils are added, the result is a rejuvenating, antiseptic, anti-inflammatory herbal formulation designed especially to relieve pain, rehydrate, soothe, and revitalize damaged skin. You can also use fresh aloe vera gel directly from a plant (simply split open a leaf, scrape or squeeze out the gel, and apply it directly to the burn), but you may find that the spray is easier to apply and feels more soothing.

1 cup commercially prepared aloe vera juice

20 drops carrot seed essential oil

20 drops rosemary (chemotype *verbenon*) essential oil

EQUIPMENT: *Glass or plastic spritzer bottle*
PREP TIME: *5 minutes*
YIELD: *Approximately 1 cup*
STORAGE: *Refrigerate; use within 4 to 6 months*
APPLICATION: *As necessary or desired*

Combine the aloe vera juice, carrot seed essential oil, and rosemary essential oil in a spritzer bottle, and shake vigorously to blend. Label and refrigerate.

APPLICATION INSTRUCTIONS: Shake well before use. Immediately or as soon as possible after experiencing sunburn, windburn, or other environmental skin damage, apply this aloe liniment, whether by pouring, spraying, or cold compress. Repeat as needed several times per day, even until the skin is completely healed. Follow with an application of Sea Buckthorn and Sesame Revitalizing Skin Treatment Oil (next recipe) or your favorite natural moisturizer or body oil.

Bonus This remedy can be used to clean, cool, and soothe any type of mild to moderate burn, not just sunburn.

SEA BUCKTHORN AND SESAME REVITALIZING SKIN TREATMENT OIL

The combination of sea buckthorn and sesame seed oils yields an ultra-revitalizing, skin-rejuvenating blend rich in nourishing essential fatty acids, proteins, and antioxidants. This vibrant orange oil supports the natural functions of the skin, helping to restore its protective barrier, leaving it soft, supple, vital, and replenished.

Note: This blend will stain light-colored fabrics due to sea buckthorn's orange pigment. Once it penetrates your skin, however, there is no need to worry about staining.

7	tablespoons unrefined sesame base oil
1	tablespoon sea buckthorn base oil
1,000	IU vitamin E oil

EQUIPMENT: *Glass or plastic bottle*
PREP TIME: *5 minutes*
YIELD: *Approximately ½ cup*
STORAGE: *Store at room temperature, away from heat and light; use within 1 year*
APPLICATION: *1 or 2 times per day*

Combine the sesame, sea buckthorn, and vitamin E oils in a storage bottle. Tightly cap the bottle and shake the mixture vigorously. Label and store in a dark cabinet.

APPLICATION INSTRUCTIONS: Shake well before using. Prior to application, cool and hydrate the skin with moist compresses of chilled water or aloe vera juice, with Aloe, Carrot, and Rosemary Hydrating Skin Rescue Spray (see previous recipe), or with a cool shower or bath. Pat the affected area almost dry, then ever-so-gently apply a small amount of this oil blend, massaging or pressing it into the skin until the oil is completely absorbed. Repeat twice daily until the skin is healed and feels comfortable again.

> **Bonus** Use this as your go-to daily conditioning body oil if you tend to suffer from "lizard skin" that is scaly, flaky, and parched.

WARTS (*Common*)

Verruca **is the technical term** for a wart, a small skin growth caused by any of 60 related human papillomavirus types that affect the outer layer of the skin, or epidermis. Warts can be spread from one location on the body to another, particularly along a scratch or cut, but most warts are not very contagious from one person to another, excepting genital warts, which are highly contagious and transmitted sexually. Anyone, at any age, can develop a wart, but they are most common in children and least common in the elderly.

Whether flat or raised, common warts tend to be firm, rough, and scaly on the top surface and vary in size depending on the particular virus that caused them and their position on the body. They most often appear in areas that are easily injured, such as the fingers, nails, face, scalp, elbows, and knees, and they can develop in clusters (mosaic warts) or as single, isolated growths. Plantar warts develop on the soles of the feet and can be quite painful due to the pressure inflicted upon them by standing or walking; they are difficult to treat, often resisting natural remedies.

A cure for these pesky, unsightly growths can be elusive because they frequently go away spontaneously and also tend to recur spontaneously in the same areas. There is no guaranteed cure, natural or chemical. Just when you think they're gone, here they come again, even if you resort to having your health-care professional freeze them off with liquid nitrogen. Alternative treatments such as laser surgery and electrodesiccation (a treatment that uses electric current) can also destroy warts, but both of these may result in scarring.

Here's an interesting tidbit: After you've been treating a wart for some time with whatever method you decide upon, you *may* notice an apparent increase in the size of the wart. This can, in some people, signal the beginning of the healing process. Warts have a root (a portion that is beneath the skin) that may get pushed outward as it is rejected by the healing tissue, so don't become alarmed if it looks as if your wart is getting bigger — it's temporary.

Tried and True Wart Remedies

Here are some simple, effective herbal wart remedies that have been around for hundreds, if not thousands, of years. Be aware that no one treatment works for everyone. Warts are stubborn creatures. Whatever method you choose to try, keep at it. Consistency is key to dissolving and ultimately removing common warts:

TEA TREE, CLOVE, AND LEMON ESSENTIAL OILS. All three essential oils have antiviral and antiseptic properties and work well at helping to dissolve common warts. If you want to give one of these essential oils a try, apply 1 tiny drop "neat" or undiluted to the wart, and cover with an adhesive bandage. Repeat twice daily.

Note: Both clove and lemon essential oils can be highly irritating when used in this manner, so take care not to get them on the surrounding skin. Tea tree essential oil is very effective yet quite gentle on the skin.

GARLIC. Enzyme-rich raw garlic is a potent antiviral. Tape a thin slice to the wart; apply a fresh piece daily. Yes, this method will make you smell a bit garlicky.

DANDELION, CALENDULA, AND MILK-WEED SAP. Folkloric wart remedies abound, and the use of the fresh sap from any of these three plants to dissolve common warts is centuries old. My grandfather taught me to apply to the wart a drop of white, sticky sap from the stem or broken root of a fresh dandelion, from the base of the calendula flower head where it joins the stem, or from the milkweed stem, and cover it with an adhesive bandage. Change the dressing daily. These saps act as corrosive agents to dissolve the wart. Take care not to get the sap onto surrounding skin. Be consistent with your applications and always use fresh plants.

VITAMIN A OIL. Vitamin A is important for the health and integrity of the cell membrane. It is part of a group of compounds called *retinoids*, and it contains *retinoic acid,* which is used in many of today's anti-aging creams and lotions to exfoliate the skin and minimize fine lines and wrinkles, resulting in a smoother, more toned appearance. Many people have had success in dissolving a wart by applying natural vitamin A oil, derived from carotenoid sources, to the wart on a twice-daily basis. You might want to give it a try.

WOMEN'S INTIMATE CONCERNS

Just as men have special physical and intimate-care needs, so do women. We have monthly periods, often with some cramping or discomfort; we get pregnant and give birth, which expands and contracts our skin; we may experience perineal tears when giving birth; and many of us suffer from hormonally induced breast cysts, hot flashes, and dryness in intimate places.

Specific combinations of herbs and other natural ingredients can offer support during some of the most trying times of womanhood. In this section, I'll share a handful of my favorite useful and comforting remedies. I hope you'll find them as beneficial and enjoyable as I do. Most of these remedies can multitask, just like most women do all day long!

Rub thy face with violets and goat's milk, and there is not a prince in the world who will not follow thee.

— Old Gaelic beauty tip

Sweet Violet "Breast Health" Massage Oil

The beautiful sweet violet is particularly valued as an ally for the lymphatic system, one of the body's key filtration and drainage systems. When processed into an infused oil and massaged into the breasts on regular basis, it helps improve lymphatic circulation and soften the lumps found in cystic breasts. It contains methyl salicylate and thus acts as a mild analgesic, easing breast tenderness, plus it offers anti-inflammatory and mild astringent properties with a cooling energy.

This massage oil can be used every day for the treatment of cysts, swollen lymph glands, or tenderness in the breasts; try applying it daily during the 2 weeks prior to the onset of your menstrual flow if you tend to get swollen, painful, cystic breasts due to hormonal changes. I also use this oil, among others, when performing my monthly breast exam. I simply adore the texture of sweet violet–infused oil, as it is incredibly velvety and rich — an oil fit for a queen.

On a dietary note, if you tend to get breast cysts, swollen lymph glands, and tenderness in your breasts, you can often dramatically decrease the frequency and intensity of these conditions by avoiding caffeinated beverages, chocolate, and dairy products and reducing your overall fat intake.

Note: Always use freshly wilted violet plants, as the dried version produces a much less potent medicinal oil. I generally use a ratio of 90 percent leaves to 10 percent flowers. I prefer to use the stovetop method of extraction with violets, as it makes a more potent, more effective formula.

2½ cups freshly wilted sweet violet leaves and flowers (see page 38 for information on wilting)

3 cups almond base oil

2,000 IU vitamin E oil

EQUIPMENT: *2-quart saucepan or double boiler, stirring utensil, candy or yogurt thermometer, strainer, fine filter, funnel, glass or plastic storage containers*
PREP TIME: *5 hours to infuse oil*
YIELD: *Approximately 2½ cups*
STORAGE: *Store at room temperature, away from heat and light; use within 1 year*
APPLICATION: *Once daily, or as desired*

Cut or tear the violet leaves into much smaller pieces to expose more surface area to the oil while processing. Combine the violet leaves and flowers with the almond base oil in a 2-quart saucepan or double boiler, and stir thoroughly to blend. The mixture should look like a thick, chunky, dark green leaf and flower herbal soup. Bring the mixture to just shy of a simmer, between 125° and 135°F. Do not let the oil actually simmer — it will degrade the quality of your infused oil. *Do not* put the lid on the pot.

Allow the herbs to macerate in the oil over low heat for 5 hours. Check the temperature every 30 minutes or so with a thermometer, and adjust the heat accordingly. If you're using a double boiler, add more water to the bottom pot as necessary, so it doesn't dry out. Stir the infusing mixture at least every 30 minutes or so, as the herb bits tend to settle to the bottom.

After 5 hours, remove the pan from the heat and allow to cool for 15 minutes. While the oil is still warm, carefully strain it through a fine-mesh strainer lined with a fine filter such as muslin or, preferably, a paper coffee filter, then strain again if necessary to remove all debris. Squeeze the herbs to extract as much of the precious oil as possible. Discard the marc.

Add the vitamin E oil and stir to blend. The resulting infused oil blend will be a surprisingly deep greenish-black color. Pour the finished oil into storage containers, then cap, label, and store in a dark cabinet.

APPLICATION INSTRUCTIONS: Ideally, perform breast massage after a warm bath or shower while your skin is slightly damp. Pour a small amount of oil into one palm, and rub your hands together to warm the oil. Apply to both breasts with a gentle, stroking massage, moving from the throat down to the nipples, then in light, circular movements around the breasts and under each arm, paying particular attention to cystic areas and swollen lymph glands. Be careful not to massage so firmly that it causes pain. Plan to spend at least 3 minutes massaging your breasts, underarms, and surrounding areas.

Bonus I highly recommend this infusion as a facial massage oil to help normalize hormonal skin fluctuations in those over the age of 40 who suffer from rosacea, combination skin, adult acne, sensitive skin with diffuse redness, and capillary fragility, as well as for those who have very dry skin or dry eczema. It can also be used daily while pregnant to keep stretch marks at bay.

A violet by a mossy stone
Half hidden from the eye!
Fair as a star when only one
Is shining in the sky.

— WILLIAM WADSWORTH

MENSTRUAL CRAMP RELIEF RUB

For some women, "that time of the month" can be a mere inconvenience, with minimal cramping and light bleeding, and for others it is a tolerable interruption of life, with minor bloating, a pound or two of weight gain, slightly sore breasts, and moderate bleeding. But for others, periods can be disabling, including very heavy bleeding, vomiting, diarrhea, a hormone-induced migraine, and severe cramping.

This blend contains herbs that deliver analgesic, nervine, antispasmodic, sedative, and anti-inflammatory properties. When massaged into your abdomen and lower back, it will help ease cramping and relax tense muscles. Plus, the aromatic vapors will help relieve the emotional anxiety and nervous tension that often accompany premenstrual syndrome.

This recipe calls for only a small amount of St. John's wort–infused oil. If you've made some at home (see the recipe on page 64), great. If not, then purchase a small bottle from your local health food store or herbal supplier. But I do recommend that you always have at least a cup of this multi-purpose infused oil on hand—fresh and homemade is best, and much less expensive!

8 drops lavender essential oil

8 drops Roman chamomile essential oil

5 drops ginger essential oil

5 drops sweet marjoram essential oil

3 tablespoons St. John's wort–infused oil

1 tablespoon castor base oil

EQUIPMENT: *Dropper, dark glass bottle with dropper top or screw cap*
PREP TIME: *15 minutes, plus 24 hours to synergize*
YIELD: *Approximately ¼ cup*
STORAGE: *Store at room temperature, away from heat and light; use within 1 year*
APPLICATION: *2 times per day*

Add the lavender, Roman chamomile, ginger, and sweet marjoram essential oils drop by drop directly into a storage bottle. Add the St. John's wort and castor oils. Screw the top on the bottle and shake vigorously for 2 minutes to blend. Label the bottle and place it in a dark location that's between 60° and 80°F for 24 hours so that the oils can synergize.

APPLICATION INSTRUCTIONS: Shake well before use. Massage ½ to 1 teaspoon of this blend into your lower abdomen and lower back. Cover these areas with a thin, soft cloth, such as flannel, or don an old, long T-shirt, and place a hot water bottle or heating pad on your abdomen. Lie down in a comfortable position for 30 minutes or so, until the pain subsides or at least becomes less intense. Repeat twice daily.

Check Your Diet

Don't dismiss the health of your colon with regard to menstrual cramping. If you experience uncomfortable menstrual cramping on a regular basis and are frequently constipated, it could be that your expanded colon is pressing against the uterus, spinal column, and lower back, where the "girdle of premenstrual pain" is felt.

Be sure to drink lots of water, eat a high-fiber diet that is rich in magnesium, take a good probiotic supplement, exercise regularly, and, if need be, visit your local health food store and purchase a good herbal colon-cleansing product to reestablish regularity.

Many foods can exacerbate cramping, muscular tension, and inflammation — I recommend avoiding excessive sodium, caffeine, refined foods, fats, sugar, artificial colors and flavors, and pasteurized, overprocessed, chemical- and hormone-filled dairy products. Many women experience dramatic relief from monthly cramping and breast tenderness when they adopt a clean, chemical-free, whole-foods, low-fat, vegan or vegetarian diet high in vegetables, fruits, beans, and whole grains.

This type of diet maintains estrogen and insulin levels in a healthy range, while reducing inflammation throughout the body. The addition of anti-inflammatory evening primrose oil or borage oil along with a natural B-complex supplement can also be helpful in eliminating breast tenderness, cramping, bloating, and water retention.

Bonus This blend works quite well as a sleep-enhancing oil when rubbed into your temples, under your nose, on the nape of your neck, and on your throat, chest, and hands prior to sliding under the sheets. Breathe deeply of the soothing fragrance and enjoy sweet dreams!

EVERY WOMAN'S EVERY-PURPOSE OIL

The two main ingredients in this recipe are almond oil and wheat germ oil, which just happen to be chock-full of skin-healing essential fatty acids, lecithin, squalene, proteins, vitamins (especially vitamin E), and minerals.

This basic, inexpensive, fragrance-free emollient blend conditions, strengthens, and protects the skin. If regularly massaged into your belly, buttocks, and breasts before, during, and after pregnancy, your ever-changing skin will remain elastic, soft, and in tip-top condition. It sinks right in and goes to work immediately.

This is yet another simple and effective formula that serves many personal-care needs for yourself and entire family, especially those with ultra-sensitive skin. It helps prevent the formation of scar tissue; softens dry, cracked skin, brittle nails, and ragged cuticles; comforts irritated nipples and damaged perineal tissue; makes a soothing, protective oil for blister-prone areas; prevents diaper rash; removes eye makeup and lipstick; and serves as a total-body, skin-nourishing, daily massage oil for yourself and your baby.

¾ cup almond base oil

¼ cup wheat germ base oil

1,000 IU vitamin E oil

EQUIPMENT: *Glass or plastic bottle*
PREP TIME: *5 minutes*
YIELD: *Approximately 1 cup*
STORAGE: *Store at room temperature, away from heat and light; use within 3 months*
APPLICATION: *As desired*

Combine the almond, wheat germ, and vitamin E oils in a storage bottle. Tightly cap the bottle and shake the mixture vigorously. Label and store in a dark cabinet. Wheat germ oil has a very short shelf life, so be sure to use within 3 months.

APPLICATION INSTRUCTIONS: To use this blend as a body oil, once or twice a day, preferably after bathing or showering, massage this oil into your skin, from head to toe if you wish, while your skin is still slightly damp (though it can be applied directly to dry skin as well, as it is highly absorptive). Let the oil soak in for at least 5 minutes before getting dressed. The oil should sink right in with no oily residue; if your skin remains oily after 5 minutes, blot off the excess and use less next time. Exfoliate at least twice per week to keep your skin free of the pore-clogging skin-cell buildup that inhibits moisture and oil penetration (see Exfoliate to Eliminate Dry Skin, page 151).

If you're using this oil for any other skin-conditioning purpose for yourself or a baby, apply as often as desired to dry or damp skin. Let the oil soak in for at least 5 minutes before getting dressed.

Bonus A dab massaged into the ends of frizzy, dried-out, overprocessed hair works like magic to condition damaged strands.

Coconut Oil

UNIVERSAL SKIN CONDITIONER AND PERSONAL LUBRICANT

Organic, unrefined, extra-virgin coconut oil is used by women the world over as a safe, inexpensive, and highly effective body moisturizer and personal lubricant. It serves as a basic, simple remedy for all manner of dry skin. It soothes, softens, seals in residual moisture, and lubricates even the most delicate of tissues such as the labia, perineum, vagina, and nipples and is completely safe to use before, during, and after giving birth.

Coconut oil is great for healing dry, cracked skin anywhere on the body, plus it conditions dry, brittle nails and cuticles, chapped lips, and dry eczema patches and soothes dermatitis. It is a superior oil for treating and preventing blisters on your feet, plus it can be used as a daily after-bath massage oil to keep baby's skin blissfully soft, in superior condition, and smelling of rich, ripe coconuts. I even like to use a tiny dab to de-frizz the ends of my dry, curly hair.

Coconut oil is highly spreadable. A little goes a long way, so use it judiciously — and remember that it is *not* latex friendly.

COOL-THE-FLASH HERBAL MIST

No matter what you call it — a hot flash, inner fire, or heat rush — that powerful surge of heat that spreads throughout your body or simply rises into your face, seemingly emanating from your core, can wreak havoc with your sleep patterns, emotions, and confidence to be in public places. Hot flashes can occur at the most inopportune moments, with physical manifestations ranging from a mildly red face with surface warmth to a full-blown, sweaty melt-down that soaks your clothes or bedsheets.

The recipe below contains cooling, aromatic essential oils traditionally used to subdue surging surface heat and skin inflammation and aid in balancing hormonal mood swings, nervous tension, and exhaustion. Just mist it on, breathe deep of the soothing vapors, and feel better fast! Keep a bottle handy wherever you go.

¾ cup purified water

¼ cup unflavored vodka

12 drops lavender essential oil

4 drops bergamot essential oil

4 drops geranium essential oil

2 drops clary sage essential oil

2 drops peppermint essential oil

EQUIPMENT: *Glass or plastic spritzer bottle*
PREP TIME: *5 minutes*
YIELD: *Approximately 1 cup*
STORAGE: *Store at room temperature, away from heat and light; use within 1 year*
APPLICATION: *3 or 4 times per day*

Combine the water, vodka, and lavender, bergamot, geranium, clary sage, and peppermint essential oils in a spritzer bottle and shake vigorously to blend. Label and store.

APPLICATION INSTRUCTIONS: Shake well before use. When in need of a hot flash chill-down, lightly mist your face and exposed skin, and breathe deeply. Repeat as needed, up to three or four times a day.

Bonus This blend can serve as a citrusy-floral room freshener to eliminate stale odors, as well as a pillow mist to enhance relaxation before nodding off to sleep.

PART 3 The Ingredient Dictionary

This comprehensive listing of ingredients takes a descriptive journey through my herbal medicine-maker's world. Get to know these ingredients; they are your tools to renewed well-being and wholeness. Use this compendium as a reference guide as you create and concoct your salves, balms, clay packs, liniments, oil blends, elixirs, deodorants, and infused oils.

Medicines of the Earth: My First Experiences

My first exposure to handmade herbal medicine was sipping black-cherry bark and goldenseal root tincture — mighty bitter, astringent stuff, but "good for what ails you," especially mucus-laden coughs accompanied by a burning sore throat and fever. My grandparents kept their refrigerator stocked with canning jars packed with roots, bark, dried leaves, stems, and berries surrounded by nasty-looking dark brown liquid (it was grain liquor, added as an extractive, a preservative, and to give the medicine a definite kick!). Curious about the contents of the jars, I inquired of my grandfather, I read books, I went to the woods and identified the plants, and then I learned how to make tinctures — alcoholic extracts of medicinal herbs.

The second herbal medicine I experienced was a healing paste that my grandfather made for the local, free-roaming country dogs. These mangy beasts seemed to find their way to his homestead when they had tick infestations, bite wounds, or open sores of any kind, and he would apply this thick, blackish, potent-smelling paste consisting of pine sap, raw honey, turpentine, and linseed oil, to their afflictions. I remember him telling me that country dogs usually know how to take care of themselves when sick . . . they'll fast for a few days and roll around and sleep in oak leaves out in the woods. Oak leaves are quite astringent, fight infection, and help tighten tissue – perhaps the dogs intuitively knew that these leaves had healing powers? My grandfather called this stinky paste a "salve" and taught me how to make it and other kinds of healing salves — for people — that didn't stink so bad.

Ever since then, wanting to know more about this type of medicine-making, I have studied God's Pharmacy — the wild-growing herbs — experimented with possible formulations for many years, and perfected the art of making soothing salves and balms for a myriad of ailments.

Almond Oil, Sweet (*Prunus dulcis*)

Derived from the ripened, pressed kernel of sweet almond, this is an all-purpose, pale golden, nutritious, very emollient, light- to medium-weight oil with a neutral to slightly warming energy. It can be used in salves, balms, and infused oils; it's gentle enough to use in facial and baby massage oils. It has a high fatty acid content that penetrates and reconditions the skin. Recommended for all skin types, especially dry, inflamed, or itchy skin.

POSSIBLE SUBSTITUTE: Apricot kernel or soybean oil

Aloe (*Aloe barbadensis*)

PART USED: Fresh gel from leaf, commercially prepared juice

With its cold energy and mildly astringent, anti-inflammatory, and vulnerary properties, aloe soothes "hot" ailments such as rashes, insect bites and stings, all manner of skin burns, bedsores or skin ulcers, eczema, psoriasis, hemorrhoids, dermatitis, minor infections, and blemishes. I also use aloe gel or juice as the liquid mixing agent for some clay pack recipes.

Apricot Kernel Oil (*Prunus armeniaca*)

Derived from the kernel of the apricot, this oil has properties similar to almond oil, though it's a bit lighter in weight and texture and slightly astringent. A balancing oil that penetrates readily, apricot kernel oil has an exquisite fruity aroma (if you purchase unrefined, organic oil) that is not to be missed, and it is excellent for all sensitive skin, including infant and mature skin.

POSSIBLE SUBSTITUTE: Almond oil

Arnica (*Arnica montana*)

PART USED: Flowers

A well-known plant with golden yellow daisy-like flowers, arnica has been used for centuries to relieve pain and inflammation from sprains, bruises, sore muscles, stressed ligaments and tendons, and arthritis. In fact, it is often referred to as the "aches and pains" herb. Used in infused oils, salves, or liniments, it yields a warming energy and stimulates the peripheral blood supply, enhancing circulation.

CONTRAINDICATIONS: Do not use on abraded skin or open wounds; may cause contact dermatitis in sensitive individuals.

Aloe: Gel or Juice?

Both fresh aloe gel and commercially prepared juice are effective, but the juice has the added convenience of being readily stored in the refrigerator where it can be quickly grabbed and poured on a burn (and it feels better when chilled!). Commercial juice should be at least 99 percent pure with less than 1 percent added oxidation and mold inhibitors. It has a shelf life of about 1 year. If you have an aloe plant, the gel will last 3 days if covered and refrigerated.

Avocado Oil (*Persea americana*)

Derived primarily from the seed of the fruit, this full-bodied, medium-green oil has a gently warming energy and is rich in nutritive and conditioning components such as vitamins A, B_1, B_2, D, and E, amino acids, lecithin, and essential fatty acids that are especially beneficial to very dry, chapped, irritated, or mature skin. Due to its heavy emollient texture, the oil takes a bit longer than other oils to penetrate the top layer of skin. It's especially good to use in body and facial oil blends. Avocado oil leaves a protective barrier on the skin that helps prevent moisture evaporation.

POSSIBLE SUBSTITUTE: Sesame seed, macadamia nut, or extra-virgin olive oil

Baking Soda (*Sodium Bicarbonate*)

This white, crystalline, odorless, and salty-tasting alkaline powder is found in every kitchen cupboard. Baking soda absorbs moisture and neutralizes odors, thus making it an excellent addition to herbal deodorizing body and foot powders. It relieves itchy, rashy skin when added to bathwater and softens both the water and your skin. An application of a baking soda and water paste is an old-fashioned standby to relieve the pain and itch of most bee stings and insect bites. It's cheap, effective, natural medicine!

Basil, Sweet (*Ocimum basilicum*)

PART USED: Essential oil
Like the fresh culinary leaves, the essential oil has a fresh, spicy-sweet, "green" scent that's very uplifting. An energetically warming essential oil, basil is used in formulas to stimulate hair growth as it increases blood flow and circulation to the scalp. Basil essential oil can also be used in arthritis and muscular pain relief remedies to ease pain and inflammation and in "study aid balms" to enhance mental clarity.

POSSIBLE SUBSTITUTE: Rosemary essential oil is much less expensive and can be used as an effective replacement for basil. It is also less aromatically intense, which many people prefer.

CONTRAINDICATIONS: Avoid if pregnant or epileptic.

Beeswax

Secreted by worker honeybees, pure, unrefined, unbleached beeswax is used as a thickener in salves and balms. It adds a sweet, honey-like fragrance and golden color to products. Melted beeswax hardens quickly as it cools.

POSSIBLE SUBSTITUTE: Refined vegetable emulsifying wax does not have the same alluring qualities as beeswax but is a good vegan substitute, as is candelilla wax. I prefer to use fresh beeswax, as I appreciate its skin-conditioning properties and adore the aroma.

Bergamot (*Citrus aurantium bergamia*)

PART USED: Essential oil
Cold-pressed from the nearly-ripe citrus peel, bergamot essential oil is used to flavor Earl Grey tea. It has a full, round, gently warming, floral-citrus fragrance that refreshes, balances, and helps ease anxiety, nervous tension, and depression. It also contains general antifungal and antiseptic properties. I use this essential oil in balms to encourage sleep and sweet dreams.

POSSIBLE SUBSTITUTE: Sweet orange essential oil, which has a much lighter, fruitier fragrance than bergamot. Children seem to like sweet orange better.

CONTRAINDICATIONS: Avoid use if pregnant or epileptic. May be photosensitizing (if not specified *bergaptenfree*) and a potential skin irritant.

Bhringaraj *(Eclipta alba)*
PART USED: Leaf

One of the most important herbs used in Ayurvedic hair and scalp remedies, bhringaraj (bah-RING-ah-raj) can be infused and applied as an herbal hair oil or consumed as a supplement. An energetically cooling herb, it is known for its ability to promote the growth of strong, healthy, lustrous hair and help prevent premature graying. It is also used to calm the mind and bolster the memory. I use it in scalp-stimulating formulations for those with thinning hair and alopecia.

Birch, Sweet *(Betula lenta)*
PART USED: Essential oil

Distilled from the bark of the North American sweet birch tree, the essential oil is fresh, sharp, and minty, with a candy-like sweetness. It is nearly identical in aroma and chemistry to the creeping wintergreen herb and often substituted for wintergreen essential oil. This cooling oil has analgesic, astringent, diuretic, anti-inflammatory, and antispasmodic properties, and I add it to oil blends specifically formulated to ease the pain of headaches, arthritic joints, tendonitis, sore muscles, and sprains, as well as blends used to open clogged respiratory channels. Birch essential oil is quite stimulating, and also acts to move stagnant fluids in skin and muscular tissue and increase peripheral blood circulation.

POSSIBLE SUBSTITUTE: Wintergreen essential oil

CONTRAINDICATIONS: Avoid if pregnant or epileptic. Always use highly diluted, as it is a potential skin irritant.

Cajeput *(Melaleuca cajeputi)*

Derived from the leaves and twigs of a tall evergreen tree native to Malaysia, Indonesia, northern Australia, and surrounding areas, cajeput essential oil has an uplifting, penetrating, camphorous aroma similar to that of tea tree essential oil. It acts as a hemostatic (arrests hemorrhaging), which makes it a wonderful addition to anti-bruising formulations. A highly antiseptic respiratory stimulant, cajeput helps decongest blocked sinuses and tight lungs and also acts as a warming analgesic. It is used in oil blends and balms to treat sinus and respiratory infections; to disinfect cuts, scrapes, boils, bedsores or skin ulcers, and blisters; to ease cold and flu symptoms; to heal bruises; and to deliver relief to sore muscles and joints.

CONTRAINDICATIONS: May irritate sensitive skin.

Calendula *(Calendula officinalis)*
PARTS USED: Flowers, essential oil, stem sap

Bright orange calendula flowers are known for their calming, anti-inflammatory, and vulnerary properties. Slightly astringent and antiseptic with a neutral to cooling energy, the flowers and deep orange essential oil can be used in elixirs, salves, balms, and infused oils for all types of skin, but they are especially beneficial for environmentally damaged, inflamed, abraded,

cracked, chapped, or infected skin. Calendula is excellent in formulations for children and the elderly, where gentle effectiveness is of utmost importance. The resinous, sticky, white sap from the calendula stem has been used for centuries as a wart remover, and the fresh flower juice is one of my favorite remedies to help heal minor infections, bites and stings, and skin abrasions.
POSSIBLE SUBSTITUTE: German chamomile essential oil and flowers

Calophyllum Oil (Calophyllum inophyllum)

This rich, brownish-green oil is also known as tamanu or foraha oil. Derived from the ripened seeds of a tree found from East Africa to India to northern Australia, it has a sweet, earthy fragrance reminiscent of buttercream frosting or Kahlua. It's mildly analgesic, antiseptic, anti-inflammatory, and slightly cooling. It's used in oil blends, salves, and balms specifically formulated to help fade scars, heal burns and boils, and soothe chapped skin, eczema and psoriasis. It's a perfect choice for environmentally damaged, mature, or very dry skin.

Cardamom (Elettaria cardamomum)

PART USED: Essential oil
Derived from the seeds of the cardamom pod, this essential oil has a sweet, spicy, woody, citrusy aroma that is warming and stimulating. I primarily use cardamom essential oil in a children's "tummy rub" oil blend that serves as an external carminative and antispasmodic, soothing the digestive tract and easing stomach cramps and gas.

Carrot Seed (Daucus carota)

PART USED: Essential oil
A clear, pale yellow essential oil, rich in betacarotene, with a warm, dry, woody, earthy aroma, it aids in restoring elasticity to sagging, wrinkled, or sun-damaged skin but is excellent for all skin types. Combine with rose hip seed, calophyllum, and calendula-infused oil when making regenerative and revitalizing formulas for thinning mature skin or scarred skin.
CONTRAINDICATIONS: Avoid use if pregnant or epileptic. May be photosensitizing and a potential skin irritant.

Castor Oil (Ricinus communis)

This clear to slightly amber-gold, shiny, viscous oil is processed from the beans of an annual shrub. It's highly emollient and analgesic and has a warming energy. Castor oil is the primary oil in most creamy and glossy lipsticks on the commercial market, and it provides staying power and shine to natural lip balm and gloss recipes. It's particularly good for softening rough, dry heels, knees, and elbows and patches of eczema and psoriasis, plus it works fabulously and inexpensively as a diaper rash and foot-blister preventive oil. When applied to fingernails and cuticles, it imparts a protective shield against exposure to drying detergents, hot water, and winter-dry air. Good stuff!

Cayenne (Capsicum annuum)

PART USED: Fruit
A long-time favorite medicinal plant with a heating energy, this one should be treated with delicacy and respect. Though fiery to the tongue and mucous membranes, it has pain-relieving

properties when used judiciously. The active ingredient in cayenne pepper is capsaicin, which, applied externally, acts as a powerful circulatory stimulant. It irritates the skin a bit, affecting the sensory nerves in a positive manner, reducing inflammation. I use ground cayenne pepper in liniments to ease tight muscles and relieve painful joints and also to fight minor-to-moderate infections. Yes, it will burn raw skin and sting like the devil at first, but it works like a charm to help eradicate festering bacteria!

CONTRAINDICATIONS: Use with caution, as the volatile oils are *extremely* irritating to the eyes and mucous membranes. Do not sniff the powder or rub your eyes after working with it. I recommend wearing gloves when working with this herb. Excessive contact can result in dermatitis and blistering, but if used in formulation as directed, it is generally safe.

Cedar, Atlas (*Cedrus atlantica*)

PART USED: Essential oil

Derived from the highly aromatic wood of the Atlas cedar tree, native to the Atlas Mountains of northwest Africa, this essential oil has a woody-fruity scent that imparts deeply soothing and grounding effects. Due to its warming energy and benefit as a deodorizing agent and lymph and circulatory tonic, I use this essential oil in deodorant, anti-dandruff, and skin-conditioning balms. It also has the wonderful ability to soften breast cysts when used in a lymph-moving breast salve.

POSSIBLE SUBSTITUTE: Cedarwood (*Juniperus virginiana*) essential oil

CONTRAINDICATIONS: Avoid Atlas cedar if pregnant or epileptic; cedarwood is considered safe at all times.

Chamomile, German (*Matricaria recutita*)

PARTS USED: Flower, essential oil

The pretty little yellow flowers have a sweet, apple-like fragrance that is most pleasing and relaxing to the senses. The pale golden-yellow oil infusion of the flowers is wonderful in conditioning body oils, salves, and balms to treat skin that is sensitive or inflamed. Chamomile is very gentle, so it is excellent for use in formulas for children and the elderly. The essential oil is thick, velvety, and deep blue, with an intense, pungent, herbaceous-floral aroma; it has high levels of chamazulene and bisabolol (chemical components known for calming inflammation and healing skin irritation). I add the essential oil to formulas when I need cooling, gentle astringency, and antihistamine and powerful anti-inflammatory actions. It's good for abscesses, cuts and scrapes, bruises, boils, bedsores or skin ulcers, rosacea, blemishes, hives, insect bites and stings, blisters, rashes, psoriasis, and eczema.

POSSIBLE SUBSTITUTE: For the essential oil, Moroccan blue chamomile (*Tanacetum annuum*); for the flowers, calendula flowers

Chamomile, Moroccan Blue
(*Tanacetum annuum*)

PART USED: Essential oil

This member of the tansy family, with its small yellow flowers, yields a deep blue essential oil with an intensely sweet, herbaceous aroma, which contains an even higher level of the anti-inflammatory chemical component chamazulene than German chamomile. With its cooling energy and its gently astringent, mildly antiseptic, and highly effective antihistamine properties, it is especially valued for the treatment of hives. It is also beneficial for abscesses, cuts and scrapes, bruises, boils, blemishes, rosacea, bedsores or skin ulcers, rashes, insect bites and stings, and blisters.

POSSIBLE SUBSTITUTE: German chamomile essential oil. Moroccan blue chamomile is also called blue chamomile or blue tansy but should *not* be confused with *Tanacetum vulgare*, or common tansy, which is extremely toxic.

Chamomile, Roman (*Chamaemelum nobile, Anthemis nobilis*)

PARTS USED: Flower, essential oil

The flower has a similar appearance and apple-like aroma to its German cousin, but different chemistry. It contains very little of the blue chamazulene compound, so the resultant essential oil is golden. This herb has stronger digestive and antispasmodic properties but is also used as a very mild anti-inflammatory agent. It helps relieve emotional depression and anxiety and is a wonderful sleep aid. I use the essential oil, with its neutral to cooling energy, in "tummy rub" oil blends to ease stomachache as well as in balms to induce sleep and relieve tension headaches.

Chickweed (*Stellaria media*)

PART USED: Entire plant, except the root

Known as a common lawn weed, this small, delicate herb with tiny white star-shaped flowers has a cooling energy, with soothing mucilaginous and vulnerary properties. It also acts as a gentle tissue-tightening astringent. I use it primarily to make a whole-plant infused oil that I use alone or in salves to treat rashes or eczema, cuts, scrapes, bruises, bedsores and skin ulcers, and blisters. I also use it in liniment blends and make a chickweed juice to treat inflammatory conditions such as hives that need a bit of soothing astringency plus itch relief. Chickweed is a wonderful aid for ulcerated skin and wounds that are slow to heal.

Cinnamon (*Cinnamomum zeylanicum*)

PARTS USED: Bark, essential oil of the bark, cinnamon powder, sticks

The familiar and wonderful spicy fragrance is derived from the bark of a tropical evergreen tree and adds zip to any formula. Its energy is very stimulating and hot, and when used judiciously, it adds a warming sensation to balms and liniments, along with antibacterial, analgesic, astringent, antispasmodic, and antiviral properties. It is useful in treating sinus and respiratory problems, colds and flu, muscular aches, and cold feet.

CONTRAINDICATIONS: Avoid if pregnant or epileptic or with sensitive skin. A strong irritant, it may cause tearing, stinging, or sneezing. Keep the pure essential oil away from eyes and mucous membranes. Potentially a strong skin irritant.

Clary Sage (*Salvia sclarea*)

PART USED: Essential oil

Distilled from the flowering tops and leaves of clary sage, the essential oil has an unusual nutty-musky, herbaceous aroma and a more cooling and gentler energy than the rather heating culinary sage. This herb has calming, deeply relaxing, antidepressant, antispasmodic, and astringent properties. It helps relieve insomnia, muscle tension, chronic stress, menstrual cramps, and hot flashes. The aroma will occasionally produce wild, vivid dreams and a sense of euphoria. I use it primarily in balms to induce sleep and dreams, in salves and oil blends to relieve menstrual cramps, and in liniments to cool hot flashes.

CONTRAINDICATIONS: Avoid if pregnant or epileptic.

Easy-to-Grow Healing Herbs for the Home Apothecary Gardener

Depending on your climate, most of the following herbs are generally easy to grow in a small backyard garden or condominium patio garden. Some, such as aloe, basil, clary sage, lemon balm, marjoram, peppermint, rosemary, sage, and thyme, do well in pots. A handful of others, such as comfrey, echinacea, mugwort, roses, and Solomon's seal, like to spread out and take up a good deal of space, so give them plenty of room if you have it. Calendula, chamomile, echinacea, and mullein tend to vigorously re-seed, taking up residence in different areas of the garden each year. The roots of lemon balm, peppermint, and sweet violet can quickly become invasive, so either plant them in an area where they can be the roaming free spirits that they are or cut their roots back each year to keep their size in check — they also spread by seed if allowed to flower. Be sure to dispose of their roots and flowerheads and don't simply toss them aside, as they will surely sprout up again where they land. Last but not least, chickweed, dandelion, and plantain tend to show up in almost every garden — let a few grow, as these common "weeds" are potent medicinals.

Aloe vera

Basil

Calendula

Chamomile (German and Roman)

Chickweed

Clary sage

Comfrey

Dandelion

Echinacea

Garlic

Lavender

Lemon balm

Marjoram

Mugwort

Mullein

Peppermint

Plantain

Rosemary

Rose

Sage

Solomon's seal (*Polygonatum multiflorum*)

Thyme

Violet, sweet

Yarrow

Clay: Bentonite, Green, and White

Formed by hundreds, if not thousands, of years of decay and compression of debris and rainwater, clay is extremely rich in minerals. I feel that it's one of the most overlooked, inexpensive healing substances we have today. As an agent of healing with remarkable absorbent and drawing powers, bentonite and green clays make packs or poultices that, when thickly applied to the skin and allowed to dry, actually raise the skin's temperature, increase local circulation, and encourage the release of solid and liquid toxins. Green clay and white cosmetic clay can be blended with powdered herbs, baking soda, and cornstarch to create medicinal body powders with deodorizing and astringent properties. (See page 24 for more information about clay.)

Bentonite Clay

Pale to medium gray in color, this naturally occurring volcanic ash is found in the midwestern United States and Canada (the name comes from Benton, Montana). It has a medium-fine texture and a very stimulating, invigorating energy, and it is chock-full of beneficial minerals. When mixed with water or aloe vera juice, bentonite clay has a very slippery, almost gel-like consistency. It can be lumpier and a bit grainier than other clays. I use it primarily to treat poison plant rashes and weeping eczema and as an aid in removing small splinters. It also makes a good foot pack to help heal athlete's foot and weepy or oozing blisters on the feet.

CONTRAINDICATIONS: Avoid use on very sensitive and dry skin.

Green Clay

Sometimes called French green clay, it is light sage green in color with a medium-fine texture and a high concentration of chromium, nickel, and copper. It can be used in the same manner as bentonite clay, but I tend to use it on weeping, oozing eczema and psoriasis, blemishes, and pseudofolliculitis barbae (ingrown beard hair). Blended with powdered herbs, cornstarch, and baking soda, it makes medicinal body powders with deodorizing and astringent properties.

POSSIBLE SUBSTITUTE: White cosmetic clay
CONTRAINDICATIONS: Avoid use on very sensitive and dry skin.

White Cosmetic (Kaolin) Clay

White clay is a very mild, fine-textured clay that contains a high percentage of aluminum oxide along with zinc oxide, silica, calcium, and magnesium. It can be used by any skin type except very dry, due to its gentleness. I like to use it as the base for an absorbent, anti-inflammatory clay facial pack for the treatment of pseudofolliculitis barbae (ingrown beard hair) and as part of the moisture-absorbing base in deodorant body and foot powders.

Clove (*Syzygium aromaticum,* syn. *Eugenia caryophyllata*)

PARTS USED: Essential oil, flower bud
Cloves are the dried flower buds of a slender evergreen tree that is cultivated worldwide, but Madagascar and Indonesia are the main oil-producing countries. Clove essential oil is broadly antiseptic and antiviral, with a hot, spicy, and stimulating energy, similar to cinnamon

bark. I frequently use it in combination with cinnamon essential oil for relieving bronchial and sinus congestion, cold and flu symptoms, and muscular aches and in warming foot balms. It is such a potent antiviral that it can help dissolve stubborn warts, but be careful not to get any onto surrounding skin. I also make an alcohol-based liniment, using whole or cracked cloves, to treat skin infections.

CONTRAINDICATIONS: Avoid if pregnant or epileptic. Potentially a strong skin irritant.

Cocoa Butter (*Theobroma cacao*)

Derived from roasted cocoa beans, this cream-colored, chocolatey-smelling, emollient vegetable fat is hard at room temperature but melts at body temperature. It lends a thick, creamy consistency with soothing conditioning properties for the skin. It's a wonderful addition to recipes for personal lubricants (though it *not* latex friendly), pregnant bellies and expanding breasts, and the tender skin of children and elderly. Ever so gentle and edible, to boot!

Coconut Oil (*Cocos nucifera*)

Use only organic, extra-virgin, unrefined coconut oil. Its sweet, exotic fragrance and smooth flavor are reminiscent of a tropical paradise (whereas refined coconut oil is void of both fragrance and flavor). Coconut oil is derived from the fruit of the coconut palm and is solid at temperatures below 76°F. It is highly emollient and an excellent oil for allover use, and some swear by it as the ultimate skin softener, hair conditioner, and after-sun treatment. Use this tasty, anti-inflammatory, energetically cooling oil in lip balms, dry skin and scalp-conditioning oils, baby oils, cold sore treatments, or any oil-based product from which you desire a penetrating, softening effect. It makes the perfect chemical-free intimate lubricant, too, but is not latex friendly.

Comfrey (*Symphytum officinale*)

PARTS USED: Root, leaf

Comfrey root and leaf have soothing, mildly astringent, and vulnerary properties with cooling energy. The root is particularly mucilaginous (slippery and gooey) and emollient. I make an infused oil from both the root and leaf and use it in salves for burns, cuts, scrapes, scars, stretch marks, and skin infections. The salve and infused oil can be used to mend broken bones and repair strained ligaments; in fact, comfrey is also called "knitbone."

CONTRAINDICATIONS: Do not use on *new* moderately deep cuts or puncture wounds, as some of comfrey's chemical constituents, particularly allantoin, plus zinc, protein, and tissue-tightening tannic acid, may stimulate the outer layer of skin tissue to regenerate and seal the wound closed prior to the subsurface portion of the wound healing and draining, which could result in an internal infection.

Cornstarch (*Zea mays*)

Common culinary cornstarch is a silky-textured, starchy flour made from corn that I use as part of the moisture-absorbent base blend for deodorant body and foot powders.

Dandelion *(Taraxacum officinale)*

PARTS USED: Sap from stem, root

Every part of this common lowly "weed" has a culinary use, a medicinal use, or both. The blossoms can be dipped in batter and fried like fritters; the fresh spring greens can be enjoyed as a nutritious salad, boiled, or dried and used in herbal medicine as a potassium-rich, gentle diuretic and kidney cleanser; the root can be roasted and brewed into "herbal coffee" or dried and decocted into a strong, bitter tonic for the liver, improving digestion and relieving constipation. I include the white, sticky sap as a natural wart remover (page 268).

Echinacea *(Echinacea angustifolia; E. purpurea; E. pallida)*

PART USED: Root

Native to the United States, echinacea has pretty, purplish-pink, daisy-like flowers and can be easily grown in almost any garden. With a cooling energy, and anti-inflammatory, immunostimulant, and vulnerary properties, it is one of the most effective and powerful herbs against all kinds of viral and bacterial infections. I use echinacea root primarily in anti-infective liniments.

POSSIBLE SUBSTITUTES: Usnea, thyme, garlic

Eucalyptus *(Eucalyptus radiata)*

PART USED: Essential oil

Also known as narrow-leaved peppermint eucalyptus or gray eucalyptus, this essential oil has the mildest aroma of all the eucalyptus species. The fragrance is uplifting, slightly spicy, and medicinal, with a warming energy, even though inhalation yields a cooling sensation. Very gentle and child-safe, it has surprisingly potent antiseptic, antiviral, and expectorant capacities that decongest and open respiratory channels. *E. radiata*, as with all eucalyptus plants, contains mucolytic eucalyptol, a compound that thins the flow of mucus and relaxes the mucous membranes. Eucalyptol is rapidly excreted through the lungs. This essential oil also helps treat herpes cold sores and relieves sore muscles and feet. Multiple varieties of eucalyptus are available; *E. globulus* is more common, but *E. radiata* is the most gentle.

Evening Primrose Oil *(Oenothera biennis)*

Native to eastern North America, the evening primrose is identified by a tall flower stalk with beautiful yellow blossoms that bloom late in the day, hence the name. This pale gold, medium-weight oil, rich in anti-inflammatory gamma-linolenic acid (GLA), vitamins, and minerals, is pressed from the small black seeds contained in the elongated fruit capsules. Evening primrose oil has a neutral to slightly cooling energy and is quite comforting and soothing, so I use it in formulations for eczema, psoriasis, cradle cap, dry and mature skin, and brittle nails. This oil has a rather short shelf life — always keep refrigerated.

Fir, Balsam *(Abies balsamea)*

PARTS USED: Needles, essential oil

Fir provides a familiar stimulating, woodsy aroma and is used primarily as a sinus decongestant and respiratory antiseptic. The fragrance has a warming, drying energy and seems to open the lungs and encourage deeper, fuller breathing, thus I add the needle-infused oil and essential oil to chest rubs, body oils for treating colds and flus, and sinus balms. Because it also helps relieve nervous tension, stress-related conditions, and depression and is balancing to the psyche, I add fir to sleep-enhancing balms as well as room mists to enhance mental clarity. This herb seems to evoke differing reactions in people — many find it incredibly energizing, while others react with feelings of peacefulness and serenity.

CONTRAINDICATIONS: Avoid essential oil if pregnant or epileptic; fir-needle-infused oil is safe to use by everyone, unless the skin is highly sensitive.

Garlic *(Allium sativum)*

PART USED: Bulb

Also known as the "stinking rose," garlic gets its medicinal quality and odor from the chemical constituent allicin. Garlic has a hot energy and dramatically stimulates circulation when applied topically. It has been relied upon for centuries as a powerful healing plant due to its strong antiseptic, antiviral, anthelmintic (kills worms), and antifungal properties. I use it topically in an alcohol-based liniment or infused oil to help the body fight infection in cuts, scrapes, boils, blisters, bedsores or skin ulcers, and puncture wounds as well as an antifungal treatment for athlete's foot. Yes, garlic smells bad when applied topically and can permeate your skin, eventually ending up in your bloodstream and on your breath, but when you have a stubborn bacterial or fungal infection, garlic is your go-to herb to speed healing.

Geranium, Rose *(Pelargonium graveolens, Pelargonium x asperum)*

PART USED: Essential oil

Many times you'll find this essential oil listed as simply "geranium." It is derived from the leaves, stalks, and flowers of the scented geranium, not the common variety. When its fresh, rose-like, "green" scent is inhaled, it helps relieve stress, fatigue, depression, and anxiety, thus I add it to sleep balms. This gently stimulating, energetically cooling, slightly astringent oil helps alleviate water retention in the legs resulting from poor circulation and PMS, making it a good ingredient in massage oil blends to relieve tired, heavy-feeling legs. Due to its balancing and revitalizing capacities, it is wonderful blended into facial elixirs formulated for mature, combination, and environmentally damaged skin, but because it helps balance sebum production, it can be used for all skin types. Geranium essential oil also contains antiviral, antifungal, and anti-inflammatory properties. It's a true multipurpose essential oil, worthy of your natural medicine cabinet.

Ginger *(Zingiber officinale)*

PARTS USED: Essential oil, root (rhizome)

A native of the topics, ginger has a familiar spicy, warming, soft aroma; a delicious taste; and remarkable healing powers that are particularly valued in Traditional Chinese Medicine (TCM). The essential oil and root have stimulating, circulation-enhancing, anti-inflammatory, and antispasmodic properties and are great for massage oil blends, balms, and liniments to ease muscle aches, menstrual cramps, and the pain of arthritis and gout. The balancing and grounding scent makes it a helpful addition to sleep-enhancing and dream balms. With its antiviral and antibacterial properties, it is a classic ingredient in cold and flu balms and oil blends. I use ground ginger root in stimulating body powders.

CONTRAINDICATIONS: Avoid essential oil if pregnant or epileptic. The essential oil may be a skin irritant. Ginger-root-infused oil and ginger-root-based liniments are safe for everyone, unless the skin is highly sensitive.

Glycerin, Vegetable

Derived from vegetable fats, this clear, slippery, moisturizing, super-thick, water-based liquid acts as a humectant (drawing moisture from the air to the skin), but it also pulls moisture from within the skin toward its surface. If you put a bit on your tongue, you'll notice it has a very sweet, warm taste. I occasionally add it in lieu of honey to lip balms for its sweet flavor and moisturizing quality, but in this book, it is used in vodka-based herbal liniment formulations to help ameliorate the skin-drying effect of the alcohol.

Grapefruit *(Citrus paradisi)*

PART USED: Essential oil

Cold-pressed from the fruit's peel, this light, sweet-tart, refreshing essential oil with a stimulating aroma helps balance moods, lift spirits, and boost self-esteem. Energetically warming and drying, it is commonly used in massage oil blends to alleviate water retention. Because of its calming effect on the psyche, I add it to sleep-enhancing balms to combat insomnia.

CONTRAINDICATIONS: Avoid if pregnant or epileptic. May be photosensitizing and a potential skin irritant.

Helichrysum *(Helichrysum italicum; helichrysum angustifolium)*

PART USED: Essential oil

A member of the aster family native to the Mediterranean and North Africa, this long-blooming flower is also known as everlasting or immortelle. It yields a truly multipurpose essential oil, with highly aromatic, warm, "curry-like" undertones. Helichrysum is a very potent anti-inflammatory, skin cell regenerative, antifungal, and antirheumatic, as well as a fabulous vulnerary. It's indicated for use in healing bruises, sprains, open wounds and cuts, acne, eczema, and psoriasis. When blended with rosehip seed oil, it helps reduce the appearance of scar tissue and stretch marks.

CONTRAINDICATIONS: Avoid if pregnant or epileptic.

Honey

Sweet, sticky honey acts as a humectant (it draws moisture from the air to the skin). I use it primarily to sweeten lip balms and enhance their moisturizing properties. Honey can also be applied directly to a freshly cleaned cut, scrape, puncture wound, or burn to prevent bacteria from proliferating, encourage oxygenation of the wound, and keep scarring to a minimum. I prefer to use raw, unheated, unfiltered honey since it is naturally rich in vitamins, minerals, trace minerals, bee pollen, propolis, and live enzymes, all of which promote healing of damaged skin tissue. When honey is heated to 140°F, or higher, as is the case with most commercially produced honey, the nutrients and enzyme activity are greatly diminished.

Hydrosols, Aromatic
(a.k.a. Flower Waters)
Hydrosols, also known as floral waters, flower waters, hydroflorates, or distillates, are produced by steam-distilling plant materials. They are typically the byproduct of essential oil manufacturing, but the highest quality is produced from devoted manufacturers who steam-distill small batches of fresh floral and plant material strictly to produce hydrosols. Hydrosols have similar properties to essential oils but are far less concentrated. True steam-distilled hydrosols contain nearly all of the beneficial components offered by whole plant materials. Herbal and floral hydrosols are especially recommended for use by those with ultra-sensitive, tender, or delicate skin, including the elderly and very young children, when even a tiny diluted amount of essential oil would be too irritating. There are four hydrosols used in this book.

Calendula (*Calendula officinalis*)
This skin-soothing hydrosol is derived from the calendula flower and has a neutral to cooling energy with a gently refreshing aroma. It has anti-inflammatory and vulnerary properties and is a must for the herbal medicine chest. It's wonderful sprayed on children's boo-boos or any inflamed, raw skin. It makes a perfect hydrating mist for irritated, dehydrated skin.

Lemon Balm (*Melissa officinalis*)
Derived from the leaves of lemon balm, with a cooling, emotionally uplifting energy, this hydrosol has gently relaxing, antispasmodic, antiviral, and slightly astringent properties. It's perfect for the treatment of acne, dermatitis, hives, cold sores, and general skin irritations.

Peppermint (*Mentha piperita*)
Derived from the leaves of the naturally cooling, aromatic, stimulating peppermint plant, this hydrosol is best used chilled for an ultra-cooling sensation! This super-refreshing, reviving spray comes in especially handy during hot flashes or on particularly hot days when a refreshing facial spritz is welcome. It's also recommended for use as a toner for normal to oily skin.

Rose (*Rosa damascena*)
Rose hydrosol has a subtle, deeply floral, lightly spicy aroma with an ever-so-gentle, slightly cooling energy. It's recommended as a mild, hydrating toner for all skin types, calming and soothing redness. It also relaxes the mind, eases anxiety, and serves as a mood-setting room spray.

Jojoba Oil (*Simmondsia chinensis*)

This light- to medium-textured oil (technically a liquid wax ester) is derived from the seeds of a desert shrub that is cultivated in the southwestern United States, Argentina, and Israel. Chemically similar to our own moisturizing sebum, with a neutral to slightly warm energy, jojoba oil has natural antioxidant and anti-inflammatory properties and penetrates extremely well, leaving no oily residue. It's one of my favorite base oils for facial elixirs and oil blends because it does not turn rancid and requires no refrigeration. I use it primarily in treatments for thinning hair, alopecia, and scalp disorders, but it's also an excellent conditioner for hair, skin, and nails.

POSSIBLE SUBSTITUTE: Macadamia nut oil, but it does not have the same shelf life as jojoba and takes a bit longer to penetrate.

Juniper Berry (*Juniperus communis*)

PART USED: Essential oil

The refreshing, woodsy-sweet, pine-needle-like fragrance of this essential oil, derived from the berries of the common evergreen shrub, uplifts and stimulates to improve productivity and alertness. Juniper has a heating energy, with mild analgesic, astringent, and antiseptic effects and strong diuretic properties, making it a great addition to salves, balms, and oil blends to comfort the pain of arthritis, gout, and muscle strain and to encourage fluid drainage from swollen, fatigued legs and feet. It's good in lice-deterrent formulas due to its insect-repellent properties.

POSSIBLE SUBSTITUTES: Eucalyptus (*E. radiata*), birch, sweet marjoram, helichrysum, lavender, or German chamomile essential oils for easing sore muscles, gout, and arthritic pain. Tea tree essential oil can be substituted in a lice-deterrent formulation.

CONTRAINDICATIONS: Avoid if pregnant or epileptic or if you have kidney problems. Potentially a skin irritant.

Lavender (*Lavandula angustifolia*)

PARTS USED: Essential oil, flower buds

An entire book could be written about the medicinal and comfort-enhancing uses of lavender. It's my absolute favorite herb! Lavender essential oil is steam-distilled from the mature purple buds of this popular perennial; with its soft floral-herbal scent, it is one of the most gentle, universally useful essential oils. Often referred to as a "medicine chest in a bottle," this extremely safe essential oil can be used "neat" (undiluted) and is a must for every first-aid kit. In fact, in France and other European countries, lavender essential oil is considered so safe that it is used as a carrier to which other essential oils are added.

The aroma is traditionally known for its relaxing, calming effect on the central nervous system, but it will also ease nervous jitters or uplift your emotions and nudge you toward balance if you are depressed. Lavender has a neutral to slightly cooling energy and acts as a sedative, nervine, antiseptic, antispasmodic, anti-inflammatory, antiviral, carminative, and mild diuretic. Both the essential oil and lavender-bud-infused oil, added to salves, balms, and oil blends, bring relief to all manner of ailments and can induce sleep in the most chronic insomniac. I use the undiluted essential oil by the drop to ward off potential infection, dry up blemishes, and calm inflamed insect bites and stings. A liniment from the fresh or dried flowers is also useful.

Lavender, Spike (*Lavandula latifolia*)
PART USED: Essential oil

Spike lavender has very similar properties to lavender (*Lavandula angustifolia*) essential oil, but with a more camphorous aroma and stronger anti-infectious properties. In general, it is not as mild nor as gentle on the skin. I use it in formulas to boost immunity, heal herpes outbreaks, and relieve muscular tension headaches that concentrate in the neck. Spike lavender essential oil works well in formulas designed to dry pustular acne and infected boils, too.

CONTRAINDICATIONS: Avoid if pregnant or epileptic.

Lemon (*Citrus limon*)
PART USED: Essential oil

Cold-pressed from the peel, this essential oil has a clean, light, sharp aroma and a cooling, drying energy. I use it in oil blends for thinning hair and alopecia for its gentle astringency and circulation-stimulating properties. Lemon essential oil also acts as a mental stimulant, increasing alertness and clarity, and so I add it to balms and oil blends that lift mental fog and that "stuck-in-the-mud" feeling. It is also a wonderful invigorating antiseptic and can be added to cold and flu and respiratory formulations. By the very tiny drop, it can be applied directly to stubborn warts to aid in removal, but be careful not to get the oil on surrounding skin.

CONTRAINDICATIONS: Avoid if pregnant or epileptic. May be photosensitizing and a potential skin irritant.

Lemon Balm (*Melissa officinalis*)
PARTS USED: Leaf, essential oil

Lemon balm, a member of the mint family, has a heady, tart, "lemony green" aroma and a cooling energy. It acts as a sedative, antidepressant, nervine, antispasmodic, mild astringent, anti-inflammatory, and potent antiviral. Its uplifting fragrance is said to "make the heart joyful." Lemon balm–infused oil is wonderful to use alone as a total-body massage oil as well as in balms and salves to reduce nervous tension and stress and induce relaxation and sleep. I use the leaf-infused oil primarily to treat cold sores resulting from the oral herpes simplex virus, as well as painful sores and blisters from the related chickenpox virus that also causes shingles. In fact, lemon balm leaf juice can be used as a spot treatment for all types of herpes outbreaks. Due to its exorbitant cost, I rarely use lemon balm essential oil, but offer it in two recipes as an aid in healing herpes outbreaks because many people find it unequaled in its effectiveness for this ailment and prefer it over prescription medications.

Macadamia Nut Oil (*Macadamia integrifolia*)

Rich in monounsaturated fatty acids, this very rich, light- to medium-textured oil has a rather nutty aroma. Like jojoba, it has a neutral to slightly warming energy, closely resembles the chemical makeup of sebum, and penetrates the skin well. I use it in formulations to prevent and soften stretch marks and scar tissue and to condition the ever-expanding skin of pregnant bellies and breasts.

POSSIBLE SUBSTITUTE: Jojoba oil

Marjoram, Sweet (*Origanum majorana*)

PART USED: Essential oil

A tasty culinary herb related to oregano and native to the Mediterranean, marjoram has a strong, woody-sweet, herbaceous aroma with a warming energy. I always grow a big pot of this bushy herb every summer. Inhaling the freshly crushed leaves after a long day's work is an instant de-stressor. Marjoram essential oil, distilled from the leaves, has tranquilizing, antispasmodic, carminative, anti-inflammatory, antifungal, analgesic, antiviral, and antiseptic properties. I use it in children's "tummy rub" oil blends, in sleep balms, and in salves for menstrual cramps, sore muscles, stiff joints, and tension headaches.

POSSIBLE SUBSTITUTE: Roman chamomile essential oil

CONTRAINDICATIONS: Avoid if pregnant or epileptic. Excessive use of the essential oil in aromatherapy will produce a loss of sexual desire and lethargy, which is okay if that is what you are after — just be aware of this side effect.

Meadowsweet (*Filipendula ulmaria*)

PARTS USED: Leaf, flower

A native of Europe and Asia but naturalized in eastern North America, this stout, dense, upright shrub, also known as queen of the meadow, has creamy white, slightly almond-scented flowers that grow in tight clusters. In 1838 chemists isolated salicylic acid from its flower buds (as well as from the bark of the willow tree). In 1899 the drug company Bayer formulated a new synthetic drug, acetylsalicylic acid, and called it "aspirin" — derived from the former botanical name for meadowsweet, *Spirea ulmaria*. Meadowsweet, often referred to as "herbal aspirin," has a cooling energy with astringent, antirheumatic, analgesic, diuretic, anti-inflammatory, exfoliant, and antispasmodic properties. I use the flowers primarily, but you can mix in the leaves when making infused oils for inclusion in salves and balms for easing muscular and arthritic aches and pains.

Milkweed, Common (*Asclepias syriaca*)

PART USED: Stem sap

Milkweed is a 2- to 4-foot tall perennial with large, elliptical, dark green leaves; globe-shaped, pinkish purple clusters of small flowers; and warty pods filled with silky white seed tassels. The American Indians drank the root tea as a laxative, diuretic, and expectorant; stuffed pillows and feather beds with the silk from the pods; and used the milky latex sap to treat ringworm and to dissolve moles and warts (page 268).

Mugwort *(Artemisia annua, A. vulgaris)*
PART USED: Leaf

A native of Europe and Asia but naturalized in the United States, mugwort grows 3 to 5 feet tall and has finely divided light green leaves with tiny yellow flowers. Also known as sweet wormwood or sweet mugwort, it has a sweet, herbaceous aroma and a warming energy. The *Artemisia annua* species, which I grow, is more green than the usual dusty silver and is commonly called sweet Annie, though many herbalists use *Artemesia vulgaris* for fragrance and medicinal purposes. The two species have basically the same anti-inflammatory, anthelmintic, antispasmodic, nervine, vulnerary, antiviral, antiseptic, and skin-cell regenerative properties and I use them interchangeably. I use the infused oil in anti-anxiety salves, massage oils, and sleep balms, and in herbal liniments to treat poison oak and ivy rashes.

Mullein *(Verbascum thapsus, V. olympicum)*
PART USED: Flower

Verbascum thapsus is a tall, stately herb with a single flower stalk that produces hundreds of small yellow flowers. *V. olympicum* (Greek mullein) has multiple flower stalks. Mullein has been referred to as "donkey ears" or "poor man's toilet paper" due to the huge, woolly, pale gray-green leaves that form a wide rosette at the base of the plant. A native of Europe and Asia, it grows in wastelands and woodland clearings throughout the temperate zones. Mullein has a gentle, neutral to slightly cooling energy with anti-inflammatory, vulnerary, astringent, analgesic, and sedative properties. I infuse the flowers in oil to treat burns, cuts, scrapes, earaches, and hemorrhoids, and I infuse them in ethyl alcohol, combined with sage, ginger, and peppermint, to create a soothing, sore muscle relief liniment. If you have room in your garden, invite a mullein plant — she'll be the magnificent queen of your garden! Everyone will want to know her name!

Myrrh *(Commiphora myrrha)*
PARTS USED: Essential oil resin

Myrrh, a dark reddish-brown resin that exudes from the incised trunk of a scrubby tree native to the Middle East and northeast Africa, is one of the oldest medicinals. The rich, aromatic resin was one of the three gifts said to have been brought by the three wise men to the baby Jesus to support the state of grace and preserve divine essence. Myrrh has a heating and drying energy with analgesic, astringent, anti-inflammatory, antispasmodic, antifungal, and antiseptic properties. Known as the "preserver of youth," it was used as an embalming fluid for Egyptian pharaohs, so it makes sense to use the essential oil in facial elixirs for environmentally damaged and mature skin. Added to clay packs and liniments, it treats pseudofolliculitis, athlete's foot, and bruises. I make a lovely, potent infused oil from the powdered resin that I add to salves to help heal cuts, scrapes, athlete's foot, infections, boils, bedsores or skin ulcers, and hemorrhoids.
CONTRAINDICATIONS: Avoid the essential oil if pregnant or epileptic.

Niaouli (*Melaleuca quinquenervia viridiflora*)

PART USED: Essential oil

Niaouli is considered a "sister" to cajeput and tea tree essential oils and has a rather strong, camphorous, stinky medicinal odor. A very safe, energetically cooling essential oil, it is distilled from the leaves and twigs of an evergreen tree native to Australia, New Caledonia, and Tasmania. Like tea tree, niaouli essential oil is unusual in that it is effective against all three varieties of infectious organisms: viruses, bacteria, and fungi. It is also a powerful immunostimulant, anti-inflammatory, and vulnerary, making it an excellent addition to the home medicine chest. I add this essential oil to oil blends, salves, balms, and clay packs to treat cuts and scrapes, all manner of rashes, athlete's foot, and skin, sinus, and respiratory infections. Due to its tissue-tightening quality, it is often used in the treatment of hemorrhoids. It can be applied neat (undiluted) as a spot treatment for blemishes, warts, and insect bites and stings.

POSSIBLE SUBSTITUTE: Tea tree essential oil

Olive Oil, Extra-Virgin (*Olea europaea*)

This rich, green, relatively stable, moderately heavy oil has a strong olive aroma and is derived from the first pressing of ripe olives. It contains high levels of monounsaturated fatty acids, antioxidants, enzymes, vitamins, and minerals. In formulations, it can be used alone or blended with lighter-textured, less aromatic oils. With its neutral energy, highly emollient quality, and gently antiseptic and stimulant properties, olive oil makes a wonderful base oil for medicinal salves, and many herbalists use it exclusively. It is also an excellent conditioning oil for dry skin, nails, feet, eczema, and psoriasis.

POSSIBLE SUBSTITUTES: Avocado, jojoba, macadamia nut, and sesame oils

Orange, Sweet (*Citrus sinensis*)

PART USED: Essential oil

Cold-pressed from the fresh rind, this sweet, fruity essential oil, with its familiar scent, has a warming energy with calming, balancing properties that help you unwind and relax, no matter how chaotic your day. I like to add it to oil blends and balms to reduce stress, anxiety, and insomnia. Orange essential oil also acts as a mild diuretic, thus helping to eliminate the water retention that accompanies tired, swollen legs and feet, plus I find it does wonders at neutralizing foot odor when added to herbal foot powders.

CONTRAINDICATIONS: Avoid if pregnant or epileptic. May be photosensitizing and a potential skin irritant.

Oregon Grape Root (*Mahonia aquifolium*)

PART USED: Root

This shrub, with its holly-like leaves and blue berries, grows prolifically in western North America and is the state flower of Oregon. Its bright yellow root has a cold, tightening, bitter energy and, like the root of the endangered goldenseal, contains the alkaloid berberine. The root has anti-inflammatory, antibacterial, antiviral, and astringent properties, and I use it in liniments for cuts and scrapes, blemishes, and skin infections and in salves to treat boils, blisters, bedsores or skin ulcers, hemorrhoids, insect bites and stings, eczema, and psoriasis.

Palmarosa *(Cymbopogon martinii)*
PART USED: Essential oil

A close relative to lemongrass, with a rich, heavy, sweet, lemon-rose fragrance, palmarosa is native to India and Pakistan and is now cultivated in Africa, Indonesia, and South America. The essential oil has a cooling, balancing energy with broadly antiseptic, astringent, antifungal, antiviral, and skin-cell regenerative properties. I use it in facial elixirs, oil blends, salves, and balms to treat cracked, chapped, environmentally damaged, and mature skin as well as boils, blisters, and bedsores or skin ulcers. I also use it in formulations to improve lymphatic drainage, especially to help soften and drain breast cysts.

Peppermint *(Mentha piperita, M. arvensis)*
PARTS USED: Essential oil, leaf, and menthol crystals (derived from *M. arvensis*)

A most familiar herb with myriad culinary, medicinal, and home uses, peppermint is native to Europe and parts of Asia but is naturalized and cultivated worldwide. Peppermint essential oil and concentrated menthol crystals have a cooling energy with analgesic, decongestant, antiseptic, and gently astringent properties; they are mentally and physically stimulating. I use them in sinus balms to relieve congestion; in arthritis balms to cool and loosen stiff, inflamed joints; in stimulating balms to counter fatigue; and in cooling liniment sprays to refresh and chill hot feet and relieve hot flashes. I use powdered, dried peppermint leaves in clay packs and deodorants. I prefer to grow the very narrow-leafed "white" mint (*forma pallescens*), which is extremely cooling, pungent, and aromatic and makes an excellent iced tea!

CONTRAINDICATIONS: Avoid if pregnant or epileptic.

Pine, Wild Scotch *(Pinus sylvestris)*
PART USED: Essential oil

Scotch pine essential oil, distilled from the needles of an evergreen native to Europe and Asia and grown in the eastern United States, has a fresh, dry, turpentine-like aroma. With its warming energy and expectorant, antiseptic, antiviral, deodorant, and circulation-stimulating properties, this is one of the safest and most therapeutically useful of all the *Pinus* species that produce essential oil. I use it in oil blends, balms, and salves to treat sinus and respiratory congestion and to bring relief to sore, stiff muscles and joints.

POSSIBLE SUBSTITUTES: Balsam fir or sea pine (*Pinus pinaster*) essential oil

CONTRAINDICATIONS: Avoid if pregnant or epileptic.

Plantain (*Plantago major, P. lanceolata*)

PART USED: Leaf

Another common "lawn weed" that grows in wastelands throughout the world, plantain is native to Europe, with flat, spreading leaves that grow from a rosette center. It has a cold energy with astringent, vulnerary, and anti-inflammatory properties. The leaves contain a wonderful mucilaginous substance that is quite soothing to skin irritations. I make a plantain-infused oil, and use it to treat boils, blisters, bed-sores and skin ulcers, diaper rash, cuts, scrapes, bruises, hemorrhoids, and insect bites and stings. It's ever so gentle and quite effective, and it grows practically everywhere. There's nothing like "free" medicine!

Pomegranate Seed Oil (*Punica granatum*)

The lion's share of the world's pomegranates are cultivated in the Mediterranean. The lightly amber-colored, relatively thick oil derived from the pressed seeds of the pomegranate fruit is extremely rich with antioxidant flavonoids and punicic acid and has a neutral to slightly cooling energy. The oil helps prevent and reverse signs of premature aging and environmental damage such as dryness, wrinkles, hyperpigmentation, and diminished skin elasticity. It is especially good for conditioning dry and thinning mature skin and calming redness and inflammation associated with eczema and psoriasis.

Ravensara (*Cinnamomum camphora, syn. Ravensara aromatica*)

PART USED: Essential oil

This essential oil is distilled from the leaves, and sometimes the fruit and bark, of an evergreen tree native to eastern Asia and now extensively cultivated in Madagascar. Ravensara has a camphorous, pungent odor akin to that of traditional eucalyptus, but lighter and softer. It has a warming energy and is an effective anti-viral, decongestant, expectorant, analgesic, anti-inflammatory, antiseptic, and circulatory stimulant. I use this essential oil in oil blends, salves, and balms to relieve sinus and respiratory congestion, ease tense muscles, dry up cold sores, and heal shingles.

POSSIBLE SUBSTITUTES: Eucalyptus (species *radiata*, cajeput, or tea tree essential oils

CONTRAINDICATIONS: Avoid if pregnant or epileptic.

Rose (*Rosa damascena, R. rugosa; Rose Otto*)

PARTS USED: Flower bud and petal, essential oil

The damask rose (*Rosa damascena*) is cultivated today primarily in Bulgaria, Turkey, and France, so I purchase it in dried form. The wild and invasive *Rosa rugosa* is planted as a thorny landscape hedge and has become naturalized along the east coast of the United States, so I harvest its fresh flowers. Both types of roses are particularly valued for their exquisite, deep, complex, true-rose aromas. I like to make a lovely, softly fragrant infused oil from the mature buds and petals, using either the dried or fresh roses, and combine it with palmarosa, rose otto (see next page), and rose geranium essential oils to create a most luxuriant body oil to condition dry skin, balance my mood, and basically make me feel good all over. It even helps ease tense muscles and tension headaches. It's a wonderful oil to use if you tend to "run hot" or have premenstrual anxiety. Roses have a slightly cooling energy with mild astringent, antiseptic, antispasmodic, antidepressant, nervine, skin-cell regenerative, and aphrodisiac properties.

Rose otto is the essential oil distilled from *Rosa damascena* flowers. I don't often use it as a medicinal, due to its exorbitant price, but if you absolutely adore roses, as I do, then indulge your senses and purchase a tiny bottle of this scent-from-heaven. I apply it "neat" as a perfume and also add it to my favorite body oil. It is most intoxicatingly fabulous when blended with lavender!

Rosehip Seed Oil *(Rosa rubiginosa; R. moschata)*

This medium-weight, amber-red oil pressed from rosehips has a light, slightly tart aroma. With a neutral to warming energy, it contains extremely high levels of essential fatty acids, making it an ideal nourishing and conditioning agent for scar tissue, stretch marks, wrinkles, and weathered, dry, devitalized skin. An amazing skin-cell regenerative, anti-inflammatory, and anti-aging oil, it can be used as the vegan alternative to animal-derived collagen treatments as it dramatically increases the elasticity of the skin and stimulates the formation of new collagen fibrils, resulting in a smoother, more toned appearance to the skin. I frequently combine this oil with calophyllum or evening primrose oil to enhance its healing properties. Rosehip seed oil has a short shelf life — always keep refrigerated. CONTRAINDICATIONS: Avoid use on oily, acneic, or combination skin, as it may exacerbate these conditions.

Rosemary *(Rosmarinus officinalis)*
PARTS USED: Leaf, essential oil (chemotype *verbenon*)

Everyone should have a rosemary plant for culinary, medicinal, and aromatherapeutic purposes. Native to the Mediterranean and cultivated worldwide, this shrubby evergreen with pale blue flowers, known as the "herb of remembrance," has a strong, sharp, camphorous, herbaceous aroma with a warming energy. Rosemary essential oil is distilled from the fresh flowering tops — I prefer the chemotype *verbenon* to *camphor* and *cineol* for its gentleness on the skin, more citrusy aroma, and slightly relaxing effects. From the resinous leaves I make an infused oil that I use in cooking and medicine-making. This divine herb has a multitude of properties — it's a potent skin-cell regenerative, mucolytic, antiseptic, anti-inflammatory, circulatory stimulant, vulnerary, antioxidant, antifungal, analgesic, and deodorizing agent. I use both the essential and the infused oil in formulas to relieve sinus and respiratory congestion, muscle tension and soreness, and headaches; to soften and fade scar tissue; to stimulate memory, creativity, confidence, and mental energy; and to stimulate circulation to encourage hair growth. CONTRAINDICATIONS: Avoid use of the essential oil if pregnant or epileptic.

Sage (*Salvia officinalis*)

PARTS USED: Essential oil, leaf

Called *herba sacra* or "sacred herb" by the Romans, sage, a native plant of the Mediterranean region and cultivated worldwide, is a familiar culinary herb, with a fresh, warm-spicy, herbaceous aroma that many of us associate with the Thanksgiving holiday. It has a stimulating, heating, and drying energy, with astringent, diuretic, potent respiratory antiseptic, mucolytic, antispasmodic, anti-inflammatory, vulnerary, antioxidant, and deodorizing properties. I use it in liniments as a deodorizing agent, as a disinfectant for minor cuts, abrasions, and insect bites, and to heal poison oak and ivy rash. Sage essential oil, distilled from the leaves, and sage-infused oil are both used to treat cold and flu symptoms, thinning hair and alopecia, sore or tense muscles, skin infections, and respiratory infection and congestion.

POSSIBLE SUBSTITUTE: For the essential oil, Spanish sage essential oil (*Salvia lavandulifolia*) or rosemary essential oil (chemotype *verbenon*); for the leaves, rosemary leaves

CONTRAINDICATIONS: Avoid using the essential oil if pregnant or epileptic.

Sea Buckthorn Oil (*Hippophae rhamnoides*)

PART USED: Berries

Native to Switzerland, but today primarily commercially cultivated in Italy, the sea buckthorn shrub is valued for its berries, which yield a highly valued, bright golden-orange medium-weight oil that is full of unsaturated fatty acids, carotenoids, vitamins E and C. This super-rich antioxidant cocktail helps protect the skin from harmful ultraviolet radiation and free-radical damage associated with aging. Sea buckthorn oil has a gently cooling energy, is highly anti-inflammatory, and penetrates the skin easily. I find it particularly healing when applied to environmentally damaged skin, as it supports the buildup of the skin's protective lipid layers. It's wonderful to use on dry eczema, psoriasis, newly formed scar tissue, and burns.

Note: The orange oil may temporarily stain very fair skin but will wear off. It will definitely stain light-colored towels and linens.

Sesame Seed Oil (*Sesamum indicum*)

Pressed from sesame seeds, this medium- to heavyweight, light golden, antioxidant oil has a distinct aroma and is rich in vitamins A and E, minerals, and protein. It's relatively stable, with a long shelf life, though I still prefer to refrigerate it and use it within 1 year. Traditionally used in Ayurvedic medicine as a highly emollient massage oil to nourish, condition, and protect the skin from the sun's harmful rays, it can also calm a nervous, anxious disposition. Sesame oil has a neutral to slightly warming energy, and I use it in oil blends for dry skin and as a pre-bedtime body oil to induce relaxation.

Note: Do not use the toasted variety of sesame oil in your personal-care recipes unless you want to smell like "essence of Asian stir-fry"!

Shea Butter (*Butyrospermum parkii*)

Pressed from the nuts of the karite tree, native to Africa, unrefined shea butter, creamy to pale gold in color, is a soft, solid fat often with a semi-strong fragrance that's difficult to mask. If the scent displeases you, purchase the refined butter, which is slightly firmer, whiter in color, and much less aromatic. (I actually prefer this product in the refined form.) Shea butter contributes a thick and creamy texture, with emollient, skin-softening properties, when added to salves and balms. It can even be used alone. Shea butter takes much longer to harden than beeswax, so keep that in mind when using it as the primary thickening agent. Your product will need additional time to completely set up — sometimes up to 48 hours, depending on the temperature of the room.

Solomon's Seal (*Polygonatum multiflorum*)

PART USED: Root (rhizome)

This ornamental plant, a member of the lily family, is native to the moist woodland areas of North America, northern Europe, and Asia. Solomon's seal has an arching, 2-foot-tall stem with lovely, small, bell-like white flowers that appear in the summer, followed by blue berries. The species name, *polygonatum*, means "many-jointed," referring to the nodes on the jointed rhizomes that, to me, look sometimes like the human spine and sometimes like a mass of gnarled knuckles. Most interesting and a bit eerie! The mucilaginous root has a cooling energy and anti-inflammatory, vulnerary, and mild analgesic properties and is extremely soothing. It is highly valued in Western herbalism for mending broken bones and easing sore, stiff joints and muscles, strained ligaments, and tendonitis. I make an infused oil from the root and use it alone or in salves and balms.

Soybean Oil (*Glycine max, syn. Soja hispida*)

Derived from soybeans, this light- to medium-textured, pale-gold oil with a neutral-to-warming energy is easily absorbed into the skin and nongreasy. Soybean oil is naturally high in vitamin E and lecithin and makes a lovely body oil and facial elixir base for all but the oiliest of skin types. I use it as a base oil in many salves and balms — when combined with beeswax, cocoa butter, and shea butter, it lends a velvety, creamy texture to the finished product. Use only organic soybean oil when making herbal remedies. Non-organic soybean oil (typically labeled "vegetable oil") is refined at high temperatures and chock-full of chemical residue, plus it is more than likely derived from genetically modified soybeans.

POSSIBLE SUBSTITUTE: Almond oil

Spruce, Black (*Picea mariana*)

PART USED: Essential oil

This very sweet, forest-fresh essential oil with a grounding, warming energy is derived primarily from the needles of evergreen trees growing wild in Canada. I use it in stimulating oil blends, salves, and balms to increase circulation and alertness. Inhale it directly from the bottle when you're feeling particularly lethargic, sluggish, or stressed at any time of day; it also raises spirits and energizes emotions!

CONTRAINDICATIONS: Avoid use if pregnant or epileptic.

St. John's Wort *(Hypericum perforatum)*

PARTS USED: Flower and bud, leaf

A European native, now naturalized in North America and Australia, this invasive roadside "weed" has clusters of star-shaped, bright yellow flowers atop 2- to 3-foot-tall stems, with small leaves. The petals have tiny black dots on their back edges, which is where the medicinal hypericin constituents are stored. St. John's wort has a cooling energy and serves as a highly effective nervine, astringent, analgesic, vulnerary, antispasmodic, antiviral, and anti-inflammatory agent.

The flowers and buds make a vivid, absolutely gorgeous, blood-red infused oil, also known as hypericum oil, with a lovely, sweet-tart aroma. Beware: Your hands will be stained reddish-purple if you don't wear gloves while harvesting the flowers! And throw a handful of leaves into your infusion as well, as they contain anti-inflammatory flavonoids that will augment the healing energy of the oil.

I use the infused oil to treat nervous tension, arthritis, bedsores or skin ulcers, hemorrhoids, sciatica, spinal injuries, bruises, headaches, cold sores, and shingles. It is wonderfully soothing when used to treat inflamed or injured muscles, joints, and tendons, nerve damage, and cases of chronic multiple sclerosis and arthritis.

CONTRAINDICATIONS: May be photosensitizing; avoid direct sun exposure after application.

Tea Tree *(Melaleuca alternifolia)*

PART USED: Essential oil

This very safe, energetically cooling essential oil, with its strong, penetrating, camphorous odor, is distilled from the leaves and twigs of a small, shrubby tree native to Australia. Tea tree essential oil is quite unusual in that it is effective against all three varieties of infectious organisms: viruses, bacteria, and fungi. It is also a powerful immuno-stimulant, anti-inflammatory, and vulnerary, making it an excellent addition to the home medicine chest. I add this essential oil to oil blends, salves, balms, and clay packs to treat cuts and scrapes, all manner of rashes, athlete's foot, and skin, sinus, and respiratory infections. It can be used neat (undiluted) as a spot treatment for blemishes, warts, and insect bites and stings.

POSSIBLE SUBSTITUTE: Niaouli essential oil (a relative of tea tree) or lavender essential oil, though the latter is not quite as potent.

Thyme *(Thymus vulgaris)*

PARTS USED: Essential oil (chemotype *linalool*), leaf

Thyme is a familiar, low-growing, creeping evergreen perennial with myriad uses, both culinary and medicinal, and should be in everyone's garden. The essential oil, distilled from the leaves (chemotype *linalool*), is nontoxic, skin-friendly, gentle, and slightly warming, unlike red thyme (*T. vulgaris*, chemotype *thymol*), which is hot and irritating. It has a sweet, "green," lightly medicinal aroma and is an effective antiseptic and antibacterial agent, anthelmintic, antispasmodic, and astringent. I use the essential oil and infused oil in salves and balms, and add the leaves to liniments to treat cold and flu symptoms, sinus and respiratory infections, cuts and scrapes, skin infections, poison oak and ivy rashes, and athlete's foot.

POSSIBLE SUBSTITUTE: Tea tree essential oil may be substituted for the essential oil, though it has a much more penetrating, medicinal odor.

CONTRAINDICATIONS: Avoid use of the essential oil if pregnant or epileptic; it's also a potential skin irritant.

Usnea (*Usnea barbata*)

PART USED: Lichen

This herb, also known as old man's beard, is actually a gray-green lichen that grows primarily on spruce, birch, poplar, and red oak trees in the northern hemisphere. According to herbalist David Winston, author of *Herbal Therapeutics*, usnea is a powerful antibacterial that inhibits streptococcus, staphylococcus, pneumococcus, and mycobacterium, and also acts as an antifungal against trichomonas and candida. Usnea has a cooling energy and a tissue-tightening, astringent property, and I use it in liniments to treat athlete's foot, nail fungus, and poison plant rashes. It also helps relieve the itching often associated with these conditions.

Vegetable Shortening

Vegetable shortening is a creamy, semisolid, white hydrogenated fat generally made from 100 percent soybean oil or a combination of vegetable oils. I primarily use all-vegetable shortening when I want to make a "quickie salve." This type of recipe requires no melting and blending of oils with beeswax, cocoa butter, or shea butter, nor any time to harden. Simply add the essential oils to the room-temperature vegetable shortening, stir to blend, and voilà!, you have salve. Shortening is already spreadable and sinks right into the skin when applied.

Note: Purchase only all-vegetable shortening made with 100 percent organic oils. Most brands found in the average grocery store are made from highly refined oils derived from genetically modified plants, grown using synthetic chemicals, and should be avoided. You'll find the organic brands in better health food stores.

Violet, Sweet (*Viola odorata*)

PARTS USED: Leaf, flower

Native to Europe and parts of Asia, but naturalized and cultivated throughout the world, the violet is a beautiful low-growing plant with deep violet, sometimes rose or white, sweetly scented flowers. Violet has a cooling energy, acts as a mild astringent and anti-inflammatory, and is a particularly excellent lymphatic herb. I use violet flowers and leaves to make an infused oil to treat cystic breasts and swollen lymph glands under the arms. I also like to use this infusion as a facial massage oil to help normalize "hormonal skin" conditions in those over the age of 40 who suffer from rosacea, combination skin, adult acne, sensitive skin with diffuse redness, capillary fragility, or very dry skin.

Vitamin E Oil *(D-Alpha Tocopherol or Mixed Tocopherols)*

This antioxidant oil acts as a preservative when added to oil-based products such as infused oils, oil blends, salves, and balms. When applied topically, it aids in the prevention of scar tissue. See page 44 for measuring this oil in remedies.

CONTRAINDICATIONS: Because it may irritate eyes and sensitive skin, use this oil on the body alone, and not on facial skin.

Vodka *(Ethyl Alcohol)*

Commonly derived from the fermentation of grain or potatoes, this fragrance-free, antiseptic, alcoholic product is used as an extractive solvent or menstruum when making herbal, alcohol-based liniments. When applied, the alcohol evaporates quickly from the skin, leaving behind the herb's medicinal properties. Always purchase 80- or 100-proof vodka; an inexpensive variety is fine.

CONTRAINDICATIONS: Avoid applying to dry, irritated, sensitive, burned, or abraded skin, except when using as indicated by the recipe to clean out cuts or scrapes, to treat insect stings and bites, and to prevent future infection.

Walnut, Black *(Juglans nigra)*

PART USED: Nut hull

The black walnut is a temperate-zone tree native to the forests of the eastern United States. Black walnut hulls have a cold energy and intense bitterness, with strong astringent, potent antifungal, anthelmintic, and antibacterial properties. I use this herb in the same manner as usnea and often in combination with it. It also offers tissue-tightening, astringent benefits to salves for the treatment of hemorrhoids and a drawing action to clay packs to assist in the removal of small splinters.

CONTRAINDICATIONS: Black walnut liniment will stain anything it comes into contact with, including hands, nails, clothes, and towels. Be careful.

Wheat Germ Oil *(Triticum aestivum; triticum vulgare)*

Pressed from the germ of the wheat grain, this clear to light gold, medium-weight oil has ultra-soothing, anti-inflammatory properties and a slightly cooling to neutral energy. It's rich in vitamins A, E, and D, proteins, lecithin, and squalene. I add it to oil blends for the treatment of environmentally damaged skin, dry eczema, psoriasis, and generic rashes. Wheat germ oil has a relatively short shelf life and must be refrigerated at all times.

POSSIBLE SUBSTITUTE: Vitamin E oil

Witch Hazel *(Hamamelis virginiana)*

PART USED: Bark

A small, deciduous tree with bright yellow, stringy flowers, native to the damp woodlands of eastern North America and Nova Scotia, witch hazel has a neutral to cooling energy with anti-inflammatory, hemostatic, and astringent properties. It contains high levels of tannins, which make it quite bitter and drying, plus eugenol and carvacrol, essential oil constituents that act as stimulating, anti-infectious agents.

Many topical, antiseptic and anti-inflammatory herbal remedies call for a witch hazel liniment. Though you can find this liniment in any pharmacy, I recommend making your own at home, as your formula will be stronger and more effective. It makes a good base for under-arm and foot deodorizing sprays, as well as a good treatment for boils, blisters, bruises, blemishes, minor infections, insect bites and stings, athlete's foot, contact dermatitis, and poison plant rashes. **POSSIBLE SUBSTITUTE:** Yarrow flowers and leaves

Yarrow *(Achillea millefolium)*
PARTS USED: Flower, leaf
This pretty garden herb, with clusters of tiny flowers and feathery leaves, is native to Europe and western Asia and naturalized in many regions around the world. Yarrow is also known as milfoil or soldier's wound wort because it was valued on the battlefield for closing wounds and arresting bleeding due to its strong astringent and hemostatic properties. It also has antispas-modic, vulnerary, mild antiseptic, and anti-inflammatory properties, along with a cooling to neutral energy, and it is quite bitter. I use it in liniments to treat poison plant rashes, contact dermatitis, blemishes, cuts and scrapes, punc-ture and open wounds, insect bites and stings, and infections. Yarrow-infused oil is wonderful to help shrink hemorrhoids and soothe irrita-tion, reduce the blood stagnation of bruises, and reduce redness and scaliness of psoriasis.

How to Make "Real" Witch Hazel

Over the years I have received many requests for instructions on how to make "real" witch hazel, which is superior to the store-bought product. The drugstore version is approxi-mately 14 percent isopropyl alcohol (a solvent derived from propylene — a petrochemical), and the other 86 percent is a watery extract of witch hazel. Here is my recipe, which I feel is a more potent and effective anti-inflamma-tory astringent:

- 8 tablespoons dried witch hazel bark or 16 tablespoons crushed fresh bark
- 2 cups 80-proof vodka (an inexpensive brand will do fine)

Place the witch hazel and vodka in a 1-quart canning jar. Cover the mouth of the jar with a piece of plastic wrap, tightly cap, and store in a cool, dark place to macerate for 6 to 8 weeks. The longer it soaks, the stronger the tincture or alcohol-based liniment.

Shake daily.

Strain and store in a dark-colored bottle.

Yield: Approximately 1¾ cups
Storage: Store at room temperature, away from heat and light; it will last almost indefinitely

Resources

My tried and true favorite companies!

Mail-Order Suppliers for Raw Materials, Packaging, Natural Health, and Personal Care Products

Aroma Therapeutix
800-308-6284
www.aromatherapeutix.com
Single essential oils and oil blends, bottles, soaps, herbal body and health care products, and more

Aubrey Organics, Inc.
800-282-7394
www.aubrey-organics.com
Chemical-free, natural skin, hair, and body care products, cosmetics, and fragrances

Aura Cacia
800-437-3301
www.auracacia.com
Essential oils, base oils, and natural skin and body care products

Avena Botanicals
866-282-8362
www.avenabotanicals.com
Organic tinctures; elixirs; glycerites, herbal teas; herbs; chemical-free, natural skin and body care; children's herbal health care; herbal pet care products; books

Banyan Botanicals
800-953-6424
www.banyanbotanicals.com
Traditional, hard-to-find Ayurvedic herbs and spices; base oils; body care and health products

Cape Bottle Company, Inc.
888-833-6307
www.netbottle.com
Wide variety of glass, plastic, and tin packaging

Champlain Valley Apiaries
800-841-7334
www.champlainvalleyhoney.com
Fresh beeswax, beeswax candles, raw honey, and maple syrup

Dr. Hauschka Skin Care
800-247-9907
www.drhauschka.com
Organic, chemical-free skin, hair, and body care products and fine cosmetics made with biodynamically grown ingredients

Ecco Bella
New Earth Beauty LLC
877-696-2220
www.eccobella.com
Organic, chemical-free skin, hair, and body care products, fine cosmetics, and fragrances

Frontier Natural Products Co-op
800-669-3275
www.frontiercoop.com
A large inventory of essential oils; base oils; natural and organic herbs; spices; teas; dried foods and mixes; cosmetic clays; beeswax; and natural skin, hair, and body care products

Herbalist & Alchemist, Inc.
908-689-9020
www.herbalist-alchemist.com
A full line of Western and Chinese herbal formulations, plus excellent infused oils and ointments

Honey Gardens, Inc.
800-416-2083
www.honeygardens.com
Fresh beeswax; beeswax candles; raw honey; and delicious honey-herbal blend health-promoting syrups

Jean's Greens
518-479-0471
www.jeansgreens.com
A wide range of wonderful health and personal care herb products; teas; herbs; essential oils; base oils; packaging supplies; beeswax and butters; clays; books, and more

The Jojoba Company
800-256-5622
www.jojobacompany.com
Certified organic, unrefined, superior-quality jojoba oil

Liberty Natural Products
800-289-8427
www.libertynatural.com
Just about every botanical ingredient you can imagine
for the health and personal care crafter, plus packaging supplies, flavorings, soap supplies, and more

Mountain Rose Herbs
800-879-3337
www.mountainroseherbs.com
Everything you could possibly want related to herbs:
seeds; books; essential and base oils; hydrosols; raw
ingredients; packaging; herbal health aids; teas; and
natural skin, hair, and body care products

MyChelle Dermaceuticals, LLC
800-447-2076
www.mychelle.com
Nontoxic, therapeutic skin and body care products

Original Swiss Aromatics
415-479-9120
www.originalswissaromatics.com
Superior quality, therapeutic-grade essential oils
derived from ethically wild-crafted or organically
grown plants; also facial oils; massage and body oils;
hydrosols; natural perfumes

Simplers Botanical Company
800-652-7646
www.simplers.com
Therapeutic-grade essential oils derived from ethically wildcrafted or organically or biodynamically
grown plants. Superior quality. Also carries natural
first-aid oils; hydrosols; perfume oils; infused herbal
oils; and herbal extracts.

Weleda North America
800-241-1030
http://usa.weleda.com
Organic and chemical-free skin, hair, body, and oral
care products; homeopathic medicines

Zack Woods Herb Farm
802-888-7278
www.zackwoodsherbs.com
More than 40 species of organic, Vermont-grown,
fresh and dried herbs

Herb and Garden Seeds, Plants, and Gardening Supplies

Goodwin Creek Gardens
800-846-7359
www.goodwincreekgardens.com
Organically grown herbs; everlasting flowers; and
fragrant plants; including a large number of Native
American species

Horizon Herbs, LLC
541-846-6704
www.horizonherbs.com
100 percent-certified organic, GMO-free, open-
pollinated herb seedlings and seeds; herbal extracts;
and books

Johnny's Selected Seeds
877-564-6697
www.johnnyseeds.com
Organic and non-organic, GMO-free, herb, vegetable,
flower, and farm seeds, and some plants; plus a full
line of tools and supplies for the home and commercial gardener

Pinetree Garden Seeds
207-926-3400
www.superseeds.com
Flower, vegetable, sprouting, and herb seeds; gardening supplies, books; body care kits, and some natural
skin care products

Seeds of Change
888-762-7333
www.seedsofchange.com
100 percent-certified organic, GMO-free, open-
pollinated vegetable, flower, and herb seeds; some
seedlings; gardening supplies; and greenhouses. They
offer many heirloom, rare, and traditional seed varieties as well.

Territorial Seed Company
800-626-0866
www.territorialseed.com
Flower, vegetable, and herb seeds; seedlings; fruits
and berries; mushrooms; gardening supplies; books

Herb Associations and Correspondence Courses

American College of Healthcare Sciences
800-487-8839

www.achs.edu

Specializes in accredited, online, holistic health and aromatherapy education

American Herb Association
530-265-9552

www.ahaherb.com

Offers a fabulously in-depth, thoroughly-researched, quarterly newsletter that I highly recommend to any herb enthusiast. The website also lists herb classes and seminars that may be of interest.

East West School of Planetary Herbology
800-717-5010

www.planetherbs.com

This school, run by Dr. Michael Tierra and Lesley Tierra, both herbalists and acupuncturists, offers several levels of in-depth correspondence courses incorporating Western, Ayurvedic, and Traditional Chinese healing systems; plus books and Chinese herbal formulations. Highly recommended!

The National Association for Holistic Aromatherapy
828-898-6161

www.naha.org

An educational, nonprofit organization dedicated to enhancing public awareness, perception, and knowledge of the benefits of true aromatherapy and its safe and effective application in everyday life. NAHA maintains a listing of approved aromatherapy schools and practitioners, plus offers books, a calendar of events, and an online journal to members.

Pacific Institute of Aromatherapy
415-479-9120

www.pacificinstituteofaromatherapy.com

Offers an in-depth correspondence course in French-style aromatherapy. Highly recommended!

School of Integrative Herbology
EverGreen Herb Garden

Candis Cantin, Herbalist

530-626-9288

www.evergreenherbgarden.org

Offers an extensive herbal correspondence course as well as local herb courses in the High Sierra mountains of California. These courses incorporate Western, Ayurvedic, and Chinese systems of herbal medicinal treatment. Highly recommended!

School of Natural Healing
800-372-8255

www.snh.cc

Offers comprehensive herbal correspondence courses based on Western herbalism.

The Science and Art of Herbalism
Sage Mountain Herbal Retreat Center

Rosemary Gladstar, Herbalist

802-479-9825

www.sagemountain.com

Rosemary offers a lovely, in-depth, beautifully written correspondence course for the beginner or intermediate-level Western herbalist.

United Plant Savers
802-476-6467

www.unitedplantsavers.org

A nonprofit organization dedicated to conservation and cultivation of endangered native medicinal plants.

Recommended Reading

This list contains many of the resources for this book as well as selections from my personal library. If you're interested in the study of herbs and natural self-care, you'll find them all quite educational and enlightening.

Buchman, Dian Dincin. *The Complete Herbal Guide to Natural Health and Beauty.* Doubleday, 1973.

———. *Dian Dincin Buchman's Herbal Medicine: The Natural Way to Get Well and Stay Well,* rev. ed. Wings Books, 1996.

Castleman, Michael. *The Healing Herbs: The Ultimate Guide to the Curative Power of Nature's Medicines.* Bantam, 1995.

Cech, Richo. *Making Plant Medicine.* Horizon Herbs, 2000.

Christopher, John R. *School of Natural Healing,* 25th anniversary ed. Christopher Publications, 2001.

Cooksley, Valerie Gennari. *Aromatherapy: Soothing Remedies to Restore, Rejuvenate and Heal.* Prentice Hall, 2002.

Dawson, Adele G. *Health, Happiness and the Pursuit of Herbs.* Stephen Greene Press, 1980.

Ericksen, Marlene. *Healing With Aromatherapy.* Keats Publishing, 2000.

Frawley, David and Vasant Lad. *The Yoga of Herbs: An Ayurvedic Guide to Herbal Medicine,* 2nd ed. Lotus Press, 1988.

Garland, Sarah. *The Complete Book of Herbs and Spices: An Illustrated Guide to Growing and Using Culinary, Aromatic, Cosmetic, and Medicinal Plants.* Viking Press, 1979.

Gerson, Joel. *Milady's Standard Textbook for Professional Estheticians,* 8th ed. Milady, 1999.

Gladstar, Rosemary. *Rosemary Gladstar's Herbal Recipes for Vibrant Health.* Storey Publishing, 2008.

Green, James. *The Herbal Medicine-Maker's Handbook: A Home Manual.* Crossing Press, 2000.

Griggs, Barbara. *Green Pharmacy: The History and Evolution of Western Herbal Medicine,* 2nd ed. Healing Arts Press, 1997.

Hampton, Aubrey. *Natural Organic Hair and Skin Care: Including A to Z Guide to Natural and Synthetic Chemicals in Cosmetics,* 2nd ed. Organica Press, 1990.

Hampton, Aubrey and Susan Hussey. *The Take Charge Beauty Book: The Natural Guide to Beautiful Hair and Skin.* Organica Press, 2000.

Hirschhorn, Howard H. *The Home Herbal Doctor.* Parker Publishing, 1982.

Hoffmann, David. *Herbal Prescriptions After 50: Everything You Need to Know to Maintain Vibrant Health,* 2nd ed. Healing Arts Press, 2007.

Jachens, Lueder. *Healing The Skin: Holistic Approaches to Treating Skin Conditions: A Practical Guide Based on Anthroposophic Medicine.* Temple Lodge Publishing, 2008.

Keville, Kathi. *Herbs: An Illustrated Encyclopedia: A Complete Culinary, Cosmetic, Medicinal, and Ornamental Guide.* Friedman/Fairfax Publishers, 1999.

Keville, Kathi and Mindy Green. *Aromatherapy: A Complete Guide to the Healing Art,* 2nd ed. Crossing Press, 2009.

King, Kurt. *Herbs to the Rescue: Herbal First Aid Handbook.* Christopher Publications, 1991.

Kloss, Jethro. *Back To Eden: The Classic Guide to Herbal Medicine, Natural Foods, and Home Remedies Since 1939,* 58th anniversary ed. Back to Eden Publishing Co., 1997.

Kowalchik, Claire and William H. Hylton, eds. *Rodale's Illustrated Encyclopedia of Herbs.* Rodale Press, 1998.

Lawless, Julia. *The Illustrated Encyclopedia of Essential Oils: The Complete Guide to the Use of Oils in Aromatherapy and Herbalism.* Elements Books, 1995.

Lust, John. *The Herb Book: The Complete and Authoritative Guide to More than 500 Herbs.* Beneficial Books, 2001.

Mabey, Richard. *The New Age Herbalist: How to Use Herbs for Healing, Nutrition, Body Care, and Relaxation.* With contributions by Michael McIntyre, Pamela Michael, Gail Duff, and John Stevens. Gaia Books, 1988.

McIntyre, Anne. *The Medicinal Garden: How to Grow and Use Your Own Medicinal Herbs.* Henry Holt and Company, 1997.

Merck & Co., Inc. *The Merck Manual of Medical Information: Home Edition,* 2nd ed. Pocket Books, 2003.

Mességué, Maurice. *Of People & Plants.* Healing Arts Press, 1991.

Miller, Light and Bryan Miller. *Ayurveda & Aromatherapy: The Earth Essential Guide to Ancient Wisdom and Modern Healing.* Lotus Press, 1995.

Ody, Penelope. *The Complete Medicinal Herbal: A Practical Guide to the Healing Properties of Herbs, with More Than 250 Remedies for Common Ailments.* DK Publishing, 1993.

Pénoël, Daniel and Rose-Marie Pénoël. *Life Helping Life: Unleash Your Mind/Body Potential with Essential Oils.* Essentia Publishing, 2000.

———. *Natural Home Health Care Using Essential Oils.* Essential Science Publications, 1998.

Sachs, Melanie. *Ayurvedic Beauty Care: Ageless Techniques to Invoke Natural Beauty.* Lotus Press, 1994.

Schnaubelt, Kurt. *Advanced Aromatherapy: The Science of Essential Oil Therapy.* Healing Arts Press, 1998.

———. *Medical Aromatherapy: Healing with Essential Oils.* Frog, Ltd., 1999.

Smith, Ed. *Therapeutic Herb Manual: A Guide to the Safe and Effective Uses of Liquid Herbal Extracts.* Ed Smith, 1999.

Snell, Alma Hogan. *A Taste of Heritage: Crow Indian Recipes & Herbal Medicine.* University of Nebraska Press, 2006.

Soule, Deb. *A Woman's Book of Herbs: The Healing Power of Natural Remedies.* Carol Publishing Group, 1998.

Stuart, Malcolm, ed. *The Encyclopedia of Herbs and Herbalism.* Orbis, 1979.

Tierra, Michael. *Planetary Herbology.* Lotus Press, 1988.

Tourles, Stephanie. *Natural Foot Care: Herbal Treatments, Massage, and Exercises for Healthy Feet.* Storey Publishing, 1998.

———. *Naturally Healthy Skin: Tips and Techniques for a Lifetime of Radiant Skin.* Storey Publishing, 1999.

———. *Organic Body Care Recipes: 175 Homemade Herbal Formulas for Glowing Skin & a Vibrant Self.* Storey Publishing, 2007.

Treben, Maria. *Health Through God's Pharmacy,* 15th ed. Ennsthaler, 1990.

Walters, Clare. *Aromatherapy: An Illustrated Guide.* Element Books, 1998.

Weinberg, Norma Pasekoff. *Natural Hand Care: Herbal Treatments and Simple Techniques for Healthy Hands and Nails.* Storey Publishing, 1998.

Winston, David. *Herbal Therapeutics: Specific Indications for Herbs and Herbal Formulas,* 8th ed. Herbal Therapeutics Research Library, 2003.

Wood, Matthew. *The Book of Herbal Wisdom: Using Plants As Medicine.* North Atlantic Books, 1997.

Worwood, Valerie Ann. *The Complete Book of Essential Oils & Aromatherapy.* New World Library, 1991.

Metric Conversions

Unless you have finely calibrated measuring equipment, conversions between U.S. and metric measurements will be somewhat inexact. It's important to convert the measurements for all of the ingredients in a recipe to maintain the same proportions as the original.

GENERAL FORMULA FOR METRIC CONVERSION

Ounces to grams	multiply ounces by 28.35
Grams to ounces	multiply grams by 0.035
Pounds to grams	multiply pounds by 453.5
Pounds to kilograms	multiply pounds by 0.45
Cups to liters	multiply cups by 0.24
Fahrenheit to Celsius	subtract 32 from Fahrenheit temperature, multiply by 5, then divide by 9
Celsius to Fahrenheit	multiply Celsius temperature by 9, divide by 5, then add 32

APPROXIMATE EQUIVALENTS BY VOLUME

U.S.	Metric
1 teaspoon	5 milliliters
1 tablespoon	15 milliliters
¼ cup	60 milliliters
½ cup	120 milliliters
1 cup	230 milliliters
1¼ cups	300 milliliters
1½ cups	360 milliliters
2 cups	460 milliliters
2½ cups	600 milliliters
3 cups	700 milliliters
4 cups (1 quart)	0.95 liter
1.06 quarts	1 liter
4 quarts (1 gallon)	3.8 liters

APPROXIMATE EQUIVALENTS BY WEIGHT

U.S.	Metric
¼ ounce	7 grams
½ ounce	14 grams
1 ounce	28 grams
1¼ ounces	35 grams
1½ ounces	40 grams
2½ ounces	70 grams
4 ounces	112 grams
5 ounces	140 grams
8 ounces	228 grams
10 ounces	280 grams
15 ounces	425 grams
16 ounces (1 pound)	454 grams

Metric	U.S.
1 gram	0.035 ounce
50 grams	1.75 ounces
100 grams	3.5 ounces
250 grams	8.75 ounces
500 grams	1.1 pounds
1 kilogram	2.2 pounds

Index

Page numbers in **bold** indicate a main entry for the ailment.
Page numbers in *italics* indicate an illustration or table.

Other Storey Titles You Will Enjoy

BY THE SAME AUTHOR

Natural Foot Care.
A comprehensive handbook of natural, homemade herbal
treatments, massage techniques, and exercises for healthy feet.
192 pages. Paper. ISBN 978-1-58017-054-3.

Naturally Healthy Skin.
A total reference for caring for all types of skin, with recipes,
techniques, and practical advice.
208 pages. Paper. ISBN 978-1-58017-130-4.

Organic Body Care Recipes.
Homemade, herbal formulas for glowing skin, hair, and nails,
plus a vibrant self.
384 pages. Paper. ISBN 978-1-58017-676-7.

Raw Energy.
More than 100 recipes for delicious raw snacks: unprocessed,
uncooked, simple, and pure.
272 pages. Paper. ISBN 978-1-60342-467-7.

The Herbal Home Remedy Book, by Joyce A. Wardwell.
A wealth of herbal healing wisdom, with advice on how to collect and
store herbs, make remedies, and stock a home herbal medicine chest.
176 pages. Paper. ISBN 978-1-58017-016-1.

Rosemary Gladstar's Herbal Recipes for Vibrant Health.
A practical compendium of herbal lore and know-how for wellness,
longevity, and boundless energy.
408 pages. Paper. ISBN 978-1-60342-078-50.

These and other books from Storey Publishing are available
wherever quality books are sold or by calling 1-800-441-5700.
Visit us at *www.storey.com*.